10

Do-Without Offering
To Make CHRIST Known

The
VOICE OF
THANKSGIVING
No. 4

That I may publish with the Voice of Thanksgiving,
and tell of all thy wondrous works—*Psalm 26:7*

Edited and Compiled
by
The Moody Bible Institute of Chicago

───

FULL CLOTH EDITION
60 cents per copy postpaid
50 cents per copy in quantities of 100 or more,
transportation extra

───

MOODY PRESS
153 Institute Place, Chicago, Ill.

Printed in U. S. A.

PREFACE

The Voice of Thanksgiving Number Four

published by The Moody Bible Institute, brings its message of salvation and praise seven years after the appearance of its immediate predecessor. Seven years is a long period of life for a book of this character, testifying to its value and prophesying what may be expected of its successor. Much of the finest that Number Three contained is carried over in the present book, the purpose of which is to put before the worker and worshipper an abundant treasure of song clearly uttering the glorious truths of the Christian faith. Changes and additions have been made to give the book the character of a church hymnal suited to the formal service of worship, while adapting it also to evangelism, Sunday School and social meetings.

The old masters are well represented by classic and historic hymns, while the more modern gospel songs are here, care having been taken with the words as well as the tunes to select such as represent an evangelical interpretation of the Word of God. The book is offered with the hope that it may be a satisfying means of worship to many thousands of souls, and prove indeed a "Voice of Thanksgiving."

The plan of song grouping will be observed, and the Topical Index, giving generous aid in selecting songs for various occasions. The groups of related songs are Psalter Hymns (141-145), Chorus Numbers (146-150), Invitation Songs (152-158), Patriotic Hymns (159-164), Junior Songs (165-172), followed by full-page hymns of the church, and miscellaneous hymns and songs. The thematic pages at the end make possible the use of various songs that would otherwise have been crowded out.

As in the previous books of the series of *The Voice of Thanksgiving* the services of the Music Faculty of the Institute have been freely contributed and utilized. Appreciation is due Mr. Talmage J. Bittikofer, Mr. Alfred Holzworth and Mr. George S. Schuler for special assistance as the work progressed. For the building of the book Mr. William M. Runyan and Mr. A. G. Olson, of the business staff of the Institute, should receive the credit. Mr. Olson was responsible for the details of contracts and correspondence, and Mr. Runyan for the editorial work, for which his song-writing and publishing experience of many years qualified him. All these have been team workers with but one purpose—to build a book in every way worthy of the Moody Bible Institute, and the cause of our Lord Jesus Christ which it represents.

It is a pleasure to record the generosity and courtesy of owners of copyrights where permission for use was sought.

JAMES M. GRAY

The Moody Bible Institute of Chicago
February 1, 1928

The
Voice of
Thanksgiving
NUMBER FOUR

1   ## Crown Him With Many Crowns

Matthew Bridges   DIADEMATA   George J. Elvey

1. Crown Him with man - y crowns, The Lamb up - on His throne;
2. Crown Him the Lord of love! Be - hold His hands and side,—
3. Crown Him the Lord of life! Who tri - umphed o'er the grave;
4. Crown Him the Lord of heav'n, One with the Fa - ther known,

Hark! how the heav'n-ly an-them drowns All mu - sic but its own!
Rich wounds, yet vis - i - ble a - bove, In beau - ty glo - ri - fied:
Who rose vic - to - rious in the strife For those He came to save;
One with the Spir - it thro' Him giv'n From yon-der glo-rious throne!

A - wake, my soul, and sing Of Him who died for thee;
No an - gel in the sky Can ful - ly bear that sight,
His glo - ries now we sing, Who died and rose on high,
To Thee be end - less praise, For Thou for us hast died;

And hail Him as thy matchless King Thro' all e - ter - ni - ty.
But downward bends His wond'ring eye At mys-ter - ies so bright.
Who died e - ter-nal life to bring, And lives that death may die.
Be Thou, O Lord, thro' end-less days A - dored and mag-ni - fied. A-men.

Ride On in Majesty

Henry Hart Milman

D. B. Towner

1. Ride on! ride on in maj - es - ty! Hark! all the tribes "Ho-san-na" cry;
2. Ride on! ride on in maj - es - ty! The an - gel ar - mies of the sky
3. Ride on! ride on in maj - es - ty! The last and fierc - est strife is nigh;
4. Ride on! ride on in maj - es - ty! In low - ly pomp ride on to die;

O Saviour meek, pursue Thy road With palms and scattered garments strowed.
Look down with sad and wond'ring eyes, To see th' approaching sac - ri - fice.
The Fa - ther on His sapphire throne A - waits His own a - noint-ed Son.
Bow Thy meek head to mor - tal pain, Then take, O God, Thy pow'r and reign.

Chorus

Ride on! ride on in maj - es - ty! In low - ly
Ride on! ride on in maj - es - ty! Ride on! ride on! In low - ly pomp, in

pomp ride on to die! O Christ, Thy tri-umphs now be-
low - ly pomp ride on to die! O Christ, Thy tri-umphs now be - gin, Thy

gin O'er cap - tive death and con - quered sin.
tri-umphs now be - gin O'er cap - tive death and con-quered sin.

3   Christ Receiveth Sinful Men

Arr. from NEUMASTER

JAMES McGRANAHAN

1. Sin - ners Je - sus will re - ceive: Sound this word of grace to all
2. Come, and He will give you rest; Trust Him for His word is plain;
3. Now my heart con-demns me not, Pure be - fore the law I stand;
4. Christ re - ceiv - eth sin - ful men, E - ven me with all my sin,

Who the heaven - ly path - way leave, All who lin - ger, all who fall.
He will take the sin - ful - est; Christ re - ceiv - eth sin - ful men.
He who cleansed me from all spot, Sat - is - fied its last de - mand.
Purged from ev - 'ry spot and stain, Heaven with Him I en - ter in.

REFRAIN

Sing it o'er........... and o'er a - gain;......... Christ re -
Sing it o'er a-gain,   Sing it o'er a-gain;

ceiv - - eth sin - ful men;......... Make the mes - - sage
ceiveth sin-ful men, Christ receiveth sin-ful men;   Make the message plain,

clear and plain:......... Christ re - ceiv - eth sin - ful men.
Make the message plain:

4   I Know Whom I Have Believed

EL NATHAN   JAMES McGRANAHAN

Moderato.

1. I know not why God's wondrous grace To me   He hath made known,
2. I know not how this sav-ing faith To me   He did im-part,
3. I know not how the Spir-it moves, Con-vinc-ing men of   sin,
4. I know not what of good or   ill May be   re-served for   me,
5. I know not when my Lord may come, At night   or noon-day fair,

Nor why   un-wor-thy—Christ in   love Re-deemed me for His   own.
Nor how   be-liev-ing   in   His Word Wrought peace within my   heart.
Re-veal-ing Je-sus thro' the Word, Cre-a-ting faith in   Him.
Of wea-ry ways or   gold-en days, Be-fore His face I   see.
Nor if I'll   walk the vale with Him, Or "meet Him in   the   air."

CHORUS

But "I know whom I have be-liev-ed, and am per-suad-ed that He is

a-ble To keep that which I've committed Un-to Him against that day."

5 Only a Sinner

James M. Gray

D. B. Towner

1. Naught have I got-ten but what I received; Grace hath bestowed it since I have be-lieved; Boast-ing ex-clud-ed, pride I a-base; I'm only a sin-ner saved by grace!

2. Once I was fool-ish, and sin ruled my heart, Caus-ing my footsteps from God to de-part; Je-sus hath found me, hap-py my case, I now am a sin-ner saved by grace!

3. Tears un-a-vail-ing, no mer-it had I; Mer-cy had saved me, or else I must die; Sin had a-larmed me, fear-ing God's face; But now I'm a sin-ner saved by grace!

4. Suf-fer a sin-ner whose heart o-ver-flows, Lov-ing his Sav-iour, to tell what he knows; Once more to tell it would I em-brace—I'm only a sin-ner saved by grace!

Chorus

On-ly a sin-ner saved by grace! This is my sto-ry, to God be the glo-ry,—I'm on-ly a sin-ner saved by grace!

6   Christ Returneth

H. L. Turner

James McGranahan

1. It may be at morn, when the day is a-wak-ing, When sun-light thro'
2. It may be at mid-day, it may be at twi-light, It may be, per-
3. While its hosts cry Ho-san-na, from heav'n descending, With glo-ri-fied
4. Oh, joy! oh, de-light! should we go with-out dy-ing, No sick-ness, no

dark-ness and shad-ow is break-ing, That Je-sus will come in the
chance, that the blackness of mid-night Will burst in-to light in the
saints and the an-gels at-tend-ing, With grace on His brow, like a
sad-ness, no dread and no cry-ing, Caught up thro' the clouds with the

full-ness of glo-ry, To re-ceive from the world "His own."
blaze of His glo-ry, When Je-sus re-ceives "His own."
ha-lo of glo-ry, Will Je-sus re-ceive "His own."
Lord in-to glo-ry, When Je-sus re-ceives "His own."

CHORUS

O Lord Je-sus, how long? how long Ere we shout the glad song? Christ re-

turn-eth; Hal-le-lu-jah! hal-le-lu-jah! A-men, Hal-le-lu-jah! A-men.

7 Is It the Crowning Day?

GEORGE WALKER WHITCOMB

CHARLES H. MARSH

1. Je - sus may come to - day, Glad day! Glad day! And I would
2. I may go home to - day, Glad day! Glad day! Seemeth I
3. Why should I anx - ious be? Glad day! Glad day! Lights ap-pear
4. Faith-ful I'll be to - day, Glad day! Glad day! And I will

see my Friend; Dan - gers and troub - les would end If
hear their song; Hail to the ra - di - ant throng! If
on the shore, Storms will af - fright nev - er - more, For
free - ly tell Why I should love Him so well, For

CHORUS

Je-sus should come to - day.
I should go home to - day. Glad day! Glad day! Is it the crowning
He is "at hand" to - day.
He is my all to - day.

day? I'll live for to-day, nor anx-ious be, Je-sus, my Lord, I

rit.

soon shall see; Glad day! Glad day! Is it the crown-ing day?

Here Am I

JULIA A. JOHNSTON

J. B. TROWBRIDGE

1. Je - sus, Mas - ter, hast Thou mes - sag - es to send? Here am I,
2. Sav - iour, is there not some low - ly task to do? O send me,
3. Dost Thou need a hand to bear a shin - ing light? Use my hand,
4. Working, wait - ing, what - so - e'er Thy ho - ly will, Here am I,

Here am I! Wait - ing, list'n - ing at Thy feet I low - ly bend,
O send me! Gird me now for serv - ice, make me strong and true,
Use my hand! Dost Thou need a pa - tient watch - er in the night?
Here am I! Mas - ter, let me Thy de - sire a - lone ful - fill,

CHORUS

Here am I— O do not pass me by!
Send me on some er - rand, Lord, for Thee.   Read-y for Thy serv - ice,
Let me serve Thee, Lord, at Thy com - mand.
Keep me to Thy heart for - ev - er nigh.

Mas - ter, here am I! Hush my heart to hear Thee call - ing from on high.

Choose Thou for me, let me still re - ply—O Mas - ter, here am I!

9 It Is Well With My Soul

H. G. SPAFFORD

P. P. BLISS

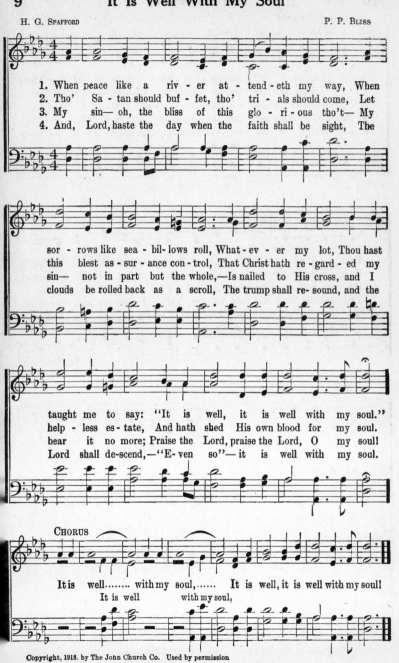

1. When peace like a riv-er at-tend-eth my way, When
sor-rows like sea-bil-lows roll, What-ev-er my lot, Thou hast
taught me to say: "It is well, it is well with my soul."

2. Tho' Sa-tan should buf-fet, tho' tri-als should come, Let
this blest as-sur-ance con-trol, That Christ hath re-gard-ed my
help-less es-tate, And hath shed His own blood for my soul.

3. My sin— oh, the bliss of this glo-ri-ous tho't— My
sin— not in part but the whole,—Is nailed to His cross, and I
bear it no more; Praise the Lord, praise the Lord, O my soul!

4. And, Lord, haste the day when the faith shall be sight, The
clouds be rolled back as a scroll, The trump shall re-sound, and the
Lord shall de-scend,—"E-ven so"— it is well with my soul.

CHORUS

It is well........ with my soul,...... It is well, it is well with my soul!
It is well with my soul,

Full Surrender

Rebecca S. Pollard

D. B. Towner

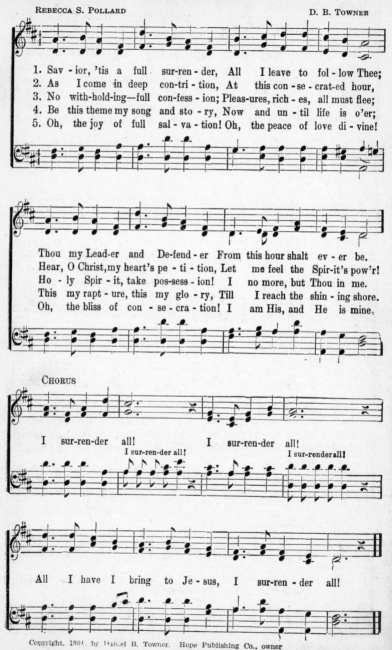

1. Sav - ior, 'tis a full sur-ren - der, All I leave to fol - low Thee;
2. As I come in deep con-tri - tion, At this con - se - crat-ed hour,
3. No with-hold-ing—full con-fess - ion; Pleas-ures, rich - es, all must flee;
4. Be this theme my song and sto - ry, Now and un - til life is o'er;
5. Oh, the joy of full sal - va - tion! Oh, the peace of love di - vine!

Thou my Lead-er and De-fend - er From this hour shalt ev - er be.
Hear, O Christ, my heart's pe - ti - tion, Let me feel the Spir-it's pow'r!
Ho - ly Spir - it, take pos-sess - ion! I no more, but Thou in me.
This my rapt - ure, this my glo - ry, Till I reach the shin - ing shore.
Oh, the bliss of con - se - cra - tion! I am His, and He is mine.

Chorus

I sur-ren-der all! I sur-ren-der all!
I sur-ren-der all! I sur-render all!

All I have I bring to Je - sus, I sur-ren - der all!

Copyright, 1901, by Daniel B. Towner. Hope Publishing Co., owner

11 What God Hath Promised

ANNIE JOHNSON FLINT

WILLIAM M. RUNYAN

1. God hath not prom-ised skies al-ways blue, Flow-er-strewn path-ways
2. God hath not prom-ised we shall not know Toil and temp-ta-tion,
3. God hath not prom-ised smooth roads and wide, Swift, eas-y trav-el,

all our lives thro'; God hath not prom-ised sun with-out rain,
troub-le and woe; He hath not told us we shall not bear
need-ing no guide; Nev-er a moun-tain, rock-y and steep,

CHORUS

Joy with-out sor-row, peace with-out pain.
Man-y a bur-den, man-y a care. But God hath prom-ised
Nev-er a riv-er tur-bid and deep.

strength for the day, Rest for the la-bor, light for the way, Grace for the

tri-als, help from a-bove, Un-fail-ing sym-pa-thy, un-dy-ing love.

That Beautiful Name

Jean Perry, alt.

Mabel Johnston Camp

1. I know of a Name, A beau-ti-ful Name, That an-gels bro't
2. I know of a Name, A beau-ti-ful Name, That un-to a
3. The One of that Name, My Sav-iour be-came, My Sav-iour of
4. I love that blest Name, That won-der-ful Name, Made high-er than

down to earth; They whis-pered it low, One night long a-go,
Babe was given; The stars glittered bright Thro'out that glad night,
Cal-va-ry; My sins nailed Him there, My bur-dens He bare,
all in heav'n; 'Twas whispered, I know, In my heart long a-go—

Chorus

To a maid-en of low-ly birth.
And an-gels praised God in heav'n. That beau-ti-ful Name, That
He suffered all this for me.
To Je-sus my life I've given.

rit.

beau-ti-ful Name, From sin has power to free us! That beau-ti-ful

cres. *ad lib.*

Name, That wonder-ful Name, That matchless Name is Je - sus!

13 Grace Enough For Me

E. O. E.

E. O. EXCELL

1. In look-ing thro' my tears one day, I saw Mount Cal-va-
2. While stand-ing there, my trem-bling heart, Once full of ag-o-
3. When I be-held my ev-'ry sin Nailed to the cru-el
4. When I am safe with-in the vale, My por-tion there will

ry; Be-neath the cross there flowed a stream Of grace, e-nough for
ny, Could scarce be-lieve the sight I saw Of grace, e-nough for
tree, I felt a flood go through my soul Of grace, e-nough for
be, To sing through all the years to come Of grace, e-nough for

CHORUS

me.
e-nough for me. Grace.. is flow-ing from Cal-va-ry,......
Grace is flow-ing from Cal-va-ry for me,

Grace as fath-om-less as the sea,...... Grace for time and e-
Grace as fath-om-less as the roll-ing sea, Grace for time and e-

ter-ni-ty, ... Grace,.... e-nough for me....
ter-ni-ty, His a-bun-dant grace I see, e-nough for me....

14 "There Remaineth a Rest"

JAMES M. GRAY

HOMER A. HAMMONTREE

1. O broth-er, be-loved in Christ Je-sus, I hail thee as
2. Think not that His rest is in heav-en, Tho' heav-en is
3. For Je-sus on Cal-va-ry's moun-tain, By dy-ing thy
4. O cease from thy works and thy la-bor, Thy doubt and mis-

one of the blest; Our God hath redeemed and hath saved thee,
promised thee, too; But here on the earth mid its tur-moil,
pen-al-ty paid, And ren-dered to God an ob-la-tion
giv-ing give o'er; Let joy and let peace in be-liev-ing

REFRAIN

But, O hast thou en-tered His rest?
A heav-en is wait-ing for you. There re-main-eth a
Which peace ev-er-last-ing hath made.
Thy sin-wound-ed spir-it re-store.

rest for God's peo-ple, O fear and an-xi-e-ty cease! If

rit.

Je-sus hath sat-is-fied heav-en, His people on earth may have peace.

15   He Is Able to Deliver

MARY SPARKES WHEELER   D. B. TOWNER.   Re-harmonized by GEO. S. SCHULER

1. When the prophet Daniel prayed to God on bended knee, With his windows o-pen
2. Where-fore is the king so sad, and wherefore does he fast, As he thinks of Dan-iel,
3. "O king, live for-ev-er! and from anxious care be free, For my God has sent His
4. From the roar-ing li-on, seeking whom he may de-vour, God is a-ble to de-

wide, de-spite the king's de-cree, And they cast him in the li-on's den, his
who with-in the den is cast? O thou serv-ant of the liv-ing God, tell
an - gel to de - liv - er me; He has shut the li-ons' mouths, my soul in
liv - er by His might-y pow'r; And the soul who comes to Je - sus with his

poco rit.   *a tempo.*

life to close, God was a - ble to de - liv - er him from all his foes.
me, I pray, From the li - on's cru - el pow - er, can He save to - day?
tri-umph sings, Oh, what joy to trust for shel - ter un - der-neath His wings."
sins oppressed, He is a - ble to de - liv - er, and to give him rest.

CHORUS

For God's an - - gel is encamping Round a - bout.... all them that fear Him;
For God's angel is encamping,   Round about all them that fear Him;

ad lib.

He is a - - - ble, to de - liv - er All who put their trust in Him.
He is a-ble to de - liv - er

16 Christian Fellowship Song

JAMES M. GRAY

D. B. TOWNER

1. One with the Lord, and one with one an-oth-er, Joined by our faith to
2. By blood redeemed, and heirs of God's sal-va-tion, Called by His Son to
3. Blended our tears as for each oth-er car-ing, Min-gled our prayers, each
4. God bless the School that D. L. Moody found-ed; Firm may she stand, by

Christ, the El-der Broth-er, Blest is our fel-low-ship, ev-er grow-ing
toil in ev-'ry na-tion, Far in the har-vest field reap-ing we may
oth-er's burdens bear-ing, Shar-ing the prom-is-es, e-ven an-gels
foes of truth surround-ed! Rich-es of grace be-stowed may she ne-ver

fond-er, Prom-ise of the bet-ter things in glo-ry o-ver yon-der!
wan-der, La-den with the gold-en grain we'll meet in glo-ry yon-der!
pon-der, Man-sions are a-wait-ing us in glo-ry o-ver yon-der!
squan-der, Keep-ing true to God and man her re-cord o-ver yon-der.

CHORUS

Glo-ry o-ver yon-der, o-ver yon-der, When Je-sus comes in
glo-ry o-ver yon-der,

1.
glo-ry, We shall part no more, ...
shall part no more,

2.
We shall part no more.

Second Timothy 2: 15

J. H. SAMMIS   D. B. TOWNER

1. Be up, my soul, and do-ing, Be strong in the Spir-it's might,
2. The shield of truth is o'er him, His mail is re-sist-less light,
3. If thou, in the day of glo-ry, Would stand in His sight ap-proved,
4. The Word of truth di-vid-ing, With prayer un-to God its source,

A faith-ful work-man show-ing Thy-self in the Mas-ter's sight.
He's not a-shamed be-fore Him, Who han-dles the Word a-right.
Hold fast the old, old sto-ry, And ne'er from the Rock be moved.
Heed not the world's de-rid-ing, Hold straight in the Word thy course.

CHORUS

Stud-y to show thy-self ap-proved un-to God
ap - proved un - to God.

A work-man that need-eth not to be a-shamed,

Right-ly di-vid - - - ing the word of truth.
Right-ly di-vid - ing the word of truth.

18   Revive Thy Work

ALFRED MIDLANE   JAMES McGRANAHAN

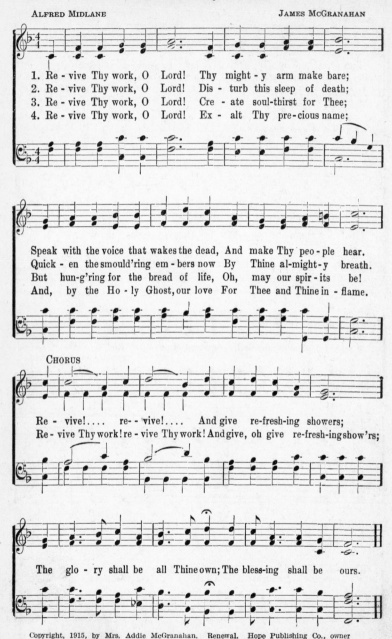

1. Re - vive Thy work, O Lord! Thy might - y arm make bare;
2. Re - vive Thy work, O Lord! Dis - turb this sleep of death;
3. Re - vive Thy work, O Lord! Cre - ate soul-thirst for Thee;
4. Re - vive Thy work, O Lord! Ex - alt Thy pre-cious name;

Speak with the voice that wakes the dead, And make Thy peo - ple hear.
Quick - en the smould'ring em - bers now By Thine al-might - y breath.
But hun-g'ring for the bread of life, Oh, may our spir - its be!
And, by the Ho - ly Ghost, our love For Thee and Thine in - flame.

CHORUS

Re - vive!.... re - vive!.... And give re-fresh-ing showers;
Re - vive Thy work! re - vive Thy work! And give, oh give re-fresh-ing show'rs;

The glo - ry shall be all Thine own; The bless-ing shall be ours.

19   A Passion for Souls

Herbert G. Tovey   Foss L. Fellers

1. Give me a pas-sion for souls, dear Lord, A pas-sion to save the lost;
2. Tho' there are dan-gers un-told and stern Con-front-ing me in the way,
3. How shall this pas-sion for souls be mine? Lord, make Thou the an-swer clear;

O that Thy love were by all a-dored, And welcomed at an-y cost.
Will-ing-ly still would I go, nor turn, But trust Thee for grace each day.
Help me to throw out the old Life Line To those who are strugg'ling near.

Chorus.

Je-sus I long, I long to be win-ning Men who are
lost, and con-stant-ly sin-ning; O may this hour be
one of be-gin-ning The sto-ry of par-don to tell.

20 Day Is Dying in the West

Mary A. Lathbury

William F. Sherwin

1. Day is dy-ing in the west; Heaven is touch-ing earth with rest;
2. While the deep-'ning shad-ows fall, Heart of Love, en-fold-ing all,
3. When for ev-er from our sight Pass the stars, the day, the night,

Wait and wor-ship while the night Sets her eve-ning lamps a-light
Through the glo-ry and the grace Of the stars that veil Thy face,
Lord of an-gels, on our eyes Let e-ter-nal morn-ing rise,

REFRAIN pp

Through all the sky.
Our hearts as-cend.
And shad-ows end.

Ho-ly, ho-ly, ho-ly,

f

Lord God of hosts! Heaven and earth are full of Thee;

ff

Heaven and earth are prais-ing Thee, O Lord Most High!

Home of the Soul

Mrs. Ellen H. Gates

Philip Phillips

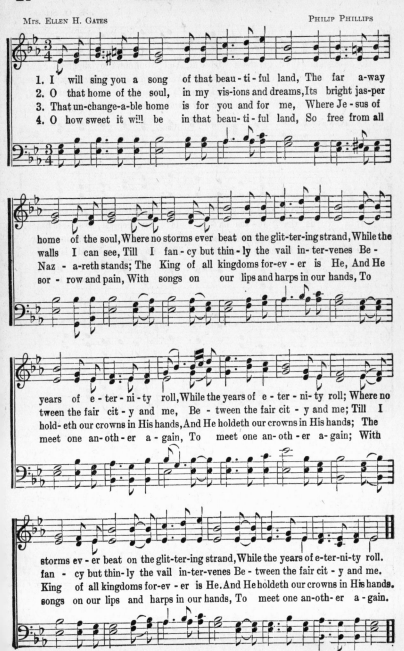

1. I will sing you a song of that beau-ti-ful land, The far a-way
2. O that home of the soul, in my vis-ions and dreams, Its bright jas-per
3. That un-change-a-ble home is for you and for me, Where Je-sus of
4. O how sweet it will be in that beau-ti-ful land, So free from all

home of the soul, Where no storms ever beat on the glit-ter-ing strand, While the
walls I can see, Till I fan-cy but thin-ly the vail in-ter-venes Be-
Naz-a-reth stands; The King of all kingdoms for-ev-er is He, And He
sor-row and pain, With songs on our lips and harps in our hands, To

years of e-ter-ni-ty roll, While the years of e-ter-ni-ty roll; Where no
tween the fair cit-y and me, Be-tween the fair cit-y and me; Till I
hold-eth our crowns in His hands, And He holdeth our crowns in His hands; The
meet one an-oth-er a-gain, To meet one an-oth-er a-gain; With

storms ev-er beat on the glit-ter-ing strand, While the years of e-ter-ni-ty roll.
fan-cy but thin-ly the vail in-ter-venes Be-tween the fair cit-y and me.
King of all kingdoms for-ev-er is He, And He holdeth our crowns in His hands.
songs on our lips and harps in our hands, To meet one an-oth-er a-gain.

22   Jesus Knows

JAMES M. GRAY   E. O. SELLERS

1. Je-sus knows my great-est tri - al, And He knows my slight-est care;
2. Je-sus knows when I am lone - ly, And when earth-ly friend-ships cease;
3. Je-sus knows my need of meek-ness Pa - tient-ly to suf - fer wrong;
4. Je-sus knows when I am wea - ry And my feet are trav - el-stained;

Not a shad - ow on life's di - al, But is traced by Je - sus there.
Then it is that "Je - sus on - ly" Is my deep-est, sweet-est peace.
And be-comes my strength in weakness, Till my moan-ing ends in song.
Thus the way is nev - er drear - y, Till the jour-ney's end is gained.

REFRAIN

Je - sus knows,...... yes, Je - sus knows!...... Heav'n-ly
Je - sus knows,   yes, Je-sus knows!

com - - fort for our woes!...... Je-sus knows,......
Heav'n-ly com - fort   for our woes!   Je - sus knows,

yes, Je - sus knows!....... And from Him my com - fort flows.
Je - sus knows!

23

Wonderful Jesus!

The Gipsy Smith Campaign Song

ANNIE B. RUSSELL

ERNEST O. SELLERS

1. There is nev-er a day so drear-y, There is nev-er a
2. There is nev-er a cross so heav-y, There is nev-er a
3. There is nev-er a care or bur-den, There is nev-er a
4. There is nev-er a guilt-y sin-ner, There is nev-er a

night so long (so long), But the soul that is trust-ing Je-sus Will
weight of woe (of woe), But that Je-sus will help to car-ry Be-
grief or loss (or loss), But that Je-sus in love will light-en When
wan-dr'ing one (not one), But that God can in mer-cy par-don Thro'

CHORUS

some-where find a song (a song). Won-der-ful, won-der-ful Je-sus,
cause He lov-eth so (loves so).
car-ried to the cross (the cross).
Je-sus Christ, His Son (His Son).

In the heart He im-plant-eth a song:...... A song of de-

He plant-eth a song:

liv-'rance, of courage, of strength, In the heart He im-plant-eth a song (a song).

24 What a Wonderful Saviour!

E. A. H.

Elisha A. Hoffman

1. Christ has for sin a-tone-ment made, What a won-der-ful Sav-iour!
2. I praise Him for the cleansing blood, What a won-der-ful Sav-iour!
3. He cleansed my heart from all! its sin, What a won-der-ful Sav-iour!
4. He walks be-side me all the way, What a won-der-ful Sav-iour!
5. He gives me o-ver-com-ing pow'r, What a won-der-ful Sav-iour!
6. To Him I've giv-en all my heart, What a won-der-ful Sav-iour!

We are re-deemed! the price is paid! What a won-der-ful Sav-iour!
That rec-on-ciled my soul to God; What a won-der-ful Sav-iour!
And now He reigns and rules there-in; What a won-der-ful Sav-iour!
And keeps me faith-ful day by day; What a won-der-ful Sav-iour!
And tri-umph in each try-ing hour; What a won-der-ful Sav-iour!
The world shall nev-er share a part; What a won-der-ful Sav-iour!

Chorus

What a won-der-ful Sav-iour is Je-sus, my Je-sus!

What a won-der-ful Sav-iour is Je-sus, my Lord!

Thou Art Enough For Me

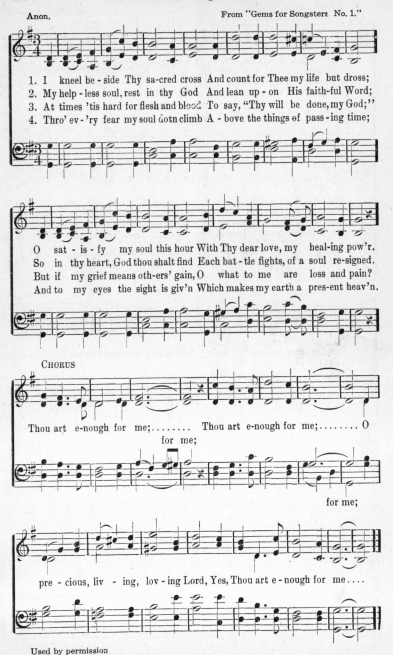

Anon.

From "Gems for Songsters. No. 1."

1. I kneel be - side Thy sa-cred cross And count for Thee my life but dross;
2. My help - less soul, rest in thy God And lean up - on His faith-ful Word;
3. At times 'tis hard for flesh and blood To say, "Thy will be done, my God;"
4. Thro' ev - 'ry fear my soul doth climb A - bove the things of pass - ing time;

O sat - is - fy my soul this hour With Thy dear love, my heal-ing pow'r.
So in thy heart, God thou shalt find Each bat - tle fights, of a soul re-signed.
But if my grief means oth-ers' gain, O what to me are loss and pain?
And to my eyes the sight is giv'n Which makes my earth a pres-ent heav'n.

CHORUS

Thou art e-nough for me;........ Thou art e-nough for me;........ O
for me;

for me;

pre - cious, liv - ing, lov - ing Lord, Yes, Thou art e - nough for me....

Moment By Moment

D. W. Whittle

May Whittle Moody

1. Dy-ing with Je-sus, by death reckoned mine; Liv-ing with Je-sus, a
2. Nev-er a tri-al that He is not there, Nev-er a bur-den that
3. Nev-er a heart-ache, and nev-er a groan, Nev-er a tear-drop and
4. Nev-er a weak-ness that He doth not feel, Nev-er a sick-ness that

new life di-vine; Look-ing to Je-sus till glo-ry doth shine, Moment by
He doth not bear, Nev-er a sor-row that He doth not share, Moment by
nev-er a moan; Nev-er a dan-ger but there on the throne, Moment by
He can-not heal; Moment by moment, in woe or in weal, Je-sus, my

CHORUS

moment, O Lord, I am Thine.
moment I'm un-der His care; Moment by moment I'm kept in His love;
moment He thinks of His own.
Saviour, a-bides with me still.

Mo-ment by mo-ment I've life from a-bove; Look-ing to Je-sus till

glo-ry doth shine; Mo-ment by mo-ment, O Lord, I am Thine.

27 The King's Business

Dr. E. T. Cassel

Flora H. Cassel

1. I am a stran-ger here, with-in a for-eign land, My home is
2. This is the King's command, that all men ev-'rywhere, Re-pent and
3. My home is bright-er far than Sharon's ros-y plain, E-ter-nal

far a-way, up-on a gold-en strand; Am-bas-sa-dor to be of
turn a-way, from sin's se-duc-tive snare; That all who will o-bey, with
life and joy throughout its vast do-main; My Sov'reign bids me tell how

CHORUS

realms be-yond the sea, I'm here on business for my King.
Him shall reign for aye, And that's my business for my King. This is the
mor-tals there may dwell, And that's my business for my King.

mes-sage that I bring, A message angels fain would sing; "Oh, be ye

reconciled," Thus saith my Lord and King, "Oh, be ye reconciled to God."

Draw Me Nearer

FANNY J. CROSBY

W. H. DOANE

1. I am Thine, O Lord, I have heard Thy voice, And it told Thy
2. Con-se-crate me now to Thy serv-ice, Lord, By the pow'r of
3. O the pure de-light of a sin-gle hour That be-fore Thy
4. There are depths of love that I can-not know Till I cross the

love to me; But I long to rise in the arms of faith,
grace di-vine; Let my soul look up with a stead-fast hope
throne I spend, When I kneel in prayer, and with Thee, my God,
nar-row sea; There are heights of joy that I may not reach

REFRAIN

And be clos-er drawn to Thee. Draw me near - er,
And my will be lost in Thine.
I commune as friend with friend!
Till I rest in peace with Thee.

near - er, near - er,

near - er, bless-ed Lord, To the cross where Thou hast died; Draw me

near-er, near-er, near-er, bless-ed Lord, To Thy precious, bleeding side.

29 Safe in Jehovah's Keeping

Sir Robert Anderson

D. B. Towner

1. Safe in Je-ho-vah's keep-ing, Led by His glo-rious arm, God is Him-
2. Safe in Je-ho-vah's keep-ing, Safe in temp-ta-tion's hour, Safe in the
3. Sure is Je-ho-vah's prom-ise, Naught can my hope as-sail; Here is my

self my ref-uge, A pres-ent help from harm. Fears may at times dis-
midst of per-ils, Kept by Al-might-y power. Safe when the tem-pest
soul's sure anchor, Entered with-in the veil. Blest in His love e-

tress me, Griefs may my soul an-noy; God is my strength and por-tion,
rag-es, Safe tho' the night be long; E'en when my sky is dark-est
ter-nal, What can I want be-side! Safe thro' the blood that cleanseth,

Chorus

God my ex-ceed-ing joy.
God is my strength and song. Safe in Je-ho-vah's keep-ing, Led by His
Safe in the Christ that died.

glo-rious arm, God is Himself my ref-uge, A pres-ent help from harm.

30   The Old Rugged Cross

G. B.   GEO. BENNARD

Solo and Chorus

1. On a hill far a-way stood an old rugged cross, The em-blem of
2. Oh, that old rugged cross, so de-spised by the world, Has a wondrous at-
3. In the old rugged cross, stained with blood so di-vine, A won-drous
4. To the old rugged cross I will ev-er be true, Its shame and re-

suf-f'ring and shame, And I love that old cross where the dear-est and best
trac-tion for me, For the dear Lamb of God left His glo-ry a-bove,
beau-ty I see, For 'twas on that old cross Je-sus suf-fered and died,
proach gladly bear; Then He'll call me some day to my home far a-way,

CHORUS

For a world of lost sin-ners was slain.
To bear it to dark Cal-va-ry.   So I'll cher-ish the old rugged
To par-don and sanc-ti-fy me.
Where His glo-ry for-ev-er I'll share.   cross, the

cross,........ Till my tro-phies at last I lay down; I will cling to the
old rug-ged cross,

old rug-ged cross,........ And ex-change it some day for a crown.
cross, the old rugged cross,

31 Tell Me the Old, Old Story

Miss Kate Hankey

W. H. Doane

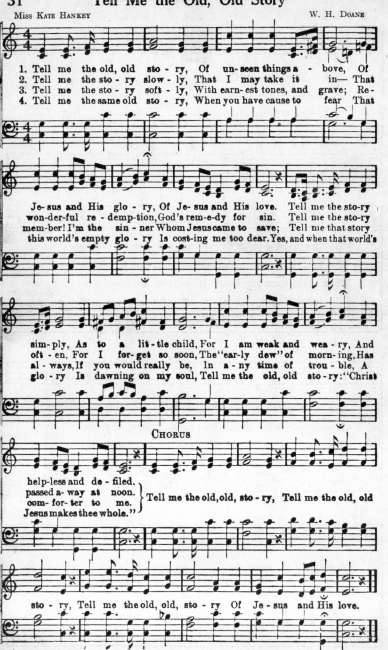

1. Tell me the old, old sto-ry, Of un-seen things a - bove, Of
2. Tell me the sto-ry slow-ly, That I may take it in— That
3. Tell me the sto-ry soft-ly, With earn-est tones, and grave; Re-
4. Tell me the same old sto-ry, When you have cause to fear That

Je-sus and His glo-ry, Of Je-sus and His love. Tell me the sto-ry
won-der-ful re - demp-tion, God's rem-e-dy for sin. Tell me the sto-ry
mem-ber! I'm the sin - ner Whom Jesus came to save; Tell me that story
this world's empty glo - ry Is cost-ing me too dear. Yes, and when that world's

sim - ply, As to a lit - tle child, For I am weak and wea - ry, And
oft - en, For I for-get so soon, The "ear-ly dew" of morn- ing, Has
al - ways, If you would really be, In a - ny time of trou - ble, A
glo - ry Is dawning on my soul, Tell me the old, old sto - ry: "Christ

Chorus

help-less and de - filed.
passed a- way at noon.
com- for- ter to me. } Tell me the old, old, sto - ry, Tell me the old, old
Jesus makes thee whole."

sto - ry, Tell me the old, old, sto - ry Of Je - sus and His love.

Awake, O Church of Christ

H. D. C.   HARRY D. CLARKE

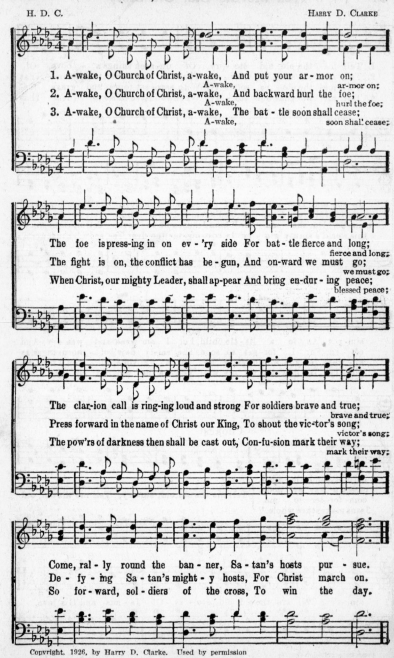

1. A-wake, O Church of Christ, a-wake, And put your ar-mor on;
   A-wake,   *ar-mor on;*
2. A-wake, O Church of Christ, a-wake, And backward hurl the foe;
   A-wake,   *hurl the foe;*
3. A-wake, O Church of Christ, a-wake, The bat-tle soon shall cease;
   A-wake,   *soon shall cease;*

The foe is press-ing in on ev-'ry side For bat-tle fierce and long;
fierce and long;
The fight is on, the conflict has be-gun, And on-ward we must go;
we must go;
When Christ, our mighty Leader, shall ap-pear And bring en-dur-ing peace;
blessed peace;

The clar-ion call is ring-ing loud and strong For soldiers brave and true;
brave and true;
Press forward in the name of Christ our King, To shout the vic-tor's song;
victor's song;
The pow'rs of darkness then shall be cast out, Con-fu-sion mark their way;
mark their way;

Come, ral-ly round the ban-ner, Sa-tan's hosts pur-sue.
De-fy-ing Sa-tan's might-y hosts, For Christ march on.
So for-ward, sol-diers of the cross, To win the day.

33 Go Ye Into All the World

J. McG.

James McGranahan

1. Far, far a-way, in hea-then darkness dwell-ing, Mil-lions of souls for-
2. See o'er the world wide-o-pen doors in-vit-ing, Sol-diers of Christ, a-
3. "Why will ye die?" the voice of God is call-ing, "Why will ye die?" re-
4. God speed the day, when those of ev-'ry na-tion "Glo-ry to God!" tri-

ev-er may be lost; Who, who will go, sal-va-tion's sto-ry tell-ing,
rise and en-ter in! Christians, a-wake! your forc-es all u-nit-ing,
ech-o in His Name; Je-sus hath died to save from death ap-pall-ing,
um-phant-ly shall sing; Ransomed, redeemed, re-joic-ing in sal-va-tion,

CHORUS

Look-ing to Je-sus, minding not the cost?
Send forth the gospel, break the chains of sin. "All pow'r is giv-en un-to Me,
Life and sal-va-tion therefore go pro-claim.
Shout "Hal-le-lu-jah, for the Lord is King."

All pow'r is giv-en un-to Me, Go ye in-to all the world and

preach the gos-pel, And lo, I am with you al-way."

34 The Child of a King

HATTIE E. BUELL.

ART. BY JOHN B. SUMNER.

1. My Fa - ther is rich in hous - es and lands, He hold - eth the
2. My Fa - ther's own Son, the Sav - iour of men, Once wander'd o'er
3. I once was an out - cast stran - ger on earth, A sin - ner by
4. A tent or a cot - tage, why should I care? They're build - ing a

wealth of the world in His hands! Of ru - bies and dia - monds, of
earth as the poor - est of them; But now He is reign - ing for -
choice, and an al - ien by birth! But I've been a - dopt - ed, my
pal - ace for me o - ver there! Tho' ex - iled from home, yet

sil - ver and gold, His cof - fers are full,—He has rich - es un - told.
ev - er on high, And will give me a home in heav'n by and by.
name's writ - ten down,—An heir to a man - sion, a robe and a crown.
still I may sing: All glo - ry to God, I'm the child of a King.

CHORUS

I'm the child of a King. The child of a King!

ad lib.

With Je - sus, my Sav - iour, I'm the child of a King!

35 Channels Only

John 7: 37, 38.

MARY E. MAXWELL   ADA ROSE GIBBS

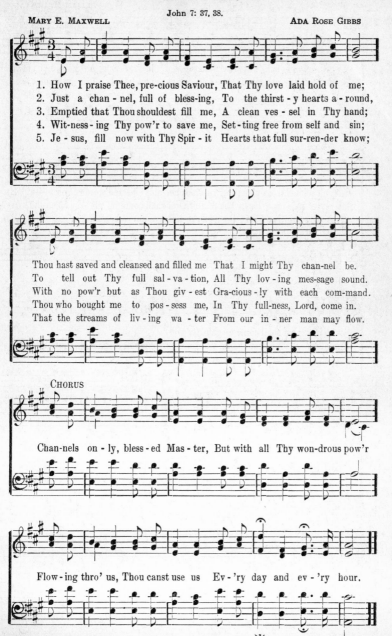

1. How I praise Thee, pre-cious Saviour, That Thy love laid hold of me;
2. Just a chan - nel, full of bless-ing, To the thirst - y hearts a - round,
3. Emptied that Thou shouldest fill me, A clean ves - sel in Thy hand;
4. Wit-ness - ing Thy pow'r to save me, Set-ting free from self and sin;
5. Je - sus, fill now with Thy Spir - it Hearts that full sur-ren-der know;

Thou hast saved and cleansed and filled me That I might Thy chan-nel be.
To tell out Thy full sal - va - tion, All Thy lov - ing mes-sage sound.
With no pow'r but as Thou giv - est Gra-cious - ly with each com-mand.
Thou who bought me to pos - sess me, In Thy full-ness, Lord, come in.
That the streams of liv - ing wa - ter From our in - ner man may flow.

CHORUS

Chan-nels on - ly, bless - ed Mas - ter, But with all Thy won-drous pow'r

Flow - ing thro' us, Thou canst use us Ev - 'ry day and ev - 'ry hour.

36 Again He'll Come

W. M. R.

WILLIAM M. RUNYAN

1. From Ol-ive's Hill, the mul-ti-tude up-gaz-ing, Be-held, un-til the
2. A - gain, but not in weak-ness or in sor-row; A - gain, but not for
3. O Zi - on, clothe thy-self in rai-ment ho - ly, Lift up thine eyes to

Saviour passed from view; But ra-diant her-alds ut-tered words of prom-ise, He
bit - ter pain and loss; The Son of God shall come in glo - ry splen-did, A-
greet thy com-ing King; Re-joice, re-joice, no more be robed in sor - row, Re-

rit.

CHORUS

who has gone shall come a - gain to you.
gain, but not to bear shame's bitter cross. A-gain, a-gain, the nations shall be-
joice, O Zi - on, lift thy voice and sing.

hold Him! A - gain, a - gain, en-robed in maj - es - ty; In clouds of glo - ry

ev - 'ry eye shall see Him, A - gain, a - gain, the King of Glo - ry see!

37   There Is Power in the Blood

L. E. J.   L. E. JONES

1. Would you be free from your bur-den of sin? There's pow'r in the blood;
2. Would you be free from your pas-sion and pride? There's pow'r in the blood;
3. Would you be whit-er—much whiter than snow? There's pow'r in the blood;
4. Would you do serv-ice for Je-sus your King? There's pow'r in the blood;

pow'r in the blood; Would you o'er e-vil a vic-to-ry win?
pow'r in the blood; Come for a cleans-ing to Cal-va-ry's tide,
pow'r in the blood; Sin-stains are lost in its life-giv-ing flow,
pow'r in the blood; Would you live dai-ly, His prais-es to sing?

CHORUS

There's won-der-ful pow'r in the blood. There is pow'r, pow'r,
there is pow'r,

won-der-working pow'r, In the blood of the Lamb; There is
In the blood of the Lamb;

pow'r, pow'r, wonder-working pow'r, In the pre-cious blood of the Lamb.
There is pow'r,

Bought By Christ

MERRILL E. DUNLOP

HOWARD S. BERGLUND

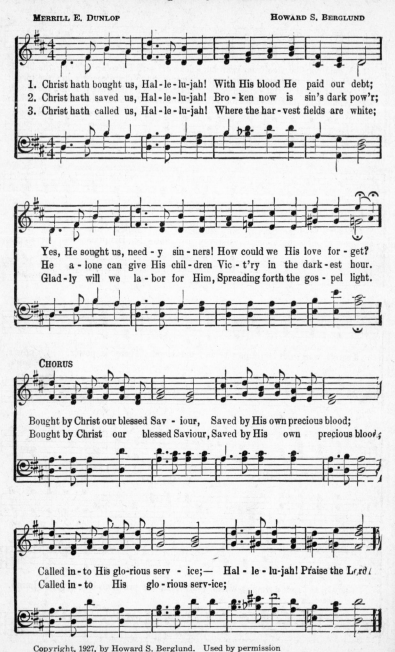

1. Christ hath bought us, Hal - le - lu - jah! With His blood He paid our debt;
2. Christ hath saved us, Hal - le - lu - jah! Bro - ken now is sin's dark pow'r;
3. Christ hath called us, Hal - le - lu - jah! Where the har - vest fields are white;

Yes, He sought us, need - y sin - ners! How could we His love for - get?
He a - lone can give His chil - dren Vic - t'ry in the dark - est hour.
Glad - ly will we la - bor for Him, Spreading forth the gos - pel light.

CHORUS

Bought by Christ our blessed Sav - iour, Saved by His own precious blood;
Bought by Christ our blessed Saviour, Saved by His own precious blood;

Called in - to His glo - rious serv - ice;— Hal - le - lu - jah! Praise the Lord!
Called in - to His glo - rious serv - ice;

Naught But His Blood Can Avail

Anna B. Russell. Alt.

Guy C. Latchaw

Moderato with breadth (Unison, Solo, or Parts)

1. Look at the Lamb with-out blem-ish or spot, Slain for re-
2. None are re-deemed by cor-rupt-i-ble things, Such as our
3. Nor by the works of the law are we saved, Nor by the

demp-tion of man; Know-ing no sin, He was made sin for us, Thro'
sil-ver and gold; But by the stripes of the Lamb are we healed, The
deeds we have done; But by the way, yea, the way of the cross, Thro'

Chorus *Little Faster*

God's most won-der-ful plan. Naught but His blood can a-vail,
Lamb whom prophets foretold. Naught but His blood,
faith in Je-sus, God's Son. Naught but His blood,

Naught but His blood can a-vail; There's no oth-er way
Naught but His blood,

rit.

The soul's ran-som to pay; Naught but His blood can a-vail. (can a-vail.)

40 Can Others See Jesus in You?

Dedicated to Charles M. Alexander

L. C. V.

"He that saith he abideth in him ought himself so to walk,
even as he walked."—1 JOHN 2:6

LEONARD C. VOKE

1. Christ Je-sus hath tri-umphed o'er Sa-tan and Death, And now, praise His name, I am free. Al-tho' He has gone to the Fa-ther's right hand,
2. O will you give heed to this mes-sage to-night, And to your com-mis-sion be true? Are you re-pre-sent-ing the Sav-iour a-right,
3. The har-vest is plen-teous, the fields they are white, A-las! for the la-b'rers are few. 'Tis far bet-ter not to pro-fess Je-sus' name,

CHORUS

May oth-ers see Je-sus in me. May oth-ers see Je-sus in me;
Can oth-ers see Je-sus in you? Can oth-ers see Je-sus in you?
If the world can-not see Him in you. Can oth-ers see Je-sus in you?

May oth-ers see Je-sus in me; For how will the
Can oth-ers see Je-sus in you? For how will the
Can oth-ers see Je-sus in you? For how will the

lost know of Je-sus If they can-not see Je-sus in me?
lost know of Je-sus If they can-not see Je-sus in you?
lost know of Je-sus If they fail to see Je-sus in you?

41 He's Looking On You

James M. Gray, arr.

George S. Schuler

1. I saw One hang-ing on the tree,... In vis-ions of my soul,
2. A gen-tle but condemning pow'r Was stored within that eye;
3. An-oth-er look He gave, which said: "I free-ly all for-give;
4. O sin-ner, thou must meet that gaze In judgment or in grace;

rit.

Who turned His lov-ing eyes on me As near His cross I stole.
And ne'er can I for-get that hour, From hence-forth till I die.
My blood is for a ran-som shed, I die that thou may'st live."
Re-pent, believe and change thy ways, Ere thou be-hold His face!

CHORUS

He's look-ing on you, He's look-ing on you! O nev-er were

love and com-pas-sion, love and compassion so true; How can you re-

so...........

true;

ad lib.

fuse Him, How can you re-fuse Him? He's look-ing, looking on you.

42 The Lily of the Valley

J. R. MURRAY

Arr. by THORO HARRIS

1. I've found a friend in Je-sus, He's ev-'ry-thing to me, He's the fairest of ten
2. He all my griefs has tak-en, and all my sorrows borne; In temp-ta-tion He's my
3. He'll nev-er, nev-er leave me, nor yet forsake me here, While I live by faith and

thousand to my soul; The Lil - y of the Val-ley in Him a-lone I see, All I
strong and mighty tow'r; I've all for Him forsaken, I've all my idols torn From my
do His bless-ed will; A wall of fire about me, I've nothing now to fear; With His

need to cleanse and make me fully whole. In sorrow He's my comfort, in trouble He's my
heart, and now He keeps me by His pow'r. Tho' all the world forsake me, and Satan tempts me
manna He my hungry soul shall fill; Then sweeping up to glory, we'll see His blessed

CHORUS. — *In sorrow He's my comfort, in trouble He's my*

stay, He tells me ev-'ry care on Him to roll. Hallelujah! He's the Lil-y of the
sore, Thru Je-sus I shall safely reach the goal. He's the Lil-y of the
face, Where rivers of delight shall ev - er roll, He's the Lil-y of the

stay; He tells me ev-'ry care on Him to roll. (Hallelujah!) He's the Lil-y of the

D. S.

Valley, the bright and morning Star, He's the fairest of ten thousand to my soul.

Valley, the bright and morning Star, He's the fairest of ten thousand to my soul.

43 Wonderful Peace

W. D. CORNELL. Alt.

W. G. COOPER

1. Far a-way in the depths of my spir-it to-night, Rolls a
2. What a treas-ure I have in this won-der-ful peace, Bur-ied
3. I am rest-ing to-night in this won-der-ful peace, Rest-ing
4. And me-thinks when I rise to that Cit-y of peace, Where the
5. Ah, soul! are you here with-out com-fort or rest, March-ing

mel - o - dy sweet-er than psalm; In ce - les - tial like strains it un -
deep in the heart of my soul; So se - cure that no pow-er can
sweet-ly in Je-sus' con - trol; For I'm kept from all dan - ger by
Au - thor of peace I shall see, That one strain of the song which the
down the rough path-way of time? Make Je - sus your friend ere the

ceas - ing - ly falls O'er my soul like an in - fi - nite calm.
mine it a - way, While the years of e - ter - ni - ty roll.
night and by day, And His glo - ry is flood-ing my soul.
ran - somed will sing, In that heav - en - ly king-dom shall be:
shad - ows grow dark; Oh, ac - cept this sweet peace so sub - lime.

CHORUS

Peace! peace! wonderful peace, Coming down from the Fa-ther a - bove; Sweep

o - ver my spir-it for - ev-er, I pray, In fathomless bil-lows of love.

44 O the Bitter Pain and Sorrow

Theodor Monod. Arr.

Mrs. Lewis S. Chafer

1. O the bit-ter pain and sor-row, That a time could ev - er be,
2. Yet He found me, I be-held Him, Bleed-ing on th' ac-curs-ed tree,
3. Day by day His ten-der mer-cies, Heal-ing, help - ing, full, and free,
4. High-er than the high-est heav-ens, Deep-er than the deep-est sea,

When I proud - ly said to Je - sus, All of self and none of Thee.
And my wist - ful heart said faint - ly, Some of self and some of Thee.
Brought me low - er, while I whis-pered, Less of self and more of Thee.
Lord, Thy love at last hath conquered, None of self and all of Thee.

All of self and none of Thee, All of self and none of Thee;
Some of self and some of Thee, Some of self and some of Thee;
Less of self and more of Thee, Less of self and more of Thee;
None of self and all of Thee, None of self and all of Thee;

When I proud - ly said to Je - sus, All of self and none of Thee.
And my wist - ful heart said faint - ly, Some of self and some of Thee.
Brought me low - er, while I whis-pered, Less of self and more of Thee.
Lord, Thy love at last hath con-quered, None of self and all of Thee.

45 Saved By Grace

FANNY J. CROSBY

GEO. C. STEBBINS

1. Some day the sil - ver cord will break, And I no more as now shall sing;
2. Some day my earth - ly house will fall, I can-not tell how soon 'twill be,
3. Some day, when fades the gold-en sun Be-neath the ro - sy-tint - ed west,
4. Some day, till then I'll watch and wait, My lamp all trimmed and burning bright,

But, O the joy when I shall wake With-in the pal-ace of the King!
But this I know—my All in All Has now a place in heav'n for me.
My blessed Lord shall say, "Well done!" And I shall en - ter in - to rest.
That when my Sav-iour ope's the gate, My soul to Him may take its flight.

CHORUS

And I shall see Him face to face, And tell the
shall see to face,

sto - ry—Saved by grace; And I shall see Him face to
shall see

face, And tell the sto - ry— Saved by grace.
to face,

Triumphant Zion

P. DODDRIDGE   J. B. TROWBRIDGE

1. Tri-um-phant Zi-on! lift thy head From dust and darkness and the dead;
2. Put all thy beauteous garments on, And let thy va-rious charms be known;
3. No more shall foes un-clean in - vade, And fill thy hallowed walls with dread;
4. God from on high has heard thy prayer; His hand thy ru - in shall re - pair;

Tho' humbled long, a - wake at length, And gird thee with Mes-si-ah's strength.
The world thy glo-ries shall con - fess, Decked in the robes of right-eous-ness.
No more shall hell's in-sult - ing host Their vict'ry and thy sor-rows boast.
Nor will thy watch-ful Mon-arch cease To guard thee in e - ter - nal peace.

CHORUS

Rise, crowned with light, O Is-ra - el, lift up thy head,— Rise in thy
Rise, O Is - ra - el, a - rise, Is - ra - el, lift up thy head,—

might from dust and darkness and the dead; Lift up thine eyes— Behold, Mes-
might,— dark-ness and the dead; Lift thy long-ing eyes to heav'n,
ho - ly might,— dust and darkness and the dead;

si - ah now ap-pears— Glo-rious in pow'r–the Monarch of the years.
See, Mes - si - ah now ap-pears—

47 Hiding in Thee

W. O. Cushing

Ira D. Sankey

1. O safe to the Rock that is high - er than I, My
2. In the calm of the noon - tide, in sor - row's lone hour, In
3. How oft in the con - flict, when pressed by the foe, I have

soul in its con - flicts and sor - rows would fly; So sin - ful, so
times when temp - ta - tion casts o'er me its pow'r; In the tem - pests of
fled to my Ref - uge and breathed out my woe; How oft - en, when

wea - ry, Thine, Thine, would I be; Thou blest "Rock of
life, on its wide, heav - ing sea, Thou blest "Rock of
tri - als like sea - bil - lows roll, Have I hid - den in

REFRAIN

A - ges," I'm hid - ing in Thee.
A - ges," I'm hid - ing in Thee. Hid - ing in Thee, Hid - ing in
Thee, O Thou Rock of my soul.

Thee, Thou blest "Rock of A - ges," I'm hid - ing in Thee.

48 I've Found a Friend

Rev. J. G. SMALL   GEO. C. STEBBINS

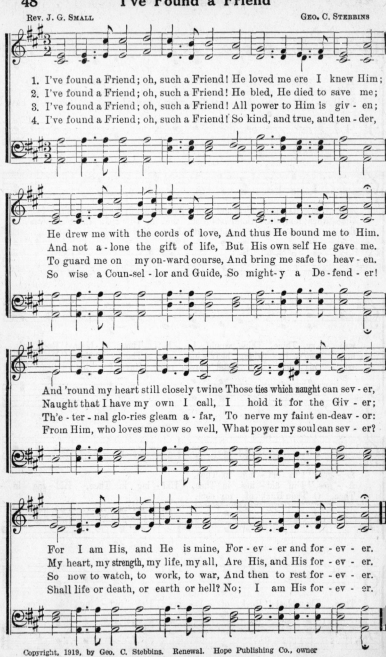

1. I've found a Friend; oh, such a Friend! He loved me ere I knew Him;
2. I've found a Friend; oh, such a Friend! He bled, He died to save me;
3. I've found a Friend; oh, such a Friend! All power to Him is giv-en;
4. I've found a Friend; oh, such a Friend! So kind, and true, and ten-der,

He drew me with the cords of love, And thus He bound me to Him.
And not a-lone the gift of life, But His own self He gave me.
To guard me on my on-ward course, And bring me safe to heav-en.
So wise a Coun-sel-lor and Guide, So might-y a De-fend-er!

And 'round my heart still closely twine Those ties which naught can sev-er,
Naught that I have my own I call, I hold it for the Giv-er;
Th'e-ter-nal glo-ries gleam a-far, To nerve my faint en-deav-or:
From Him, who loves me now so well, What power my soul can sev-er?

For I am His, and He is mine, For-ev-er and for-ev-er.
My heart, my strength, my life, my all, Are His, and His for-ev-er.
So now to watch, to work, to war, And then to rest for-ev-er.
Shall life or death, or earth or hell? No; I am His for-ev-er.

49   I Am Waiting, Thou Art Willing

Arr. by James M. Gray

D. B. Towner

1. Ho - ly Spir - it, bend - ing low - ly, Bring I Thee my heart and will;
2. Lord, I ask it, hard - ly knowing What this won-drous gift may be;
3. Make me in Thy roy - al pal - ace Ves - sel wor - thy for my King;
4. Prom-ise and command com - bin - ing Doubt to chase and faith to lift;

Cleanse Thou me and make me ho - ly, And with Thine own ful - ness fill.
But Thy mer - cy, ev - er flow - ing, Will its mean-ing let me see.
With Thy good-ness fill my chal - ice From Thy nev - er - fail - ing spring.
Self re-nounc-ing, all re - sign - ing, I would seek this might - y gift.

Chorus

Ho - ly Spir - it, Thy in - fill - ing Is the gift for which I pray;

I am wait-ing, Thou art will - ing, Fill me with Thy-self to - day.

I Am His, and He Is Mine

Wade Robinson

J. Mountain

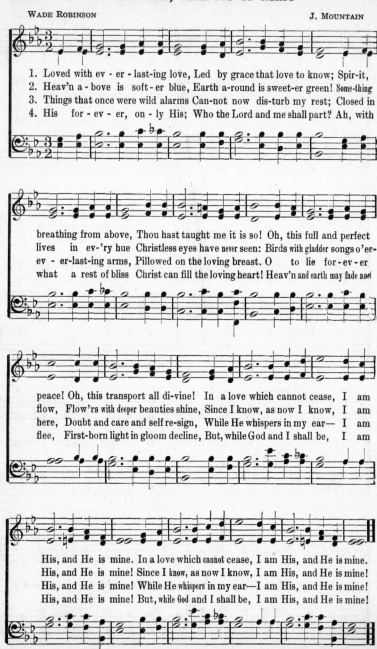

1. Loved with ev - er - last-ing love, Led by grace that love to know; Spir-it,
2. Heav'n a - bove is soft - er blue, Earth a-round is sweet-er green! Some-thing
3. Things that once were wild alarms Can-not now dis-turb my rest; Closed in
4. His for - ev - er, on - ly His; Who the Lord and me shall part? Ah, with

breathing from above, Thou hast taught me it is so! Oh, this full and perfect
lives in ev'ry hue Christless eyes have never seen: Birds with gladder songs o'er-
ev - er-last-ing arms, Pillowed on the loving breast. O to lie for-ev-er
what a rest of bliss Christ can fill the loving heart! Heav'n and earth may fade and

peace! Oh, this transport all di-vine! In a love which cannot cease, I am
flow, Flow'rs with deeper beauties shine, Since I know, as now I know, I am
here, Doubt and care and self re-sign, While He whispers in my ear— I am
flee, First-born light in gloom decline, But, while God and I shall be, I am

His, and He is mine. In a love which cannot cease, I am His, and He is mine.
His, and He is mine! Since I know, as now I know, I am His, and He is mine!
His, and He is mine! While He whispers in my ear—I am His, and He is mine!
His, and He is mine! But, while God and I shall be, I am His, and He is mine!

51 Jesus, I Come

William T. Sleeper

Geo. C. Stebbins

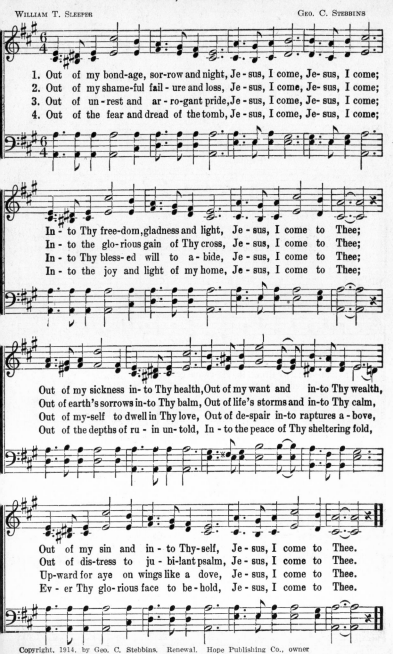

1. Out of my bond-age, sor-row and night, Je-sus, I come, Je-sus, I come;
2. Out of my shame-ful fail - ure and loss, Je-sus, I come, Je-sus, I come;
3. Out of un - rest and ar - ro-gant pride, Je-sus, I come, Je-sus, I come;
4. Out of the fear and dread of the tomb, Je-sus, I come, Je-sus, I come;

In - to Thy free-dom, gladness and light, Je-sus, I come to Thee;
In - to the glo-rious gain of Thy cross, Je-sus, I come to Thee;
In - to Thy bless- ed will to a - bide, Je-sus, I come to Thee;
In - to the joy and light of my home, Je-sus, I come to Thee;

Out of my sickness in- to Thy health, Out of my want and in-to Thy wealth,
Out of earth's sorrows in-to Thy balm, Out of life's storms and in-to Thy calm,
Out of my-self to dwell in Thy love, Out of de-spair in-to raptures a - bove,
Out of the depths of ru - in un-told, In - to the peace of Thy sheltering fold,

Out of my sin and in - to Thy-self, Je-sus, I come to Thee.
Out of dis-tress to ju - bi-lant psalm, Je-sus, I come to Thee.
Up-ward for aye on wings like a dove, Je-sus, I come to Thee.
Ev - er Thy glo-rious face to be-hold, Je-sus, I come to Thee.

52 It Never Grows Old

JAMES M. GRAY   GEORGE S. SCHULER

1. O tell me the sto-ry that nev-er grows old, The sto-ry of One whom the
2. O tell me the sto-ry that nev-er grows old, The sto-ry the an-gel at
3. O tell me the sto-ry that nev-er grows old, The sto-ry the gospels re-
4. O tell me the sto-ry that nev-er grows old, The sto-ry the a-ges to

proph-ets fore-told; The Horn of sal-va-tion, the Scep-ter and Star,
Beth-le-hem told; The Babe in the man-ger, of low-li-est birth,
peat man-i-fold; The love and com-pas-sion in Je-sus we trace,
come will un-fold; The kind-ness of God in re-deem-ing the lost,

The Light in the darkness they saw from afar.
The highest arch-an-gel ex-cel-ling in worth.   It nev-er grows old,   it
The pow-er and pa-tience, the glo-ry and grace.
The death of our Saviour in pay-ing the cost.

nev-er grows old, The sto-ry of Je-sus will nev-er grow old; It nev-er grows

old,   it nev-er grows old, The sto-ry of Je-sus will nev-er grow old.

53 Christ Arose!

R. L.

ROBERT LOWRY

Slow

1. Low in the grave He lay—Je - sus, my Sav - iour! Wait-ing the com-ing day—
2. Vainly they watch His bed—Je - sus, my Sav - iour! Vain - ly they seal the dead—
3. Death cannot keep his prey—Je - sus, my Sav - iour! He tore the bars a - way—

CHORUS *faster*

Je - sus, my Lord! Up from the grave He a - rose

He a - rose,

With a

might-y triumph o'er His foes;

He a - rose!

He a - rose a Vic - tor from the

dark do-main, And He lives for - ev - er with His saints to reign; He a-

rit.

rose! He a - rose! Hal - le - lu - jah! Christ a - rose!

He a - rose! He a - rose!

54 O That Will Be Glory

C. H. G.

CHAS. H. GABRIEL

1. When all my la-bors and tri-als are o'er, And I am safe on that
2. When, by the gift of His in-fin-ite grace, I am ac-cord-ed in
3. Friends will be there I have loved long a-go; Joy like a riv-er a-

beau-ti-ful shore, Just to be near the dear Lord I a-dore,
heav-en a place, Just to be there and to look on His face,
round me will flow; Yet, just a smile from my Sav-ior, I know,

Rit. — — — — — — **CHORUS.**

Will thro' the a-ges be glo-ry for me . . O that will be
O . . . . . . that will

glo-ry for me, Glo-ry for me, glo-ry for me; When by His grace
be glo-ry for me, Glo-ry for me, glo-ry for me; . . . .

rit. > > > >

I shall look on His face, That will be glo-ry, be glo-ry for me.

55 I Would Be Like Jesus

JAMES ROWE

B. D. ACKLEY

1. Earth-ly pleas-ures vain-ly call me; I would be like Je-sus;
2. He has bro-ken ev-'ry fet-ter, I would be like Je-sus;
3. All the way from earth to Glo-ry, I would be like Je-sus;
4. That in Heav-en He may meet me, I would be like Je-sus;
would be like Jesus;

Noth-ing world-ly shall en-thrall me; I would be like Je-sus.
That my soul may serve Him bet-ter, I would be like Je-sus.
Tell-ing o'er and o'er the sto-ry, I would be like Je-sus.
That His words "Well done" may greet me, I would be like Je-sus.
would be like Je-sus.

CHORUS

Be like Je-sus, this my song, In the home and in the throng;

Be like Je-sus, all day long! I would be like Je-sus.

56 Throw Out the Life-Line

E. S. UFFORD

E. S. U. Arr. by GEO. C. STEBBINS

1. Throw out the Life-Line a-cross the dark wave, There is a broth-er whom
2. Throw out the Life-Line with hand quick and strong; Why do you tar-ry, why
3. Throw out the Life-Line to dan-ger-fraught men, Sink-ing in an-guish where
4. Soon will the sea-son of res-cue be o'er, Soon will they drift to e-

some one should save; Some-bod-y's brother! oh, who then, will dare To
lin-ger so long? See! He is sink-ing; oh, has-ten to-day—And
you've nev-er been: Winds of temp-ta-tion and bil-lows of woe Will
ter-ni-ty's shore, Haste then, my brother, no time for de-lay, But

CHORUS

throw out the Life-Line, his per-il to share?
out with the Life-Boat! a-way, then, a-way! Throw out the Life-Line!
soon hurl them out where the dark wa-ters flow.
throw out the Life-Line and save them to-day.

Throw out the Life-Line! Some one is drift-ing a-way; Throw out the

Life-Line! Throw out the Life-Line! Some one is sink-ing to-day.

57 Under His Wings

W. O. Cushing

Ira D. Sankey

1. Un - der His wings, I am safe - ly a - bid - ing; Though the night
2. Un - der His wings, what a ref - uge in sor - row! How the heart
3. Un - der His wings, O what pre - cious en - joy - ment! There will I

deep - ens and tem - pests are wild, Still I can trust Him, I
yearn - ing - ly turns to His rest! Oft - en when earth has no
hide till life's tri - als are o'er; Shel - tered, pro - tect - ed, no

know He will keep me; He has re-deemed me, and I am His child.
balm for my heal - ing, There I find com - fort, and there I am blest.
e - vil can harm me, Rest-ing in Je - sus I'm safe ev - er - more.

Chorus

Un - der His wings, un - der His wings, Who from His love can sev - er?

Un - der His wings my soul shall a - bide, Safe - ly a - bide for - ev - er.

58 Faith in the Word of God

M. J. C. ROM. 4: 20, 21. MABEL JOHNSTON CAMP

1. God says who-so-ev-er be-lieves on His Son, Has
2. He says He makes right-eous and cleans-es from sin The
3. O soul with-out God, with-out hope, with-out peace, Just

par-don ob-tained and a new life be-gun; His sins blot-ted
one who the chief-est of sin-ners has been; He sanc-ti-fies
now come to Him, let your doubt-ings all cease; He says He'll re-

out, not by aught he has done, But thro' faith in the word of God!
whol-ly and jus-ti-fies him Who has faith in the word of God!
ceive you, your joys will in-crease, O have faith in the word of God!

CHORUS

His word is a strong e-ter-nal rock, Un-shak-en it stands thro' fiercest shock;

sfz rit.

Tho' Sa-tan and all his hosts may mock, I have faith in the word of God!

Speed Away

FANNY J. CROSBY

I. B. WOODBURY, arr.

1. Speed a-way, speed a-way on your mis-sion of light,
2. Speed a-way, speed a-way with the life-giv-ing Word,
3. Speed a-way, speed a-way with the mes-sage of rest,

To the lands that are ly-ing in dark-ness and night; 'Tis the
To the na-tions that know not the voice of the Lord; Take the
To the souls by the tempt-er in bond-age op-pressed; For the

Mas-ter's command; go ye forth in His name, The won-der-ful
wings of the morn-ing and fly o'er the wave, In the strength of your
Sav-ior has pur-chased their ran-som from sin, And the ban-quet is

Gos-pel of Je-sus pro-claim; Take your lives in your hand, to the
Mas-ter the lost ones to save; He is call-ing once more, not a
read-y, O gath-er them in; To the res-cue make haste, there's no

work while 'tis day; Speed a-way, speed a-way, speed a-way.
mo-ment's de-lay; Speed a-way, speed a-way, speed a-way.
time for de-lay; Speed a-way, speed a-way, speed a-way.

60   I Am Happy in Him

E. O. E.   E. O. Excell

1. My soul is so hap-py in Je-sus, For He is so precious to me;....
2. He sought me so long ere I knew Him, When wand'ring afar from the fold;..
3. His love and His mercy surround me, His grace like a riv-er doth flow;...
4. They say I shall some day be like Him, My cross and my burden lay down;..

His voice, it is mu-sic to hear it, His face it is heaven to see......
Safe home in His arms He hath bro't me, To where there are pleasures untold...
His Spir-it, to guide and to comfort, Is with me wher-ev-er I go......
Till then I will ev-er be faith-ful In gath-er-ing gems for His crown..

CHORUS

I am hap-py in Him,...... I am hap-py in Him;.....
I.......... am hap-py in Him, I.......... am hap-py in Him;

My soul with de-light He fills day and night, For I am hap-py in Him.

He Is Near

HORATIUS BONAR

GEO. C. STEBBINS

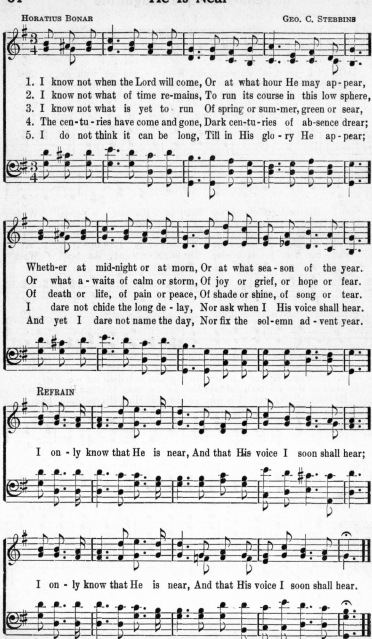

1. I know not when the Lord will come, Or at what hour He may ap-pear,
2. I know not what of time re-mains, To run its course in this low sphere,
3. I know not what is yet to run Of spring or sum-mer, green or sear,
4. The cen-tu-ries have come and gone, Dark cen-tu-ries of ab-sence drear;
5. I do not think it can be long, Till in His glo-ry He ap-pear;

Wheth-er at mid-night or at morn, Or at what sea-son of the year.
Or what a-waits of calm or storm, Of joy or grief, or hope or fear.
Of death or life, of pain or peace, Of shade or shine, of song or tear.
I dare not chide the long de-lay, Nor ask when I His voice shall hear.
And yet I dare not name the day, Nor fix the sol-emn ad-vent year.

REFRAIN

I on-ly know that He is near, And that His voice I soon shall hear;

I on-ly know that He is near, And that His voice I soon shall hear.

62 In Tenderness He Sought Me

W. Spencer Walton   A. J. Gordon

1. In ten-der-ness He sought me, Wear-y and sick with sin, And
2. He washed the bleeding sin-wounds, And poured in oil and wine; He
3. He point-ed to the nail-prints, For me His blood was shed, A
4. I'm sit-ting in His pres-ence, The sun-shine of His face, While
5. So while the hours are pass-ing, All now is per-fect rest; I'm

on His shoulders brought me Back to His fold a-gain. While
whis-pered to as-sure me, "I've found thee, thou art Mine;" I
mock-ing crown so thorn-y, Was placed up-on His head: I
with a-dor-ing won-der His bless-ings I re-trace. It
wait-ing for the morn-ing, The bright-est and the best, When

an-gels in His pres-ence sang Un-til the courts of heav-en rang.
nev-er heard a sweet-er voice, It made my ach-ing heart re-joice!
wondered what He saw in me, To suf-fer such deep ag-o-ny.
seems as if e-ter-nal days Are far too short to sound His praise.
He will call us to His side, To be with Him, His spot-less bride.

Chorus

Oh, the love that sought me! Oh, the blood that bought me! Oh, the grace that
brought me to the fold, Wondrous grace that brought me to the fold!

63 The Shepherd of Love

A. S. R.

ALBERT SIMPSON REITZ

Duet

1. The Shepherd of Love is seeking the lost In paths that are rough and steep;
2. The Shepherd of Love knows His sheep by name And tenderly leads the way;
3. The Shepherd of Love our ransom hath paid And of-fers sal-va-tion free;
4. The Shepherd of Love now seeketh His sheep He seeketh what-e'er the cost;

rit.

He's calling the lambs that have gone astray, He's calling, calling His sheep.
O wea-ry one come to the Shepherd's fold, He's calling, calling to-day.
He's pa-tient-ly wait-ing for thee to come, He's calling, calling for thee.
Be-hold, He is call-ing the wand'rer home, He's calling, calling the lost.

CHORUS

Out of your darkness of sin and shame, In-to His love for-ev-er the same,
Call - - ing, call - ing, Call - - ing, call - - ing,

ad lib.

Come to Him now, be-lieve on His name, O answer the call to-day.

3

On the Jesus Way

ANNIE JOHNSON FLINT, by per.

MAY AGNEW STEPHENS

1. Oh, there's man-y a thorn on the Je-sus way, Man-y a thorn I
2. Oh, there's man-y a storm on the Je-sus way, Man-y a storm I
3. Oh, there's man-y a foe on the Je-sus way, Man-y a foe to

know; There is grief and loss and the pain of the Cross Wher-
see, When black is the cloud and the wind is loud, And
fight; And all the day we must watch and pray To

ev-er my feet may go. But the Lord will heal all the
waves go o-ver me. But the Lord Him-self is in
keep our ar-mor bright. But the Lord for-ev-er will

wounds I feel When the thorns have pricked me sore; And He's
my lit-tle ship, And the storms o-bey His will; At the
be at my side The tempt-er's wiles to meet; Tho' the

plant-ed a rose where the bri-ar grows, For He's walked this path be-fore.
word He hath said, "Be not a-fraid," My heart and the sea grow still.
foe be strong, and the strife be long, He can nev-er know de-feat.

65   O Lord, Send a Revival!

JAMES M. GRAY   D. B. TOWNER

1. Of self I am wea-ry, My sin I ab-hor, I long to be
2. Thy church, O my Sav-iour, Thy bod-y and bride, The saints Thou hast
3. The world, in its sor-row, The world need-eth Thee; Re-vive Thy dis-
4. Thy glo-ri-ous com-ing—We long for the day! But are we pre-

ho-ly And pure to the core; O why do I la-bor On
ran-somed, For whom Thou hast died—How cold are we grow-ing In
ci-ples, Be-gin-ning in me! En-due us with boldness Thy
par-ing The ho-ly high-way? Our hand seem-eth weakened, And

husks to be fed, Or spend my poor mon-ey For what is not bread?
serv-ice and pray'r! Our love needs re-kind-ling, Our al-tars re-pair.
grace to pro-claim; O help us with pow-er To speak in Thy name!
fee-ble the knee; O send a re-viv-al, Be-gin-ning in me!

CHORUS

O Lord, send a re-viv-al! Lord, send a re-viv-al!

O Lord, send a re-viv-al, And let it be-gin in me!

My Heart is Resting, O My God

ANNA L. WARING

SWISS MELODY

1. My heart is rest-ing, O my God, I will give thanks and sing.
2. I thirst for springs of heav'nly life, And here all day they rise;
3. And a "new song" is in my mouth, To long-loved mu-sic set—
4. I have a her-i-tage of joy That yet I must not see;
5. There is a cer-tain-ty of love, That sets my heart at rest;

My heart is at the se-cret source Of ev-'ry pre-cious thing.
I seek the treas-ure of Thy love, And close at hand it lies.
Glo-ry to Thee for all the grace I have not tast-ed yet!
The hand that bled to make it mine Is keep-ing it for me.
A calm as-sur-ance for to-day That what Thou dost is best.

CHORUS

O peace of God that pass-eth thought, I dai-ly, hour-ly sing,

My heart is at the se-cret source Of ev-'ry pre-cious thing.

67 Jesus! I am Resting, Resting

JEAN SOPHIA PIGOTT

J. MOUNTAIN

1. Je - sus! I am rest - ing, rest - ing In the joy of what Thou art;
2. Oh, how great Thy lov - ing kind - ness, Vast - er, broad - er than the sea!
3. Sim - ply trust - ing Thee, Lord Je - sus, I be - hold Thee as Thou art;
4. Ev - er lift Thy face up - on me, As I work and wait for Thee;

CHO.—Je - sus, I am rest - ing, rest - ing, In the joy of what Thou art;

FINE.

I am find - ing out the great - ness Of Thy lov - ing heart.
Oh, how mar - vel - ous Thy good - ness, Lav - ished all on me!
And Thy love so pure, so change - less, Sat - is - fies my heart.
Rest - ing 'neath Thy smile, Lord Je - sus, Earth's dark shad - ows flee.

I am find - ing out the great - ness Of Thy lov - ing heart.

Thou hast bid me gaze up - on Thee, And Thy beau - ty fills my soul;
Yes, I rest in Thee, be - lov - ed, Know what wealth of grace is Thine;
Sat - is - fies its deep - est long - ings, Meets, sup - plies its ev - 'ry need;
Brightness of my Fa - ther's glo - ry, Sun - shine of my Fa - ther's face;

D. C. Chorus

For by Thy trans - form - ing pow - er, Thou hast made me whole.
Know Thy cer - tain - ty of prom - ise, And have made it mine.
Com - pass - eth me round with bless - ings, Thine is love in - deed.
Keep me ev - er trust - ing, rest - ing, Fill me with Thy grace.

68   Jesus Saves

Priscilla J. Owens   Wm. J. Kirkpatrick

1. We have heard the joy-ful sound, Je-sus saves, Je-sus saves;
2. Waft it on the roll-ing tide, Je-sus saves, Je-sus saves;
3. Sing a-bove the bat-tle's strife, Je-sus saves, Je-sus saves;
4. Give the winds a might-y voice, Je-sus saves, Je-sus saves;

Spread the glad-ness all a-round, Je-sus saves, Je-sus saves;
Tell to sin-ners far and wide, Je-sus saves, Je-sus saves;
By his death and end-less life, Je-sus saves, Je-sus saves;
Let the na-tions now re-joice, Je-sus saves, Je-sus saves;

Bear the news to ev-'ry land, Climb the steeps and cross the waves,
Sing, ye is-lands of the sea, Ech-o back, ye o-cean caves,
Sing it soft-ly thro' the gloom, When the heart for mer-cy craves,
Shout sal-va-tion full and free, High-est hills and deep-est caves,

On-ward, 'tis our Lord's command, Je-sus saves, Je-sus saves.
Earth shall keep her ju-bi-lee, Je-sus saves, Je-sus saves.
Sing in tri-umph o'er the tomb, Je-sus saves, Je-sus saves.
This our song of vic-to-ry, Je-sus saves, Je-sus saves.

Rescue the Perishing

FANNY J. CROSBY

WILLIAM H. DOANE

1. Res - cue the per-ish-ing, Care for the dy - ing. Snatch them in pit - y from
2. Tho' they are slighting Him, Still He is wait-ing, Wait-ing the pen - i - tent
3. Down in the human heart, Crushed by the tempter, Feel-ings lie bur-ied that
4. Res - cue the per-ish-ing, Du - ty de-mands it; Strength for thy la - bor the

sin and the grave; Weep o'er the err - ing one, Lift up the fall - en,
child to re - ceive; Plead with them ear-nest-ly, Plead with them gen - tly:
grace can re - store; Touched by a lov - ing heart, Wak-ened by kind - ness,
Lord will pro - vide; Back to the nar-row way Pa - tient-ly win them;

CHORUS

Tell them of Je - sus the might-y to save.
He will for-give if they on - ly be - lieve. Res - cue the per - ish-ing,
Chords that are bro-ken will vi-brate once more.
Tell the poor wan-d'rer a Sav-iour has died.

Care for the dy - ing; Je - sus is mer - ci - ful, Je - sus will save.

Copyright property of W. H. Doane. Used by permission

The Comforter Has Come!

F. Bottome

Wm. J. Kirkpatrick

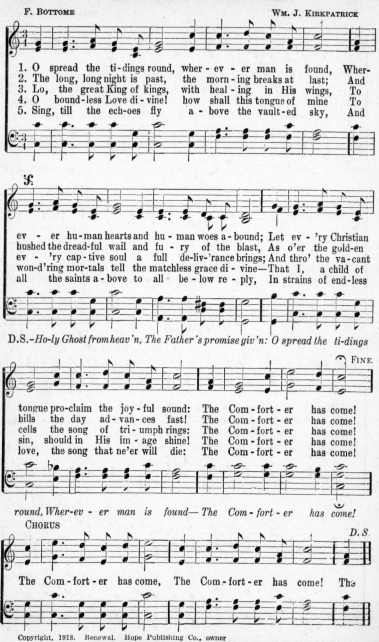

1. O spread the ti-dings round, wher-ev-er man is found, Wher-
2. The long, long night is past, the morn-ing breaks at last; And
3. Lo, the great King of kings, with heal-ing in His wings, To
4. O bound-less Love di-vine! how shall this tongue of mine To
5. Sing, till the ech-oes fly a-bove the vault-ed sky, And

ev-er hu-man hearts and hu-man woes a-bound; Let ev-'ry Christian
hushed the dread-ful wail and fu-ry of the blast, As o'er the gold-en
ev-'ry cap-tive soul a full de-liv-'rance brings; And thro' the va-cant
won-d'ring mor-tals tell the matchless grace di-vine—That I, a child of
all the saints a-bove to all be-low re-ply, In strains of end-less

D.S.—*Ho-ly Ghost from heav'n, The Father's promise giv'n: O spread the ti-dings*

FINE.

tongue pro-claim the joy-ful sound: The Com-fort-er has come!
hills the day ad-van-ces fast! The Com-fort-er has come!
cells the song of tri-umph rings: The Com-fort-er has come!
sin, should in His im-age shine! The Com-fort-er has come!
love, the song that ne'er will die: The Com-fort-er has come!

round, Wher-ev-er man is found—The Com-fort-er has come!

CHORUS

D.S.

The Com-fort-er has come, The Com-fort-er has come! The

71 Send the Power Again

W. C. POOLE.　　　　　　　　　　　　CHAS. H. GABRIEL

1. There was pow'r, O Lord, in the days of old, To kin - dle a
2. There was pow'r by which ev - 'ry tongue could speak, New life - giv - ing
3. There was pow'r to set ev - 'ry cap - tive free And give to Thy
4. There was pow'r, O Lord, in the old-time prayer, It thrilled ev - 'ry

fire in hearts grown cold; That we on Thy Word may now lay hold,
pow'r un - to the weak, That sent them the wand'ring ones to seek—
ser - vants lib - er - ty To speak and to pray and work for Thee—
heart and lin-gered there, Till we in Thy glo - ry seemed to share—

CHORUS

Lord, send that pow'r a - gain. Lord, send the pow'r a - gain!
A - men!

O send the pow'r a - gain! We be - lieve on Thy name,
A - men!

And Thy prom-ise we claim, Lord, send the pow'r a - gain.

72 The Name of Jesus

Rev. W. C. Martin

E. S. Lorenz

1. The name of Je - sus is so sweet, I love its mu - sic to re-peat;
2. I love the name of Him whose heart Knows all my griefs, and bears a part;
3. That name I fond - ly love to hear; It nev - er fails my heart to cheer;
4. No word of man can ev - er tell How sweet the name I love so well;

It makes my joys full and complete, The precious name of Je - sus.
Who bids all anx - ious fears de-part—I love the name of Je - sus.
Its mu - sic dries the fall - en tear; Ex - alt the name of Je - sus.
Oh, let its prais - es ev - er swell, Oh, praise the name of Je - sus.

1. The precious name

CHORUS

"Je - sus," oh, how sweet the name! "Je - sus," ev - 'ry day the same;

"Je - sus," let all saints proclaim Its wor - thy praise for - ev - er.

Its wor - thy praise

73 Nothing Between

Words and Music by C. A. TINDLEY

Arr. by F. A. CLARK

1. Noth-ing be-tween my soul and the Sav-iour, Naught of this world's de-
2. Noth-ing be-tween, like world - ly pleas-ure, Hab - its of life tho'
3. Noth-ing be-tween, like pride or sta-tion, Self or friends shall
4. Noth-ing be-tween, e'en man-y hard tri - als, Tho' the whole world a-

lu - sive dream; I have re-nounced all sin - ful pleas-ure,
harmless they seem, Must not my heart from Him ev - er sev - er,
not in - ter-vene, Tho' it may cost me much trib-u - la-tion,
gainst me convene; Watching with pray'r and much self-de - ni - al, I'll

CHORUS

Je - sus is mine; there's noth-ing be-tween.
He is my all; there's noth-ing be-tween. Noth-ing be-tween my
I am resolved; there's noth-ing be-tween.
tri-umph at last, with noth-ing be-tween.

soul and the Sav-iour, So that His blessed face may be seen; Noth-ing pre-

vent-ing the least of His fa - vor, Keep the way clear! Let nothing between.

74 Teach Me to Pray

A. S. R.   ALBERT SIMPSON REITZ

1. Teach me to pray, Lord, teach me to pray; This is my heart-cry, day un-to day; I long to know Thy will and Thy way; Teach me to pray, Lord, teach me to pray.

2. Pow-er in prayer, Lord, pow-er in prayer, Here 'mid earth's sin and sor-row and care; Men lost and dy-ing, souls in des-pair: O give me pow-er, pow-er in prayer!

3. My weakened will, Lord, Thou canst re-new; My sin-ful na-ture Thou canst subdue; Fill me just now with pow-er a-new: Pow-er to pray and pow-er to do!

4. Teach me to pray, Lord, teach me to pray; Thou art my Pat-tern, day un-to day; Thou art my Sure-ty, now and for aye; Teach me to pray, Lord, teach me to pray.

CHORUS

Liv-ing in Thee, Lord, and Thou in me; Constant a-bid-ing, this is my plea; Grant me Thy pow-er, boundless and free: Power with men and pow-er with Thee.

75   I'll Go Where You Want Me to Go

MARY BROWN   CARRIE E. ROUNSEFELL

1. It may not be on the mountain height, Or o-ver the storm-y sea,
2. Per-haps to-day there are lov-ing words Which Je-sus would have me speak;
3. There's surely somewhere a low-ly place In earth's harvest fields so wide,

It may not be at the bat-tle's front My Lord will have need of me;
There may be now in the paths of sin Some wand'rer whom I should seek:
Where I may la-bor thro' life's short day For Je-sus, the Cru-ci-fied;

But if, by a still, small voice He calls To paths that I do not know,
O Sav-ior, if Thou wilt be my guide, Tho' dark and rug-ged the way,
So trust-ing my all to Thy ten-der care, And know-ing Thou lov-est me,

FINE.

I'll answer, dear Lord, with my hand in Thine, I'll go where you want me to go.
My voice shall ech-o the mes-sage sweet, I'll say what you want me to say.
I'll do Thy will with a heart sin-cere, I'll be what you want me to be.

D.S.—I'll say what you want me to say, dear Lord, I'll be what you want me to be.

REFRAIN.   *D.S.*

I'll go where you want me to go, dear Lord, Over mountain, or plain, or sea;

We're Marching to Zion

ISAAC WATTS

ROBERT LOWRY

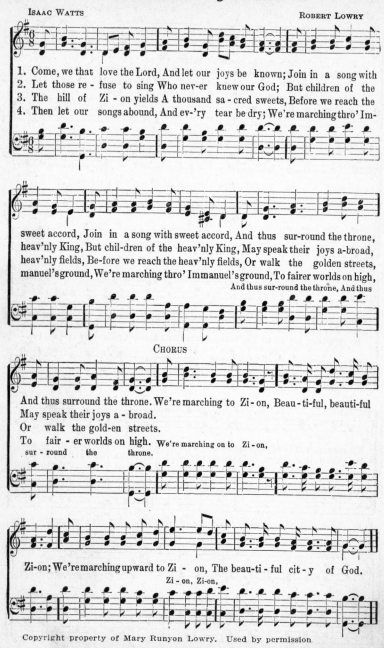

1. Come, we that love the Lord, And let our joys be known; Join in a song with
2. Let those re - fuse to sing Who nev-er knew our God; But children of the
3. The hill of Zi - on yields A thousand sa - cred sweets, Before we reach the
4. Then let our songs abound, And ev'ry tear be dry; We're marching thro' Im-

sweet accord, Join in a song with sweet accord, And thus sur-round the throne,
heav'nly King, But chil-dren of the heav'nly King, May speak their joys a-broad,
heav'nly fields, Be-fore we reach the heav'nly fields, Or walk the golden streets,
manuel's ground, We're marching thro' Immanuel's ground, To fairer worlds on high,

And thus sur-round the throne, And thus

CHORUS

And thus surround the throne. We're marching to Zi - on, Beau - ti-ful, beautiful
May speak their joys a - broad.
Or walk the gold-en streets.
To fair - er worlds on high. We're marching on to Zi - on,
sur - round the throne.

Zi-on; We're marching upward to Zi - on, The beau-ti - ful cit - y of God.
Zi - on, Zi-on,

Copyright property of Mary Runyon Lowry. Used by permission.

77 Trust and Obey

Rev. J. H. Sammis

D. B. Towner

1. When we walk with the Lord In the Light of His Word What a glo- ry He
2. Not a shad-ow can rise, Not a cloud in the skies, But His smile quickly
3. Not a bur-den we bear, Not a sor-row we share, But our toil He doth
4. But we nev-er can prove The de-lights of His love Un-til all on the
5. Then in fel-low-ship sweet We will sit at His feet, Or we'll walk by His

sheds on our way! While we do His good-will, He a-bides with us still,
drives it a-way; Not a doubt or a fear, Not a sigh or a tear
rich-ly re-pay; Not a grief or a loss, Not a frown or a cross
al-tar we lay; For the fa-vor He shows, And the joy He be-stows,
side in the way; What He says we will do, Where He sends we will go—

CHORUS

And with all who will trust and o-bey.
Can a-bide while we trust and o-bey.
But is blest if we trust and o-bey.   Trust and o-bey, for there's
Are for them who will trust and o-bey.
Nev-er fear, on-ly trust and o-bey.

no oth-er way To be hap-py in Je-sus, But to trust and o-bey.

No Night There

John R. Clements

H. P. Danks

1. In the land of fade-less day Lies "the cit - y four-square,"
2. All the gates of pearl are made, In "the cit - y four-square,"
3. And the gates shall nev - er close, To "the cit - y four-square,"
4. There they need no sun-shine bright, In "that cit - y four-square,"

It shall nev - er pass a - way, And there is "no night there."
All the streets with gold are laid, And there is "no night there."
There life's crys - tal riv - er flows, And there is "no night there."
For the Lamb is all the light, And there is "no night there."

mf CHORUS

God shall "wipe away all tears;" There's no death, no pain, nor fears;
God shall "wipe a - way all tears;" There's no death, no pain, nor fears;

f   *dim.*   *mf*

And they count not time by years,... For there is "no night there."
not time by years, by years, "no night there."

Copyright, 1927. Renewal. Hope Publishing Co., owner

He Lifted Me

CHARLOTTE G. HOMER   CHAS. H. GABRIEL

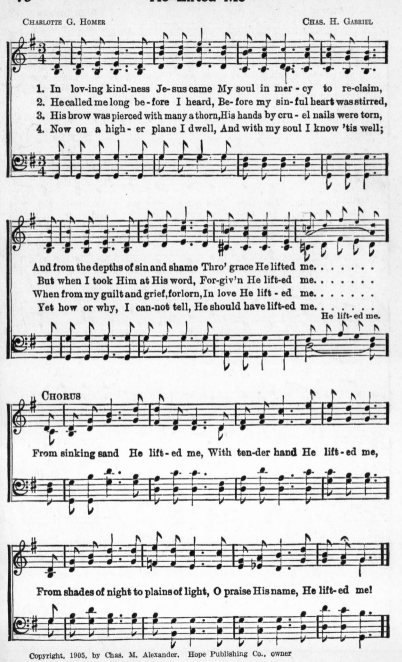

1. In lov-ing kind-ness Je-sus came My soul in mer - cy to re-claim,
2. He called me long be - fore I heard, Be- fore my sin- ful heart was stirred,
3. His brow was pierced with many a thorn, His hands by cru - el nails were torn,
4. Now on a high - er plane I dwell, And with my soul I know 'tis well;

And from the depths of sin and shame Thro' grace He lifted me......
But when I took Him at His word, For-giv'n He lift-ed me......
When from my guilt and grief, forlorn, In love He lift - ed me......
Yet how or why, I can-not tell, He should have lift-ed me....

He lift- ed me.

CHORUS

From sinking sand He lift - ed me, With ten-der hand He lift - ed me,

From shades of night to plains of light, O praise His name, He lift- ed me!

80 Move Forward!

G. W. CROFTS

D. B. TOWNER

1. Move for-ward! val-iant men and strong, Ye who have prayed and la-bored long; The time has come for you to rise, For lo! the sun rolls up the skies.
2. Move for-ward! each and ev-'ry one; The gold-en har-vest is be-gun, Ye reap-ers, come from glen and glade, And wield the sick-le's glit-t'ring blade.
3. Move for-ward! reap-ing as you move! An-gels are watch-ing from a-bove! A-round are wit-ness-es a host; A-rouse ye now and save the lost.
4. Move for-ward! day will die full soon; How quick-ly eve-ning fol-lows noon! Now is the time to work and pray: Let glo-ry crown the dy-ing day.

CHORUS

Move for-ward, move for-ward, move for-ward, All a-long the line,........ Move for-ward, move for-ward, The light be-gins to shine.

81 Jesus, Our Master

GEORGINA M. MARSHALL

DONALD G. DAVIS

Prayerfully.

1. Je - sus, Mas - ter, Thou hast bought us With Thy blood on
2. Je - sus, Mas - ter, Thou art ris - en; Seat - ed on Thy
3. Je - sus, Mas - ter, Thou art com - ing, We shall meet Thee

Cal - va - ry; All we are and have we of - fer For Thy
Fa - ther's throne, In - ter - ced - ing for Thy chil - dren, Thee as
on the way; Gathered home from ev - 'ry na - tion, We shall

CHORUS

serv - ice glad and free.
King and Priest we own. Dy - ing, ris - en, com - ing
own Thy glo - rious sway.

Sav - iour, At Thy feet we bow and pray; Fill, oh,

fill us with Thy Spir - it, Lead us all a - long life's way.

Kept By the Power of God

ETHEL R. HARPER

EDNA P. WRIGHT

1. We praise Thee, O God, all glo-rious in pow'r, For strength all-suf-
2. We praise Thee, O Christ, Be-lov-ed of Heav'n, That in-to Thy
3. We praise Thee, O Spir-it, Thou Com-fort-er blest, That Thou in our

fi - cient in temp-ta - tion's hour; Our strength is but weakness; we
keep-ing all pow-er is giv'n; A - bid-ing in Thee, all
hearts art a most gra - cious Guest; O fill us, we pray, from

lose in the fight, But great is the vic - t'ry when clad in Thy might.
strength is sup-plied, To bring help-less wan-d'rers to Thy wound-ed side.
self set us free, That we in our serv - ice may glo - ri - fy Thee.

CHORUS

Kept by His pow'r! we can-not fail, Tho' all Satan's legions our strong-hold as-sail,

Tri-um-phant we follow the pathway He trod, Kept by the in-fi-nite pow'r of God.

Praise Him! Praise Him!

FANNY J. CROSBY

CHESTER G. ALLEN

1. Praise Him! praise Him! Jesus, our blessed Re-deem-er! Sing, O earth—His
2. Praise Him! praise Him! Jesus, our blessed Re-deem-er! For our sins He
3. Praise Him! praise Him! Jesus, our blessed Re-deem-er! Heav'nly por-tals,

won-der-ful love pro-claim! Hail Him! hail Him! high-est arch-an-gels in
suf-fered, and bled, and died; He our rock, our hope of e-ter-nal sal-
loud with ho-san-nas ring! Je-sus, Sav-iour, reigneth for-ev-er and

D.S.—Praise Him! praise Him! tell of His ex-cel-lent

FINE

glo-ry; Strength and honor give to His ho-ly name! Like a shep-herd,
va-tion, Hail Him! hail Him! Jesus, the cru-ci-fied. Sound His prais-es!
ever: Crown Him! crown Him! Prophet, and Priest, and King! Christ is com-ing!

greatness, Praise Him! praise Him! ever in joy-ful song!

D.S.

Je-sus will guard His children, In His arms He car-ries them all day long;
Je-sus who bore our sorrows, Love unbounded; wonder-ful, deep and strong;
o-ver the world vic-torious, Pow'r and glo-ry un-to the Lord be-long.

Leaving It All With Jesus

James M. Gray   O. F. Pugh

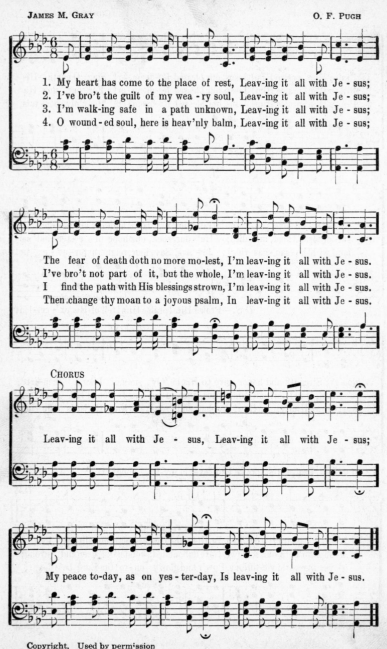

1. My heart has come to the place of rest, Leav-ing it all with Je-sus;
2. I've bro't the guilt of my wea-ry soul, Leav-ing it all with Je-sus;
3. I'm walk-ing safe in a path unknown, Leav-ing it all with Je-sus;
4. O wound-ed soul, here is heav'nly balm, Leav-ing it all with Je-sus;

The fear of death doth no more mo-lest, I'm leav-ing it all with Je-sus.
I've bro't not part of it, but the whole, I'm leav-ing it all with Je-sus.
I find the path with His blessings strown, I'm leav-ing it all with Je-sus.
Then change thy moan to a joyous psalm, In leav-ing it all with Je-sus.

CHORUS

Leav-ing it all with Je - sus, Leav-ing it all with Je - sus;

My peace to-day, as on yes-ter-day, Is leav-ing it all with Je - sus.

Thou Alone, Lord Jesus

Anon.

ED. MAURER, Har. by R. L. H.

1. Thou a - lone, Lord Je - sus, canst true peace im - part; Thou dost
2. Hearts bowed down with sad-ness, la - den with their sin, Thro' Thy
3. World - ly joy is fleet - ing, — van - i - ty it - self; Vain the

know the sor - row of the hu - man heart; Thou who cam'st from
blood, Lord Je - sus, bold - ly en - ter in, Glad - ly hear Thee
daz - zling bright-ness, vain the stores of wealth; Vain the pomp and

glo - ry here that heart to win, And in love for sin - ners
call - ing, "Come to Me and rest," Lose their heav - y bur - den
glo - ry; on - ly Thou canst give Peace and sat - is - fac - tion,

suf-fer'dst once for sin! There is none, Lord Je - sus, there is none like
on Thy lov-ing breast. There is none, Lord Je - sus, there is none like
whilst on earth we live. There is none, Lord Je - sus, there is none like

Thee, For the bro - ken - heart - ed there is none like Thee!
Thee, For the heav - y - la - den there is none like Thee!
Thee, For the soul that thirst - eth there is none like Thee!

"Thou Remainest"

EL NATHAN

JAMES McGRANAHAN

Moderato, with expression

1. "Thou re-main-est," blest Redeem-er, Lord of peace and Lord of strife;
2. Sat - is - fy - ing ev-ery long-ing Of my sin-ful soul for grace;
3. Earth-ly joys may soon be fad-ing, Wintry frosts sweet flowers destroy;
4. One by one my loved may leave me, Voic-es sweet no more be heard;
5. When from earth Thou, Lord, shalt call me, Calm I'll lay my bur-den down;

Je - sus, Sav-iour, Lord for - ev - er, "Thou re-mainest," Christ my life.
From my weakness nev - er turn-ing, "Thou re-mainest," Christ my peace.
But a - bove the cloud that's shading, "Thou re-mainest," Christ my joy.
But of God naught can be - reave me, "Thou re-mainest," Christ my Lord.
For I know, what-e'er be - fall me, "Thou re-mainest," Christ my crown.

CHORUS

"Thou re-main-est," "Thou re-main-est,"
"Thou re-main-est," "Thou re-main-est,"

"Thou re - main-est," Christ my all; (Christ my all;) Peace or

con - flict, joy or sor - row, "Thou re-main-est," Christ my all.

I'm a Pilgrim

Mary Dana Shindler

George S. Schuler

1. I'm a pil-grim, and I'm a stran-ger, I can tar-ry but a
2. Of that cit-y to which I jour-ney, My Re-deem-er is the
3. There the sunbeams are ev-er shin-ing; O my long-ing heart is

night; Do not de-tain me, for I am go-ing To where the
light; There is no sor-row, nor an-y sigh-ing, Nor an-y
there; Here in this coun-try, so dark and drear-y, I long have

CHORUS

streamlets are ev-er flow-ing.
tears there, nor an-y dy-ing.   I'm a pil-grim, and I'm a stran-ger,
wan-dered, for-lorn and wear-y.

I can tar-ry, I can tar-ry but a night;.... I'm a

ad lib.

pil-grim, and I'm a stran-ger, I can tar-ry, I can tar-ry but a night.

I can tar-ry, I can tar-ry but a night;

The Old Time Fire

W. H. BATHURST, arr.

D. B. TOWNER

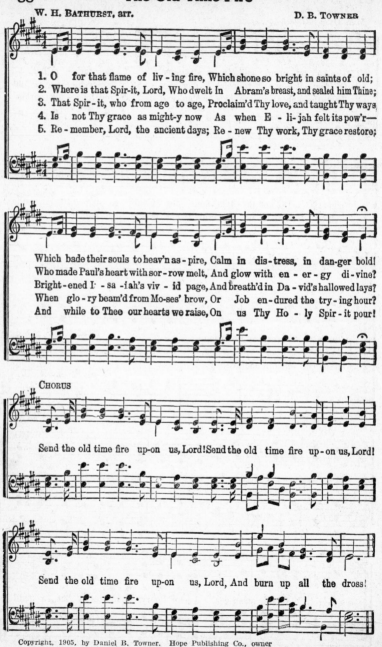

1. O for that flame of liv-ing fire, Which shone so bright in saints of old;
2. Where is that Spir-it, Lord, Who dwelt In Abram's breast, and sealed him Thine;
3. That Spir-it, who from age to age, Proclaim'd Thy love, and taught Thy ways,
4. Is not Thy grace as might-y now As when E - li - jah felt its pow'r-
5. Re - member, Lord, the ancient days; Re - new Thy work, Thy grace restore;

Which bade their souls to heav'n as-pire, Calm in dis-tress, in dan-ger bold!
Who made Paul's heart with sor-row melt, And glow with en - er-gy di-vine?
Bright-ened I - sa - iah's viv - id page, And breath'd in Da - vid's hallowed lays?
When glo - ry beam'd from Mo-ses' brow, Or Job en-dured the try-ing hour?
And while to Thee our hearts we raise, On us Thy Ho - ly Spir-it pour!

CHORUS

Send the old time fire up-on us, Lord! Send the old time fire up-on us, Lord!

Send the old time fire up-on us, Lord, And burn up all the dross!

Christ Is a Wonderful Savior

JEAN SHEWELL

GRACE DICKSON WHITE

1. Christ is a won-der-ful Sav - ior, He bore all my sins on the
2. Christ is a won-der-ful Sav - ior, My weak-ness no lon - ger I
3. Christ is a won-der-ful Sav - ior, From self I am al - so set
4. Christ is a won-der-ful Sav - ior, A ref - uge to whom I can

tree; He suf - fered and died, And I'm jus - ti - fied,— His
see; On Him I'll de - pend Un - til my life's end, His
free; No more my own way, For His I now pray,— His
flee; He has my whole heart, My all I im - part,— His

CHORUS

blood was suf-fi-cient for me.
strength is suf-fi-cient for me.
will is suf-fi-cient for me.
love is suf-fi-cient for me.

A won - der - ful Sav - ior,
A won-der-ful, won-der-ful Sav - ior is He,

A won - der - ful Sav - ior, I'll praise Him for aye,
A won-der-ful, won-der-ful Sav - ior is He,

I'll trust and o - bey,—For His grace is suf - fi - cient for me.

90   What Are You Doing for Them?

Mrs. H. S. L.

Mrs. H. S. LEHMAN

1. Is - ra-el's sheep scat-tered far   and wide, Wan-der-ing on with no
2. "First to the Jew" was the or - der He gave; First to the Jew came
3. Hid for a mo-ment His face at their call, Soon in His mer-cy He'll

shep-herd to guide, Far from the Sav-iour who for them has died; What are you
Je - sus to save; First to the Jew when sins He for-gave; What are you
gath - er them all; Loved for their fathers, e'en far tho' they fall; What are you

CHORUS

do-ing for them?
do-ing for them? How Je - sus loved them! but we have de-spised, For-
do-ing for them?

got-ten, neg-lect-ed, in scorn un - dis-guised. Think you to face Him and

hear His "Well done," With Is - rael, His cho-sen, left dy - ing a - lone?

91 Believe On the Lord Jesus Christ

AVIS B. CHRISTIANSEN

HARRY D. CLARKE

1. "What must I do?" the trembling jail-or cried, When dazed by
2. What must I do! O wea - ry, trembling soul, Just turn to-
3. His blood is all thy plea for sav-ing grace, The pre-cious

fear and won-der. "Be-lieve on Christ!" was all that Paul re-
day to Je - sus. He will re-ceive, for-give and make thee
fount of cleans-ing! O come, ac-cept His love, be-hold His

CHORUS

plied, "And thou shalt be saved from sin." Be-lieve on the
whole—Christ a-lone can set thee free.
face, And be saved for ev - er-more. Be-lieve

Lord Je-sus Christ, Be-lieve on the Lord Je-sus Christ, Be-
Be - lieve

lieve on the Lord Je-sus Christ, And thou shalt be saved!
Be - lieve

92 Until the Day Break

A. A. P.

D. B. TOWNER

1. The day is break-ing, Christian! The morn-ing draw-eth near! Re-deem the
2. The dead in Christ shall hear Him. And, thrilled with life a - rise! And we shall
3. O hope that pu - ri - fi - eth The souls that wait for Him! O look that
4. O, hark! what "Al - le - lu - ias," Like might y thun-der-ings, Pro-claim His

precious mo-ments! The King will soon ap-pear! A - mid in-creas-ing per - il He
join our loved ones In nev - er sundered ties! Then sor-row not, O Christian Nor
sat - is - fi - eth The eyes by tears made dim! We count all things as worthless To
reign tri - um-phant—The glor'ous King of Kings! Be-hold, with clouds He cometh, As

bids us watch and pray, O, may He find us faith - ful Un - til the break of day.
from thy Sav - iour stray! Be com-fort-ed, be - lov - ed, Un - til the break of day.
win the Christ for aye— A-bid-ing in His presence Un - til the break of day.
when He went a - way! O, ea - ger heart, be pat-'ent Un - til the break of day.

CHORUS

Un - til the day break! Al - le - lu-ia! Un - til the day break! Al - le - lu - ia!

Un - til the day break! Al - le - lu - ia! And the shadows, the shadows flee a-way.

93   Jesus is All the World to Me

W. L. T.

WILL L. THOMPSON

1. Je - sus is all the world to me, My life, my joy, my all;
2. Je - sus is all the world to me, My friend in tri - als sore;
3. Je - sus is all the world to me, And true to Him I'll be;
4. Je - sus is all the world to me, I want no bet - ter friend;

He is my strength from day to day, With-out Him I would fall;
I go to Him for bless - ings, and He gives them o'er and o'er;
Oh, how could I this friend de - ny, When He's so true to me?
I trust Him now, I'll trust Him when Life's fleet-ing days shall end;

When I am sad, to Him I go, No oth - er one can cheer me so;
He sends the sun-shine and the rain, He sends the har-vest's gold-en grain;
Fol - low - ing Him I know I'm right, He watch-es o'er me day and night;
Beau - ti - ful life with such a friend; Beau-ti-ful life that has no end;

When I am sad, He makes me glad, He's my friend.
Sun - shine and rain, har - vest of grain, He's my friend.
Fol - low - ing Him, by day and night, He's my friend.
E - ter - nal life, e - ter - nal joy, He's my friend.

94 Saved by the Blood

S. J. HENDERSON

D. B. TOWNER

1. Saved by the blood of the Cru-ci-fied One! Ran-somed from
2. Saved by the blood of the Cru-ci-fied One! The an-gels re-
3. Saved by the blood of the Cru-ci-fied One! The Fa-ther He
4. Saved by the blood of the Cru-ci-fied One! All hail to the

sin and a new work be-gun, Sing praise to the Fa-ther and
joic-ing be-cause it is done, A child of the Fa-ther, joint-
spoke, and His will it was done; Great price of my par-don, His
Fa-ther, all hail to the Son, All hail to the Spir-it, the

praise to the Son, Saved by the blood of the Cru-ci-fied One!
heir with the Son, Saved by the blood of the Cru-ci-fied One!
own pre-cious Son; Saved by the blood of the Cru-ci-fied One!
great Three in One! Saved by the blood of the Cru-ci-fied One!

CHORUS

Saved!...... saved!...... My sins are all pardoned, my guilt is all gone!
Glo-ry, I'm saved! glo-ry, I'm saved!

Saved!...... saved!...... I am saved by the blood of the Cru-ci-fied One!
Glo-ry, I'm saved! glo-ry, I'm saved!

95 I Find Thee so Precious

JAMES M. GRAY   JAMES McGRANAHAN

DUET OR SOLO (*Small notes for Solo*)

1. O what are the pleasures that sil - ver can buy? They come and they go,
2. I care not if all the proud world turn a-way, The plau - dits of men
3. As well in the cot-tage as un - der the dome, Be - side my own cot,

but can-not sat-is-fy; But, praised be the Sav-iour! I cease not to cry,
on - ly last for a day; Their frowns do not fright-en, or cause me dis-may,
or wher-ev - er I roam, The hon - ey from heav-en still drips from the comb:

CHORUS

I find Thee so pre-cious, my Sav - iour! O sweet-er and sweet-er, as

day fol-lows day, As the gold of the morning breaks forth thro' the gray; As I

lift up my soul, as I praise and I pray, I find Thee more precious, my Sav-iour!

96 No, Not One!

JOHNSON OATMAN

GEO. C. HUGG

1. There's not a friend like the low-ly Je-sus, No, not one! no, not one!
2. No friend like Him is so high and ho-ly, No, not one! no, not one!
3. There's not an hour that He is not near us, No, not one! no, not one!
4. Did ev-er saint find this Friend forsake him? No, not one! no, not one!
5. Was e'er a gift like the Sav-iour giv-en? No, not one! no, not one!

None else could heal all our soul's dis-eas-es, No, not one! no, not one!
And yet no friend is so meek and low-ly, No, not one! no, not one!
No night so dark but His love can cheer us, No, not one! no, not one!
Or sin-ner find that He would not take him? No, not one! no, not one!
Will He re-fuse us a home in heav-en? No, not one! no, not one!

CHORUS

Je-sus knows all a-bout our strug-gles, He will guide till the day is done;

There's not a friend like the low-ly Je-sus, No, not one! no, not one!

97 Complete In Thee!

Rev. A. R. WOLFE (Cho. added by J. M. G) T. J. BITTIKOFER

1. Complete in Thee! no work of mine May take, dear Lord, the place of Thine;
2. Complete in Thee—no more shall sin, Thy grace hath conquered, reign within;
3. Complete in Thee—each want supplied, And no good thing to me de-nied;
4. Dear Sav-iour! when be-fore Thy bar All tribes and tongues as-sem-bled are,

Thy blood hath par-don bought for me, And I am now com-plete in Thee.
Thy voice shall bid the tempt-er flee, And I shall stand com-plete in Thee.
Since Thou my por-tion, Lord, wilt be, I ask no more, com-plete in Thee.
A-mong Thy cho-sen will I be, At Thy right hand—com-plete in Thee.

CHORUS

Yea, jus-ti-fied! O bless-ed tho't! And sanc-ti-fied! Sal-va-tion wrought!

Thy blood hath par-don bought for me, And glo-ri-fied, I too, shall be!

William Williams
& Gipsy Smith

Arr. from Welsh by
E. Edwin Young

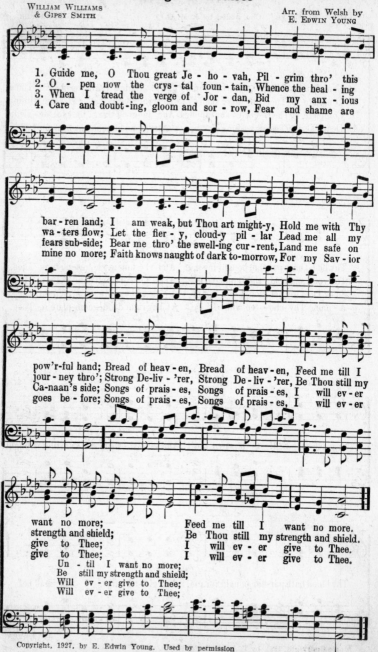

1. Guide me, O Thou great Je - ho - vah, Pil - grim thro' this
2. O - pen now the crys - tal foun - tain, Whence the heal - ing
3. When I tread the verge of Jor - dan, Bid my anx - ious
4. Care and doubt-ing, gloom and sor - row, Fear and shame are

bar - ren land; I am weak, but Thou art might-y, Hold me with Thy
wa - ters flow; Let the fier - y, cloud-y pil - lar Lead me all my
fears sub-side; Bear me thro' the swell-ing cur - rent, Land me safe on
mine no more; Faith knows naught of dark to-morrow, For my Sav - ior

pow'r-ful hand; Bread of heav - en, Bread of heav - en, Feed me till I
jour - ney thro'; Strong De-liv - 'rer, Strong De - liv - 'rer, Be Thou still my
Ca-naan's side; Songs of prais - es, Songs of prais - es, I will ev - er
goes be - fore; Songs of prais - es, Songs of prais - es, I will ev - er

want no more; Feed me till I want no more.
strength and shield; Be Thou still my strength and shield.
give to Thee; I will ev - er give to Thee.
give to Thee; I will ev - er give to Thee.
Un - til I want no more;
Be still my strength and shield;
Will ev - er give to Thee;
Will ev - er give to Thee;

99 What Did He Do?

JAMES M. GRAY (From the Welsh) W. OWEN

1. O lis-ten to our wondrous sto-ry! Count-ed once a-mong the lost,
2. No an-gel could our place have ta-ken, High-est of the high tho' he;
3. And yet this wondrous tale pro-ceed-eth, Stir-ring heart and tongue aflame!
4. Will you sur-ren-der to this Sav-iour—To His scep-ter hum-bly bow?

Yet One came down from heaven's glo-ry, Sav-ing us at aw-ful cost.
The loved One, on the cross for-sa-ken, Was one of the God-head Three!
As our High Priest in heav'n He pleadeth, And Christ Je-sus is His name!
You, too, shall come to know His fa-vor, He will save you, save you now!

CHORUS

Who saved us from e-ter-nal loss? What did He do?
Who but God's Son upon the cross? He

Where is He now? In heav-en in-ter-ced-ing!
died for you! Be-lieve it thou, In heav-en in-ter-ced-ing!

He is So Real to Me

W. M. R.

William M. Runyan

1. Some say it is a fa-ble and that Je-sus nev-er came, And some,that for our
2. The Bi-ble, say the doubters, is a sheaf of fa-bled lore; And Jesus, our bless'd
3. Back to the life of sin and doubt, thro' grace, I'll never turn, For Je-sus is the

Christian faith the dreamers are to blame; But when God's Spirit glo - ri - fied the
Je - sus, is a myth, and noth-ing more! But where the Bi-ble has been sent God's
liv - ing bread for which my soul did yearn; Im-part-ing peace and joy each day He's

liv - ing Christ in me The scales fell from my blinded eyes and now, praise God, I see!
blessings have been poured, And joy abounds in ev-'ry heart that makes this Jesus Lord.
all in all to me. How can I ev-er doubt Him more who saved and set me free!

CHORUS

He is so real (so real) to me, He is so real (so real) to me, From

sin's sad bond-age Je-sus set me free; His glo-rious presence thrills me, His

He Is So Real to Me

bless-ed Spir - it fills me,—Hal-le - lu-jah! He is so real (so real) to me!

101 God Will Take Care of You

C. D. MARTIN   Dedicated to my wife, Mrs. John A. Davis   W. S. MARTIN

1. Be not dis-mayed what-e'er be-tide, God will take care of you;
2. Thro' days of toil when hearts doth fail, God will take care of you;
3. All you may need He will pro-vide, God will take care of you;
4. No mat-ter what will be the test, God will take care of you;

Be - neath His wings of love a - bide, God will take care of you.
When dan-gers fierce your path as - sail, God will take care of you.
Noth- ing you ask will be de - nied, God will take care of you.
Lean, wea- ry one, up - on His breast, God will take care of you.

CHORUS

God will take care of you, Thro' ev - 'ry day, O'er all the way;

He will take care of you, God will take care of you.......
take care of you.

Faith Is the Victory

JOHN H. YATES

IRA D. SANKEY

1. En-camped a - long the hills of light, Ye Chris - tian sol - diers, rise,
2. His ban - ner o - ver us is love, Our sword the Word of God;
3. On ev - 'ry hand the foe we find Drawn up in dread ar - ray;
4. To him that o - ver - comes the foe, White rai - ment shall be given;

And press the bat - tle ere the night Shall veil the glow - ing skies.
We tread the road the saints a - bove With shouts of tri - umph trod.
Let tents of ease be left be - hind, And—on - ward to the fray.
Be - fore the an - gels he shall know His name con - fessed in heaven.

A - gainst the foe in vales be - low Let all our strength be hurled;
By faith, they like a whirl-wind's breath, Swept on o'er ev - 'ry field;
Sal - va - tion's hel - met on each head, With truth all girt a - bout,
Then on - ward from the hills of light, Our hearts with love a - flame;

Faith is the vic - to - ry, we know, That o - ver - comes the world.
The faith by which they con-quered death Is still our shin - ing shield.
The earth shall trem - ble 'neath our tread, And ech - o with our shout.
We'll van - quish all the hosts of night, In Je - sus' con-quering name.

Faith Is the Victory

Chorus

Faith.... is the vic-to-ry! Faith..... is the vic-to-ry!
Faith is the vic-to-ry! Faith is the vic-to-ry!

Oh, glo-ri-ous vic-to-ry, That o-ver-comes the world.

---

103 Let the Lower Lights Be Burning

P. P. B.

P. P. Bliss

1. Bright-ly beams our Fath-er's mer-cy, From His light-house ev-er-more,
2. Dark the night of sin has set-tled, Loud the an-gry bil-lows roar;
3. Trim your fee-ble lamp, my broth-er: Some poor sail-or tem-pest-tossed,

But to us He gives the keep-ing   Of the lights a-long the shore.
Ea-ger eyes are watch-ing, long-ing, For the lights a-long the shore.
Try-ing now to make the har-bor, In the dark-ness may be lost.

FINE

D.C.—*Some poor faint-ing, strug-gling sea-man You may res-cue, you may save.*

Chorus

D.C.

Let the low-er lights be burn-ing! Send a gleam a-cross the wave!

104   One Day!

J. Wilbur Chapman   Chas. H. Marsh

1. One day when heav - en was filled with His prais - es, One day when
2. One day they led Him up Cal - va - ry's moun - tain, One day they
3. One day they left Him a - lone in the gar - den, One day He
4. One day the grave could con - ceal Him no lon - ger, One day the
5. One day the trum - pet will sound for His com - ing, One day the

sin was as black as could be, Je - sus came forth to be
nailed Him to die on the tree; Suf - fer - ing an - guish, de -
rest - ed, from suf - fer - ing free; An - gels came down o'er His
stone rolled a - way from the door; Then He a - rose, o - ver
skies with His glo - ry will shine; Won - der - ful day, my be -

born of a vir - gin—Dwelt amongst men, my ex - am - ple is He!
spised and re - ject - ed: Bearing our sins, my Re - deem - er is He!
tomb to keep vig - il; Hope of the hope - less, my Sav - iour is He!
death He had con - quered; Now is as - cend - ed, my Lord ev - er - more!
lov - ed ones bring - ing; Glo - ri - ous Sav - iour, this Je - sus is mine!

CHORUS

Liv - ing, He loved me; dy - ing, He saved me; Bur - ied, He

car - ried my sins far a - way, Ris - ing, He jus - ti - fied

One Day!

cres. > > > > *rit.* > >

free - ly for - ev - er: One day He's com-ing— Oh, glo - ri-ous day!

105   Search Me, O God

GERTRUDE E. SWALLEN   WALTER J. MAIN

1. Search me, O God, and know my heart, Thy per-fect love to
2. Search out in me all hid - den sin, And may Thy pu - ri-
3. O search my life, my will, my all, As now on Thee, my

me im - part; Try me and know my ev - 'ry tho't,
ty with - in So cleanse my life, that it may be
Lord, I call; Purge me from self, and sanc - ti - fy

REFRAIN

That I may live as Thou hast taught. Search me, O God;
A tem - ple whol - ly fit for Thee.
My life, while Thee I glo - ri - fy. Search me,.. search me,

Repeat pp

search me, O God; O search Thou me, Al - might - y God.
O my God;

106 Make Me a Blessing

IRA B. WILSON
(To the Moody Memorial Church Choir) GEORGE S. SCHULER

1. Out in the high-ways and by-ways of life, Man-y are
2. Tell the sweet sto-ry of Christ and His love, Tell of His
3. Give as 'twas giv-en to you in your need, Love as the

wea-ry and sad;......... Car-ry the sun-shine where darkness is rife,
   are wea-ry and sad;
pow'r to for-give;........ Oth-ers will trust Him if on-ly you prove
   His pow'r to for-give;
Mas-ter loved you;......... Be to the help-less a help-er in-deed,
   the Mas-ter loved you;

rit.   **CHORUS.** *Men or Unison*

Mak-ing the sor-row-ing glad...... True, ev-'ry mo-ment you live...... Un-to your mis-sion be true ..... Make me a bless-ing,

Women

Make me a bless-ing, Out of my life........ may Je-
   Men   Out of my life

rit.   *Unison*   *Women*

sus shine;.... Make me a bless-ing, O Sav-iour,

Make Me a Blessing

I pray,...... Make me a bless-ing to some one to-day.
I pray Thee, my Sav-iour,

Tenors.

107   Just For Today

Arranged by J. M. G.   J. B. TROWBRIDGE

1. Lord, for to-mor-row and its needs   I do not pray; Keep me, my
2. Let   me both dil-i-gent-ly work, And du-ly pray; Let me be
3. Let   me be slow to do my will; Prompt to o-bey; Help me to
4. Let   me no wrong or i-dle word Un-think-ing say; Set Thou a

CHORUS

God, from stain of sin—   Just for   to-day.
kind in word and deed—   Just for   to-day. Just for to-day,
sac-ri-fice my-self—   Just for   to-day.
seal up-on my lips—   Just for   to-day.

Just for to-day. Lord, keep me, guide me, hold me, Just for to-day.

108   "Great Is Thy Faithfulness"

T. O. Chisholm   William M. Runyan

1. "Great is Thy faith-ful-ness," O God my Fa-ther, There is no
2. Sum-mer and win-ter, and spring-time and har-vest, Sun, moon and
3. Par-don for sin and a peace that en-dur-eth, Thy own dear

shad-ow of turn-ing with Thee; Thou chang-est not, Thy com-
stars in their cours-es a-bove, Join with all na-ture in
pres-ence to cheer and to guide; Strength for to-day and bright

pas-sions, they fail not, As Thou hast been Thou for-ev-er wilt be.
man-i-fold wit-ness, To Thy great faith-ful-ness, mer-cy and love.
hope for to-mor-row, Bless-ings all mine, with ten thou-sand be-side!

Chorus

"Great is Thy faith-ful-ness! Great is Thy faith-ful-ness!" Morn-ing by

morn-ing new mer-cies I see; All I have need-ed Thy

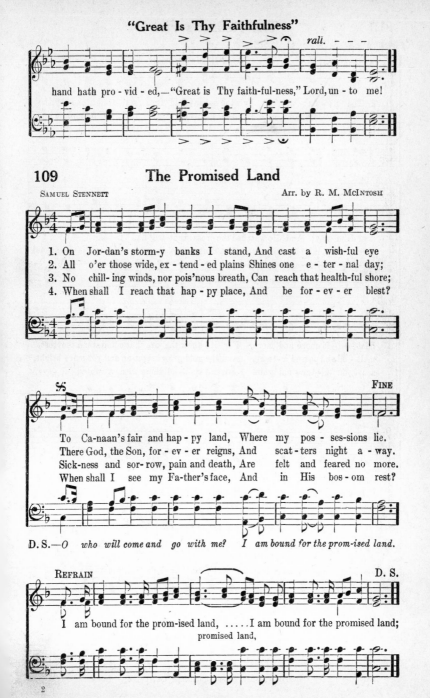

"Great Is Thy Faithfulness"

hand hath pro - vid - ed,— "Great is Thy faith-ful-ness," Lord, un - to me!

109   The Promised Land

SAMUEL STENNETT

Arr. by R. M. McINTOSH

1. On   Jor-dan's storm-y banks I stand, And cast a   wish-ful eye
2. All   o'er those wide, ex - tend - ed plains Shines one   e - ter - nal day;
3. No   chill- ing winds, nor pois'nous breath, Can reach that health-ful shore;
4. When shall I reach that hap - py place, And   be for - ev - er   blest?

To Ca-naan's fair and hap - py land, Where my pos - ses-sions lie.
There God, the Son, for - ev - er reigns, And   scat - ters night a - way.
Sick-ness and sor - row, pain and death, Are   felt and feared no more.
When shall I   see my Fa-ther's face, And   in His bos - om rest?

FINE

D. S.—O who will come and go with me?   I am bound for the prom-ised land.

REFRAIN

D. S.

I am bound for the prom-ised land, ... I am bound for the promised land;
promised land,

110   The Refiner's Fire

Arr. by James M. Gray

D. B. Towner

1. The Re - fin - er sat by the seven-fold fire, As He watched by the
2. So He laid our gold in the flam - ing fire, Tho' we fain would have
3. Should we think it pleased such a lov - ing heart For to cause us a

pre-cious ore, And He bent more close with a search-ing gaze, As He
said Him nay; And He watched the dross that we had not seen, And it
mo-ment's pain? 'Tis not so, but that thro' the pres - ent cross He should

heat - ed it more and more, For He knew the ore that could stand the test,
melt - ed and passed a - way, And the gold grew bright-er and yet more bright,
see an e - ter - nal gain. So He wait - ed there with a watch-ful eye,

And He want - ed the fin - est gold For to mould as a crown for the
But our eyes were so dim with tears That we saw but the fire, not the
And a love that is strong and sure; And His gold did not suf - fer a

CHORUS

King to wear, Set with gems with a price un - told.
Mas-ter's hand, And we ques-tioned with anx-ious fears. He knew He had
bit more heat Than was need - ed to make it pure.

The Refiner's Fire

ore that could stand the test, And He want-ed the fin-est gold To

mould as a crown for the King to wear, Set with gems with a price un-told.

111 **Prayer**

JAMES MONTGOMERY

FOSS L. FELLERS

1. Prayer is the soul's sin-cere de-sire, Ut-tered or un-ex-pressed;
2. Prayer is the bur-den of a sigh, The fall-ing of a tear,
3. Prayer is the sim-plest form of speech That in-fant lips can try;
4. Prayer is the Chris-tian's vi-tal breath, The Chris-tian's na-tive air,
5. O Thou, by whom we come to God, The Life, the Truth, the Way!

The mo-tion of a hid-den fire That trem-bles in the breast.
The up-ward glanc-ing of an eye, When none but God is near.
Prayer the sublimest strains that reach The Maj-es-ty on high.
His watchword at the gates of death; He en-ters heav'n with prayer.
The path of prayer Thy-self hast trod: Lord! teach us how to pray! A - MEN.

My Anchor Holds!

W. C. Martin

D. B. Towner

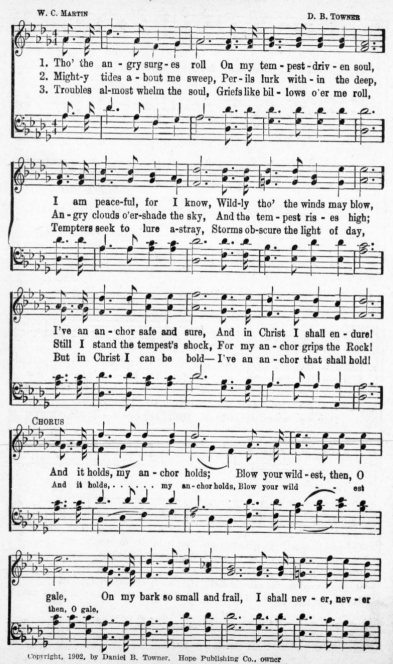

1. Tho' the an-gry surg-es roll On my tem-pest-driv-en soul,
2. Might-y tides a-bout me sweep, Per-ils lurk with-in the deep,
3. Troubles al-most whelm the soul, Griefs like bil-lows o'er me roll,

I am peace-ful, for I know, Wild-ly tho' the winds may blow,
An-gry clouds o'er-shade the sky, And the tem-pest ris-es high;
Tempters seek to lure a-stray, Storms ob-scure the light of day,

I've an an-chor safe and sure, And in Christ I shall en-dure!
Still I stand the tempest's shock, For my an-chor grips the Rock!
But in Christ I can be bold— I've an an-chor that shall hold!

CHORUS

And it holds, my an-chor holds; Blow your wild-est, then, O
And it holds, ... my an-chor holds, Blow your wild - - est

gale, On my bark so small and frail, I shall nev-er, nev-er
then, O gale,

My Anchor Holds!

fail; For my an - chor holds, my an-chor holds!
For my an - chor holds, it firm - ly holds,

113   Have You Any Room For Jesus?

Arr. by W. W. D. from L. W. M.

C. C. WILLIAMS

1. Have you an - y room for Je - sus, He who bore your load of sin;
2. Room for pleasure, room for busi-ness, But for Christ the cru - ci - fied,
3. Have you an - y room for Je - sus, As in grace He calls a - gain?
4. Room and time now give to Je - sus, Soon will pass God's day of grace;

As He knocks and asks ad-mis - sion, Sin - ner, will you let Him in?
Not a place that He can en - ter, In the heart for which He died?
O to - day is time ac-cept - ed, To-mor-row you may call in vain.
Soon thy heart left cold and si - lent, And Thy Sav-iour's pleading cease.

CHORUS

Room for Je - sus, King of glo - ry! Has - ten now His word o - bey;

Swing the heart's door wide-ly o - pen, Bid Him en - ter while you may.

114 My Redeemer

P. P. BLISS

JAMES McGRANAHAN

1. I will sing of my Re-deem-er, And His won-drous love to me;
2. I will tell the wondrous sto - ry, How my lost es-tate to save,
3. I will praise my dear Re-deem-er, His tri- umph-ant pow'r I'll tell;
4. I will sing of my Re-deem-er, And His heav'n-ly love to me;

On the cru - el cross He suf - fered, From the curse to set me free.
In His boundless love and mer - cy, He the ran - som free-ly gave.
How the vic - to - ry He giv - eth O - ver sin, and death, and hell.
He from death to life hath brought me, Son of God with Him to be.

CHORUS

Sing, oh, sing.............. of my Re - deem - er,
of my Re-deem - er, Sing, oh, sing of my Re-deem-er,

With His blood.............. He pur-chased me,..............
He purchased me, With His blood He purchased me,

On the cross............... He sealed my par - don,
He sealed my par - don, On the cross He sealed my par-don,

My Redeemer.—Concluded.

Repeat pp after last verse.

Paid the debt................. and made me free.................
and made me free, and made me free.

115

God Holds the Key

LLANELLY, 8. 4. 8. 8. 8. 4.

REV. JOHN PARKER   DAVID E. ROBERTS

1. God holds the key of all un-known, And I am glad,
2. What if to-mor-row's cares were here With-out its rest,
3. The ver-y dim-ness of my sight Makes me se-cure,
4. I can-not read His fu-ture plan, But this I know
5. E-nough; this cov-ers all my wants, And so I rest,

If oth-er hands should hold the key, Or if He
I'd rath-er He'd un-lock the day, And, as the
For, grop-ing in my mist-y way, I feel His
I have the smil-ing of His face, And all the
For, what I can-not, He can see, And, in His

rit.

trust-ed it to me, I might be sad, I might be sad.
hours swing o-pen, say, "My will is best," "My will is best."
hand; I hear Him say, "My help is sure," "My help is sure."
ref-uge of His grace, While here be-low, While here be-low.
care I safe shall be, For-ev-er blest, For-ev-er blest.

The Road Leads Home

Arr. by JAMES M. GRAY

D. B. TOWNER

1. O   pil - grim, as   you jour - ney,   Do you ev - er glad - ly say,
2. O   safe and bless - ed shel - ter, Heav'n-ly man-sions of   con - tent!
3. There's com - fort on   the jour - ney, There is al - so guide and chart;

In spite   of heav - y weath - er   And the rough-ness of   the way,
There are the ho - ly   kin - dred From our hearthstones ear - ly rent;
There's wis-dom for the ask - ing, And there's sol - ace for the heart;

That it real - ly does not mat - ter, All the strange and bit - ter stress,—
And our pre - cious, lov - ing Sav - iour, Who our sins on Cal - v'ry bore—
And there is   no need of turn - ing To the left or to   the right,

Heat and cold, and toil and sor - row,—Will be healed with bless - ed - ness!
Who would ev - er mind the jour - ney, With such bless - ed-ness in store?
And no fear need stir the bos - om At the com - ing of the night.

CHORUS

For the road leads home, Sweet, sweet home! O who would mind the

The Road Leads Home

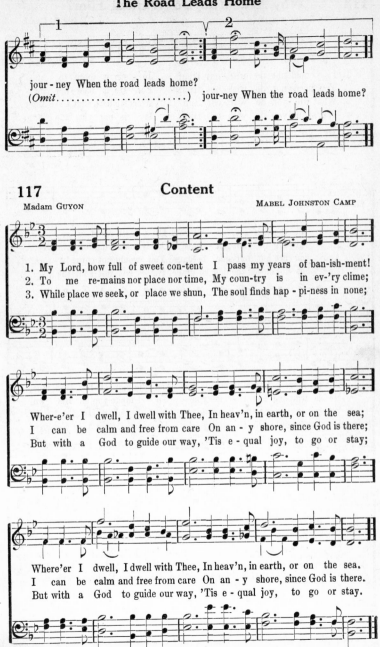

jour - ney When the road leads home?
(*Omit* . . . .) jour-ney When the road leads home?

117   **Content**

Madam GUYON   MABEL JOHNSTON CAMP

1. My Lord, how full of sweet con-tent I pass my years of ban-ish-ment!
2. To me re-mains nor place nor time, My coun-try is in ev-'ry clime;
3. While place we seek, or place we shun, The soul finds hap - pi-ness in none;

Wher-e'er I dwell, I dwell with Thee, In heav'n, in earth, or on the sea;
I can be calm and free from care On an - y shore, since God is there;
But with a God to guide our way, 'Tis e - qual joy, to go or stay;

Where'er I dwell, I dwell with Thee, In heav'n, in earth, or on the sea.
I can be calm and free from care On an - y shore, since God is there.
But with a God to guide our way, 'Tis e - qual joy, to go or stay.

118 *Why Will You Do Without Him?

FRANCES R. HAVERGAL

IVY E. CRAIG

1. I could not do with-out Him! Je - sus is more to me
2. You need not do with-out Him, For He is pass-ing by;
3. What will you do with-out Him? When He hath shut the door,
4. Why should you do with-out Him? It is not yet too late;

Than all the rich-est, fair - est gifts Of earth could ev - er be;....
He is wait-ing to be gra - cious, On-ly wait - ing for your cry;...
And you are left out-side be-cause You would not come be - fore?..
He has not closed the day of grace, He has not shut the gate...

But the more I find Him pre - cious, And the more I find Him true,
He is wait-ing to re - ceive you— To make you all His own,
When it is no use knock-ing, No use to stand and wait,
He calls you!—Oh, He calls you! He would not have you go

The more I long for you to find What He can be to you.
Why will you do with-out Him, And wan-der on a - lone?
For the word of doom tolls thro' your breast, That ter - ri - ble, "Too late!"
An - oth - er step with-out Him, Be - cause He loves you so.

Music copyright, 1920, by H. G. Tovey. Used by permission.
*From Poems—Frances R. Havergal. Used by permission of E. P. Dutton and Company

Why Will You Do Without Him?

CHORUS

Why will you do with-out Him? Is He not kind in - deed?

Did He not die to save you? Is He not all you need?

119 ## Praise Ye the Triune God!

Author unknown   INTEGER. 11s. 5.   F. F. FLEMMING

1. Praise ye the Fa - ther! for His lov-ing kind-ness, Ten - der-ly
2. Praise ye the Sav - iour! great is His com - pas - sion, Gra-cious-ly
3. Praise ye the Spir - it! Com-fort - er of Is - rael, Sent of the

cares He   for His err - ing chil - dren; Praise Him, ye an - gels,
cares He   for His cho - sen peo - ple; Young men and maid-ens,
Fa - ther and the Son to bless us; Praise ye the Fa - ther,

praise Him in the heav - ens, Praise ye Je - ho - vah!
ye old men and chil - dren, Praise ye the Sav - iour!
Son and Ho - ly Spir - it, Praise ye the Tri - une God! A - MEN.

What If It Were Today?

Mrs. C. H. M.

Mrs. C. H. Morris

1. Je - sus is com-ing to earth a-gain, What if it were to - day?
2. Sa - tan's do-min-ion will then be o'er, O that it were to - day!
3. Faith-ful and true would He find us here, If He should come to - day?

Com - ing in pow-er and love to reign, What if it were to - day?
Sor - row and sigh-ing shall be no more, O that it were to - day!
Watch-ing in glad-ness and not in fear, If He should come to - day?

Com - ing to claim His cho - sen Bride, All the re - deemed and
Then shall the dead in Christ a - rise, Caught up to meet Him
Signs of His com - ing mul - ti - ply, Morn-ing light breaks in

rit.

pu - ri - fied, O - ver this whole earth scat - tered wide,
in the skies, When shall these glo - ries meet our eyes?
east - ern sky, Watch, for the time is draw - ing nigh,

a tempo.

Chorus

What if it were to - day? Glo - ry! glo - ry!

What If It Were Today?

joy to my heart 'twill bring; Glo - ry! glo - ry! When we shall
Joy to my heart 'twill bring, When

crown Him king; Glo - ry! glo - ry! Haste to pre-pare the
we shall crown Him king, Haste to pre-

ritard.

way; Glo - ry! glo - ry! Je-sus will come some day.
pare the way;

121 ## I Am Coming to the Cross.

REV. WM. McDONALD

WM. G. FISCHER

1. I am com - ing to the cross; I am poor, and weak, and blind;
2. Long my heart has sighed for Thee, Long has e - vil reigned with-in,
3. Here I give my all to Thee, Friends, and time, and earth - ly store,

CHO.—*I am trust-ing, Lord, in Thee, Blest Lamb of Cal - va - ry;*

D.C. for Chorus.

I am count - ing all but dross; I shall full sal - va - tion find.
Je - sus sweet - ly speaks to me, "I will cleanse you from all sin."
Soul and bod - y Thine to be— Whol - ly Thine for - ev - er - more.

Hum-bly at Thy cross I bow. Save me, Je - sus, save me now.

122 Bringing Back the King

JAMES M. GRAY

JAMES McGRANAHAN

1. Why say ye not a word Of bring-ing back the King? Why
2. Dost thou not want to look Up - on His lov - ing face? Dost
3. O hark! cre - a-tion's groans, How can they be as-suaged? How
4. Come quick-ly, bless - ed Lord, Our hearts a wel - come hold! We

speak ye not of Je - sus and His reign? Why tell ye of His king-dom,
thou not want to see Him glo-ri - fied? Would'st thou not hear His wel-come,
can our bod - ies know re-demptive joy? How can the war be end - ed
long to see cre - a-tion's sec-ond birth; The prom-ise of Thy com-ing

And of its glo - ries sing, But noth-ing of His com-ing back a-gain?
And in that ver - y place, Where years a - go we saw Him cru - ci - fied?
In which we are en-gaged, Un - til He come the law - less to de - stroy?
To some is grow-ing cold, O has - ten Thy re - turn-ing back to earth.

CHORUS

Bring-ing back the King, Oh, bringing back the King! The an - gel choirs of

Bringing Back the King

heav'n their hal - le - lu - jahs sing, Ho-san - na! Bring-ing back the King, Oh,

bring-ing back the King! Ye ransomed, let your joy-ous wel-come ring!

123   **Fairest Lord Jesus**

CRUSADERS' HYMN   ARR. BY RICHARD S. WILLIS

1. Fair - est Lord Je - sus! Rul - er of all na - ture!
2. Fair are the mead - ows, Fair - er still the wood - lands,
3. Fair is the sun - shine, Fair - er still the moon - light,

O Thou of God and man the Son! Thee will I cher - ish,
Robed in the bloom-ing garb of spring; Je - sus is fair - er,
And all the twink-ling star - ry host; Je - sus shines bright - er,

Thee will I hon - or, Thou, my soul's glo - ry, joy, and crown!
Je - sus is pur - er, Who makes the woe - ful heart to sing!
Je - sus shines pur - er, Than all the an - gels heaven can boast!

Count Your Blessings

Rev. J. Oatman, Jr.

E. O. Excell

1. When up-on life's bil-lows you are tem-pest-tossed, When you are dis-
2. Are you ev-er bur-dened with a load of care? Does the cross seem
3. When you look at oth-ers with their lands and gold, Think that Christ has
4. So, a-mid the con-flict, wheth-er great or small, Do not be dis-

couraged, thinking all is lost, Count your many blessings, name them one by
heav-y you are called to bear? Count your many blessings, ev-'ry doubt will
promised you His wealth un-told; Count your many blessings, money can-not
couraged, God is o-ver all; Count your many blessings, an-gels will at-

one, And it will surprise you what the Lord hath done.
fly, And you will be singing as the days go by. Count your blessings, Name them
buy Your reward in heaven, nor your home on high.
tend, Help and comfort give you to your journey's end.

CHORUS

Count your many blessings,

one by one; Count your blessings, See what God hath done; Count your

Name them one by one; Count your many blessings, See what God hath done; Count your many

Count Your Blessings

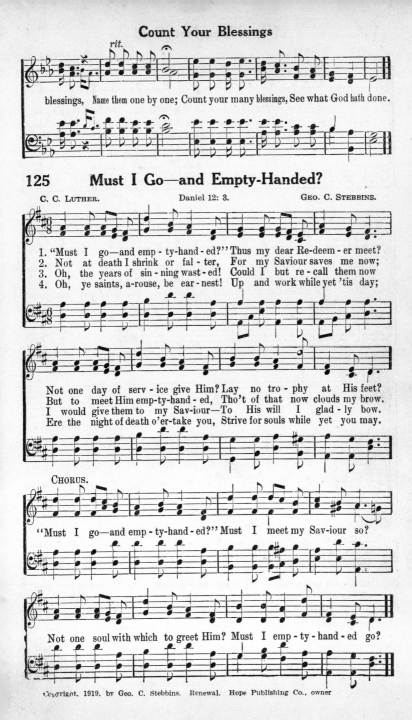

blessings, Name them one by one; Count your many blessings, See what God hath done.

125 Must I Go—and Empty-Handed?

C. C. Luther.   Daniel 12: 3.   Geo. C. Stebbins.

1. "Must I go—and emp-ty-hand-ed?" Thus my dear Re-deem-er meet?
2. Not at death I shrink or fal-ter, For my Saviour saves me now;
3. Oh, the years of sin-ning wast-ed! Could I but re-call them now
4. Oh, ye saints, a-rouse, be ear-nest! Up and work while yet 'tis day;

Not one day of serv-ice give Him? Lay no tro-phy at His feet?
But to meet Him emp-ty-hand-ed, Tho't of that now clouds my brow.
I would give them to my Sav-iour—To His will I glad-ly bow.
Ere the night of death o'er-take you, Strive for souls while yet you may.

CHORUS.

"Must I go—and emp-ty-hand-ed?" Must I meet my Sav-iour so?

Not one soul with which to greet Him? Must I emp-ty-hand-ed go?

126 Nor Silver Nor Gold

JAMES M. GRAY

D. B. TOWNER

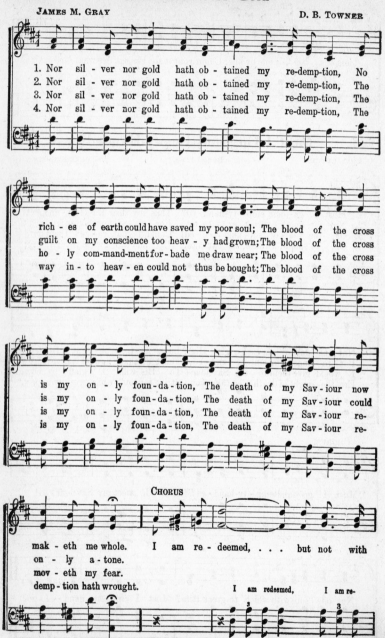

1. Nor sil - ver nor gold hath ob - tained my re-demp-tion, No
2. Nor sil - ver nor gold hath ob - tained my re-demp-tion, The
3. Nor sil - ver nor gold hath ob - tained my re-demp-tion, The
4. Nor sil - ver nor gold hath ob - tained my re-demp-tion, The

rich - es of earth could have saved my poor soul; The blood of the cross
guilt on my conscience too heav - y had grown; The blood of the cross
ho - ly com-mand-ment for-bade me draw near; The blood of the cross
way in - to heav - en could not thus be bought; The blood of the cross

is my on - ly foun - da - tion, The death of my Sav - iour now
is my on - ly foun - da - tion, The death of my Sav - iour could
is my on - ly foun - da - tion, The death of my Sav - iour re-
is my on - ly foun - da - tion, The death of my Sav - iour re-

CHORUS

mak - eth me whole. I am re - deemed, . . . but not with
on - ly a - tone.
mov - eth my fear.
demp - tion hath wrought.   I am redeemed,   I am re-

Nor Silver Nor Gold

sil - ver, I am bought..... but not with
deemed, but not with sil - ver, I am bought, I am

gold; Bought with a price.......... the blood of
bought, but not with gold; Bought with a price— the

Je - sus, Pre - cious price of love un - told!
pre - cious blood of Je - sus,

127 My Heart's Prayer

H. P. Blanchard

Ralph E. Stewart

1. My new life I owe to Thee, Je - sus, Lamb of Cal - va - ry;
2. Hum - bly at Thy cross I'd stay, Je - sus, keep me there, I pray;
3. Grant me wis - dom, grace and pow'r, Lord, I need Thee ev - 'ry hour.
4. Sav - iour, Thou hast heard my plea, Thou art near—so near to me;

Sin was can - celed on the tree, Je - sus, bless - ed Je - sus.
Teach me more of Thee, each day, Je - sus, bless - ed Je - sus.
Let my will be lost in Thine, Je - sus, bless - ed Je - sus.
Now I feel Thy strength'ning pow'r, Je - sus, bless - ed Je - sus.

5

128 The Cleansing Blood

Mrs. Elizabeth Miller

Oscar A. Miller

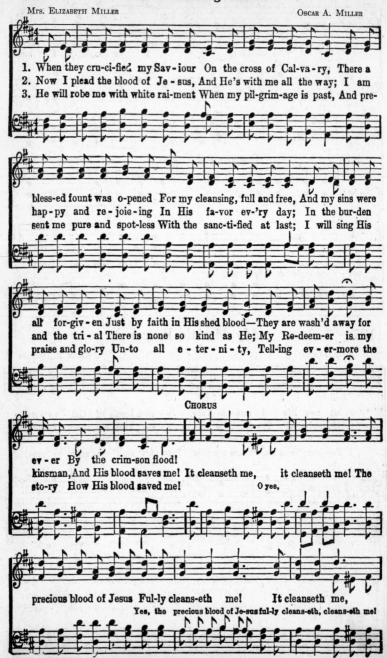

1. When they cru-ci-fied my Sav-iour On the cross of Cal-va-ry, There a
2. Now I plead the blood of Je-sus, And He's with me all the way; I am
3. He will robe me with white rai-ment When my pil-grim-age is past, And pre-

bless-ed fount was o-pened For my cleansing, full and free, And my sins were
hap-py and re-joic-ing In His fa-vor ev-'ry day; In the bur-den
sent me pure and spot-less With the sanc-ti-fied at last; I will sing His

all for-giv-en Just by faith in His shed blood—They are wash'd away for
and the tri-al There is none so kind as He; My Re-deem-er is. my
praise and glo-ry Un-to all e-ter-ni-ty, Tell-ing ev-er-more the

Chorus

ev-er By the crim-son flood!
kinsman, And His blood saves me! It cleanseth me, it cleanseth me! The
sto-ry How His blood saved me! O yes,

precious blood of Jesus Ful-ly cleans-eth me! It cleanseth me,
Yes, the precious blood of Je-sus ful-ly cleans-eth, cleans-eth me!

The Cleansing Blood

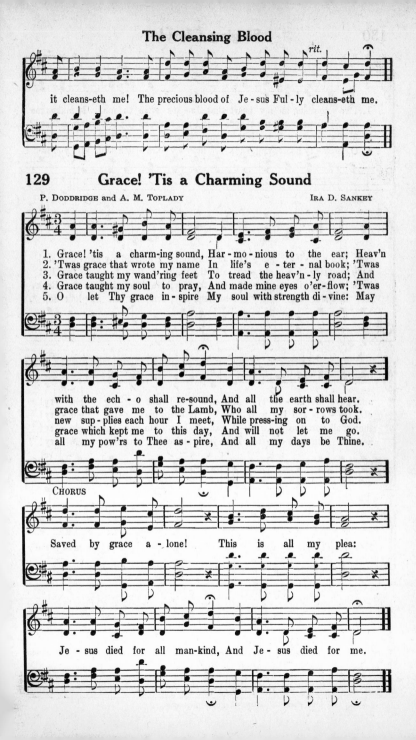

it cleans-eth me! The precious blood of Je-sus Ful-ly cleans-eth me.

129　Grace! 'Tis a Charming Sound

P. DODDRIDGE and A. M. TOPLADY

IRA D. SANKEY

1. Grace! 'tis a charm-ing sound, Har-mo-nious to the ear; Heav'n
2. 'Twas grace that wrote my name In life's e-ter-nal book; 'Twas
3. Grace taught my wand'ring feet To tread the heav'n-ly road; And
4. Grace taught my soul to pray, And made mine eyes o'er-flow; 'Twas
5. O let Thy grace in-spire My soul with strength di-vine: May

with the ech-o shall re-sound, And all the earth shall hear.
grace that gave me to the Lamb, Who all my sor-rows took.
new sup-plies each hour I meet, While press-ing on to God.
grace which kept me to this day, And will not let me go.
all my pow'rs to Thee as-pire, And all my days be Thine.

CHORUS

Saved by grace a-lone! This is all my plea:

Je-sus died for all man-kind, And Je-sus died for me.

Singing Glory!

L. R. M.   L. R. Minor

1. I've something in my heart that Je-sus gave to me, It makes me
2. My Sav-iour loosed my tongue that I might speak His praise; Since then I
3. My Sav-iour took my feet from out the mir-y clay; Since then I
4. O wea-ry heart, and sad, O heav-y-la-den soul, If you would

feel like sing-ing glo-ry all the day; He found my cap-tive soul
have been sing-ing glo-ry all the day; I love to tell the lost
have been sing-ing glo-ry all the day; He placed them on the Rock
feel like sing-ing glo-ry all the day, Just let the Sav-iour in,

and gave me lib-er-ty, And now I feel like sing-ing glo-ry!
of Je-sus and His ways, And oh, it keeps me sing-ing glo-ry!
that shall not pass a-way— I can-not keep from sing-ing glo-ry!
and let Him take con-trol: Then you will feel like sing-ing glo-ry!

CHORUS

He makes the path grow bright-er ev-'ry pass-ing day, He makes the

bur-den light-er all a-long the way; His Word is my de-light

Singing Glory!

His will I now o-bey, And all the time I'm sing-ing glo-ry!

131   More Love to Thee!

Mrs. E. Prentiss

W. H. Doane

1. More love to Thee, O Christ! More love to Thee; Hear Thou the
2. Once earth-ly joy I craved, Sought peace and rest; Now Thee a-
3. Let sor-row do its work, Send peace or pain; Sweet are thy
4. Then shall my lat-est breath Whis-per Thy praise; This be the

prayer I make On bend-ed knee. This is my ear-nest plea,
lone I seek, Give what is best. This all my prayer shall be,
mes-sen-gers, Sweet their re-frain, When they can sing with me,—
part-ing cry My heart shall raise, This still its prayer shall be:

More love, O Christ, to Thee, More love to Thee! More love to Thee!

132 The Saviour for Me

W. M. R.
DUET

WILLIAM M. RUNYAN

1. From heav-en a-bove, in His in-fi-nite love, Came Je-sus, a
2. The birds had their nest and the peo-ple their rest, While Je-sus all
3. For sil-ver be-trayed, in mock pur-ple ar-rayed, Con-demned to a

Sav-iour to be; And He scorned the deep pain our ran-som to gain,
night made His plea; On the mountain a-lone was the Father's dear Son,
death on the tree; Then they led Him a-way on that Won-der-ful Day,

O He is the Sav-iour for me...............
the Sav-iour for me.

CHORUS.

O Je-sus is will-ing to be................. A Sav-iour for
and wait-ing to be

sin-ners like me,................ And the bur-den will roll from the
e-ven me,

The Saviour for Me.

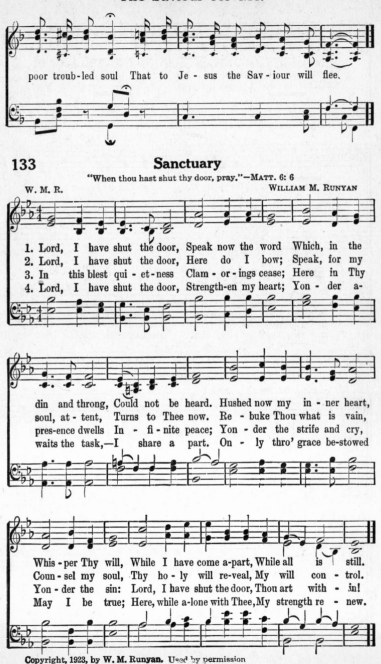

poor troub-led soul That to Je - sus the Sav - iour will flee.

133 Sanctuary

"When thou hast shut thy door, pray."—MATT. 6: 6

W. M. R.   WILLIAM M. RUNYAN

1. Lord, I have shut the door, Speak now the word Which, in the
2. Lord, I have shut the door, Here do I bow; Speak, for my
3. In this blest qui - et-ness Clam - or - ings cease; Here in Thy
4. Lord, I have shut the door, Strength-en my heart; Yon - der a-

din and throng, Could not be heard. Hushed now my in - ner heart,
soul, at - tent, Turns to Thee now. Re - buke Thou what is vain,
pres-ence dwells In - fi - nite peace; Yon - der the strife and cry,
waits the task,—I share a part. On - ly thro' grace be-stowed

Whis - per Thy will, While I have come a-part, While all is still.
Coun - sel my soul, Thy ho - ly will re-veal, My will con - trol.
Yon - der the sin: Lord, I have shut the door, Thou art with - in!
May I be true; Here, while a-lone with Thee, My strength re - new.

134 His Eye Is On the Sparrow

Mrs. C. D. Martin   Chas. H. Gabriel

1. Why should I feel dis-cour-aged, Why should the shad-ows come,
2. "Let not your heart be trou-bled," His ten-der word I hear,
3. When-ev-er I am tempt-ed, When-ev-er clouds a-rise,

Why should my heart be lone-ly And long for heaven and home, When
And rest-ing on His good-ness, I lose my doubts and fears; Though
When songs give place to sigh-ing, When hope with-in me dies, I

Je-sus is my por-tion? My con-stant friend is He: His
by the path He lead-eth, But one step I may see: His
draw the clos-er to Him, From care He sets me free; His

eye is on the spar-row, And I know He watch-es me; His
eye is on the spar-row, And I know He watch-es me; His
eye is on the spar-row, And I know He cares for me; His

eye is on the spar-row, And I know He watch-es me.
eye is on the spar-row, And I know He watch-es me.
eye is on the spar-row, And I know He cares for me.

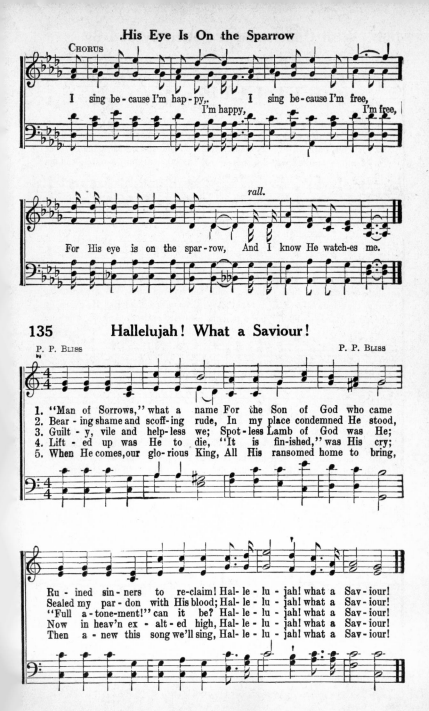

His Eye Is On the Sparrow

CHORUS

I sing be-cause I'm hap-py, I sing be-cause I'm free,
I'm happy, I'm free,

For His eye is on the spar-row, And I know He watch-es me.

rall.

135

Hallelujah! What a Saviour!

P. P. BLISS

P. P. BLISS

1. "Man of Sorrows," what a name For the Son of God who came
2. Bear - ing shame and scoff-ing rude, In my place condemned He stood,
3. Guilt - y, vile and help-less we; Spot-less Lamb of God was He;
4. Lift - ed up was He to die, "It is fin-ished," was His cry;
5. When He comes, our glo-rious King, All His ransomed home to bring,

Ru - ined sin-ners to re-claim! Hal - le - lu - jah! what a Sav-iour!
Sealed my par-don with His blood; Hal - le - lu - jah! what a Sav-iour!
"Full a-tone-ment!" can it be? Hal - le - lu - jah! what a Sav-iour!
Now in heav'n ex - alt - ed high, Hal - le - lu - jah! what a Sav-iour!
Then a - new this song we'll sing, Hal - le - lu - jah! what a Sav-iour!

136 We'll Understand It Better By and By

Words and Music by C. A. TINDLEY
Arr. by F. A. CLARK

1. We are oft-en tossed and driv-en on the rest-less sea of time, Som-ber
2. We are oft-en des-ti-tute of the things that life demands, Want of
3. Tri-als dark on ev-'ry hand, and we can-not un-der-stand All the
4. Temp-ta-tions, hid-den snares, oft-en take us un-a-wares, And our

skies and howl-ing tempest oft suc-ceed a bright sunshine; In that land of
shel-ter and of food— thirst-y hills and bar-ren lands; We are trust-ing
ways that God would lead us to that bless-ed Promised Land; But He guides us
hearts are made to bleed for a thought-less word or deed; And we won-der

per-fect day, when the mists have rolled a-way, We will un-der-stand it
in the Lord, and ac-cord-ing to His Word, We will un-der-stand it
with His eye, and we'll fol-low till we die, For we'll un-der-stand it
why the test, when we try to do our best, But we'll un-der-stand it

D. S.—*For we'll un-der-stand it*

FINE

CHORUS

bet-ter by and by.　　By and by, when the morn-ing comes,

bet-ter by and by. (by and by)

We'll Understand It Better By and By

All the saints of God are gathered home, We'll tell the sto-ry how we've o-ver-come,

137   Alone With God

MRS. B. A. THOMPSON   D. B. TOWNER

1. A-lone with God—Shut is the door; Tho' sad and troub-led, tempted sore,
2. A-lone with God—And, while we pray, Our cares take wings and fly a-way;
3. A-lone with God—O hallowed spot, Where many a les-son has been taught,
4. A-lone with God—Whom we a-dore-Drawn are the shades and closed the door,
5. A-lone with God—A-new be-gin, Go forth fresh vic-to-ries to win;

How sweet to be On bend-ed knee, As out to Him our hearts we pour—
As on His breast We sweet-ly rest, Our sorrow's night is turned to day—
And vic-t'ry won Thro' His dear Son, In man-y a bat-tle that was fought—
In this re-treat, In serv-ice sweet, We learn to love Him more and more—
Je-sus, our King, Whose praise we sing, Is now enthroned our hearts with-in—

rit.

As out to Him our hearts we pour—A-lone with God, A-lone with God.
Our sorrow's night is turned to day—A-lone with God, A-lone with God.
In many a bat-tle that was fought—A-lone with God, A-lone with God.
We learn to love Him more and more—A-lone with God, A-lone with God.
Is now enthroned our hearts with-in—A-lone with God, A-lone with God.

He Hideth My Soul

Fanny J. Crosby

Wm. J. Kirkpatrick

1. A won-der-ful Sav-iour is Je-sus my Lord, A won-der-ful Sav-iour to me; He hid-eth my soul in the cleft of the rock, Where riv-ers of pleas-ure I see.
2. A won-der-ful Sav-iour is Je-sus my Lord, He tak-eth my bur-den a-way; He hold-eth me up, and I shall not be moved, He giv-eth me strength as my day.
3. With num-ber-less bless-ings each mo-ment He crowns, And filled with His ful-ness di-vine; I sing in my rap-ture, O glo-ry to God For such a Re-deem-er as mine!
4. When clothed in His bright-ness trans-port-ed I rise To meet Him in clouds of the sky, His per-fect sal-va-tion, His won-der-ful love, I'll shout with the mil-lions on high.

CHORUS

He hid-eth my soul in the cleft of the rock, That shad-ows a dry, thirst-y land; He hid-eth my life in the depths of His love,

He Hideth My Soul

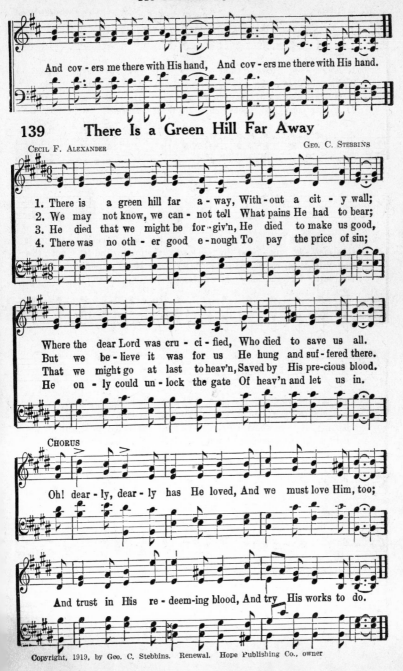

And cov - ers me there with His hand, And cov - ers me there with His hand.

139 There Is a Green Hill Far Away

CECIL F. ALEXANDER

GEO. C. STEBBINS

1. There is   a green hill far   a - way, With - out a cit - y wall;
2. We may   not know, we can - not tell What pains He had   to bear;
3. He died that we might be for - giv'n, He died   to make us good,
4. There was   no oth - er good e - nough To   pay   the price of sin;

Where the   dear Lord was cru - ci - fied, Who died to save us all.
But   we   be - lieve it was for us   He hung and suf - fered there.
That we   might go   at last   to heav'n, Saved by   His pre - cious blood.
He on - ly could un - lock the gate Of heav'n and let   us in.

CHORUS

Oh! dear - ly, dear - ly has He loved, And we   must love Him, too;

And trust in His   re - deem - ing blood, And try   His works to do.

140 Ye Must Be Born Again

W. T. Sleeper

Geo. C. Stebbins

1. A rul-er once came to Je-sus by night, To ask Him the way of sal-va-tion and light; The Mas-ter made an-swer in words true and plain, "Ye must be born a-gain." ..
2. Ye chil-dren of men, at-tend to the word So sol-emn-ly ut-tered by Je-sus, the Lord, And let not this mes-sage to you be in vain, "Ye must be born a-gain." ..
3. O ye who would en-ter that glo-ri-ous rest, And sing with the ran-somed the song of the blest, The life ev-er-last-ing if ye would ob-tain, "Ye must be born a-gain." ..
4. A dear one in heav-en thy heart yearns to see, At the beau-ti-ful gate may be watch-ing for thee; Then list to the note of this sol-emn re-frain, "Ye must be born a-gain." ..

Chorus

"Ye must be born a-gain," .. "Ye must be born a-gain," .. I

Ye Must Be Born Again

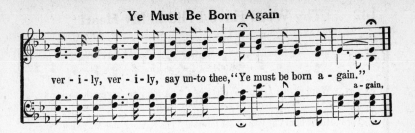

ver - i - ly, ver - i - ly, say un-to thee, "Ye must be born a - gain."

a - gain,

141 Ever Waiting for the Lord

Psalm 130

WILLIAM H. YOUNG

1. From the depths do I in - voke Thee; O Je - ho - vah, give an ear;
2. Lord, if Thou shouldst mark transgres-sions, Who before Thee, Lord, shall stand?
3. For Je - ho - vah I am wait - ing, And my hope is in His word,
4. For the Lord my soul is wait - ing, More than watchers in the night,

To my voice be Thou at - ten - tive And my sup-pli - ca-tion hear.
But with Thee there is for - give - ness That Thy name may fear command.
In His word of prom-ise giv - en; Yea, my soul waits for the Lord.
More than they for morn-ing watch-ing, Watch-ing for the morn-ing light.

CHORUS

I am wait - ing, wait - ing, Wait-ing, ev - er wait-ing for the Lord;

I am wait - ing, wait - ing, Ev - er wait-ing for the Lord.

142 Thy Word Have I Hid in My Heart

ADAPTED BY E. O. S.

E. O. SELLERS

1. Thy Word is a lamp to my feet, A light to my path al - way,
2. For - ev - er, O Lord, is Thy Word Established and fixed on high;
3. At morn-ing, at noon, and at night, I ev - er will give Thee praise;
4. Thro' Him whom Thy Word hath foretold, The Saviour and Morn-ing Star,

To guide and to save me from sin, And show me the heav'n-ly way.
Thy faith-ful-ness un - to all men A - bid-eth for-ev - er nigh.
For Thou art my por-tion, O Lord, And shall be thro' all my days.
Sal - va - tion and peace have been bro't To those who have strayed a - far.

CHORUS   Ps. 119: 11.

Thy Word have I hid in my heart,........ That I might not
in my heart,

sin a-gainst Thee;............. That I might not sin, That
a - gainst Thee;

ad lib.

I might not sin, Thy Word have I hid in my heart.

143 O How Love I Thy Law!

Psalm 19. C. M. JAMES McGRANAHAN

1. God's law is per - fect and con-verts The soul in sin that lies;
2. The stat-utes of the Lord are right And do re - joice the heart;
3. Un - spot-ted is the fear of God And ev - er doth en - dure;
4. More - o - ver, they Thy ser - vant warn How he his life should frame;

God's tes - ti - mo - ny is most sure, And makes the sim - ple wise.
The Lord's command is pure and doth Light to the eyes im - part.
The judg-ments of the Lord are truth And right-eous-ness most pure.
A great re-ward pro - vid - ed is For them that keep the same.

CHORUS (Psa. 119: 97, Prose Version)

O how love I Thy law! O how love I Thy law! It is my med - i -

ta - tion all..... the day; O how love I Thy law! O how

love I Thy law! It is my med - i - ta - tion all the day.................
all the day.

144 Whiter Than the Snow

Psalm 51. C. M.   IDANA   Charles H. Gabriel

1. O God, ac-cord-ing to Thy grace Be mer-ci-ful to me;
2. O wash me whol-ly from my guilt And make me clean with-in;
3. From out Thy pres-ence cast me not, Thy face no more to see;
4. Re-store me Thy sal-va-tion's joy, My will-ing heart up-hold;

In Thine a-bounding love blot out All my in-iq-ui-ty.
For my trans-gres-sions I con-fess, I ev-er see my sin.
Thy Ho-ly Spir-it and His grace Take not a-way from me.
Then sin-ners shall be turned to Thee When I Thy ways un-fold.

Chorus

Whit-er than the snow,.... Whit-er than the snow,....
Whit-er, whit-er than the snow, Whit-er, whit-er than the snow,

Wash   me   wash   me and I shall be whit-er than snow.
Wash me and I shall be whit-er than snow, and I shall be whit-er than snow.

145 O Thou My Soul, Bless God the Lord

PSALM 103. C. M.
JAMES McGRANAHAN

1. O thou my soul, bless God the Lord, And all that in me is,
2. Bless, O my soul, the Lord thy God, And not for-get-ful be,
3. All thy in-iq-ui-ties who doth Most gra-cious-ly for-give,
4. The Lord Je-ho-vah gra-cious is, And He is mer-ci-ful,

Be lift-ed up, His ho-ly name To mag-ni-fy and bless.
Of all His gra-cious ben-e-fits, He hath bestowed on thee.
Who thy dis-eas-es all and pains Doth heal and thee re-lieve.
Long-suf-fer-ing and slow to wrath, In kind-ness plen-ti-ful.

CHORUS

"Bless the Lord, Bless the Lord, Bless the Lord, O my
Bless the Lord, Bless the Lord;

soul, And all that is with-in me, Bless His ho-ly name.
Bless His ho-ly

5 He will not chide continually,
　Nor keep His anger still;
With us He dealt not as we sinned,
　Nor did requite our ill.

6 For as the heaven in its height
　The earth surmounteth far;
So great to those that do Him fear
　His tender mercies are.

7 As far as east is distant from
　The west, so far hath He
From us removed, in tender love,
　All our iniquity.

8 O ye His angels, that excel
　In strength, bless ye the Lord;
Ye who obey, what He commands,
　And hearken to His word.

9 O bless and magnify the Lord,
　Ye glorious hosts of His;
Ye ministers that do fulfill
　Whate'er His pleasure is.

10 O bless the Lord, all ye His works,
　Wherewith the world is stored,
In His dominions everywhere;
　My soul bless thou the Lord.

Scotch Version

146 Wounded for Our Transgressions

Mrs. C. H. M.   Mrs. C. H. MORRIS

Adagio

1. Sing we the prais-es of Je-sus, the won-der-ful Sav-ior of men;....
2. To Beth-le-hem of Ju-de-a a Babe in a man-ger He came;...
3. Glo - ry to God in the highest, our glad hearts exultingly sing,....

Sing how He died for our ransom, yet liv-eth in glo-ry a - gain;....
Lived He a life of the low-ly, en-dur-ing the cross and its shame; ..
Prais - es for-ev - er and ev - er to Je - sus our Sav-ior and King;....

Tell how His grace is suf-fi-cient a world of lost sin-ners to save;...
Tempt-ed in all points as we are, and yet without sin was He found;..
No more de-spised and re-ject-ed, for sin-ners to suf-fer and die,....

Tell how who-ev -er be-liev-eth a per-fect sal-va-tion shall have....
God - man, our frailties He knows, and His grace doth to sinners abound..
Worshiped, enthroned and exalted, He liv-eth for-ev - er on high......

Wounded for Our Transgressions

CHORUS *Largo* *pp rit.* — — — — — —

Wound-ed for our trans-gres-sions, Treading the wine-press a-lone;....

p tempo adagio

Brought as a lamb to the slaugh-ter, Je-sus the In-fi-nite

f

One........ Shall we not praise Him for-ev — er,

Harmony

Wor-ship His name and a-dore?.... He who was slain, but now

liv-eth a-gain, Is our Sav-ior for-ev-er-more......

ev-er-more.

147 Hallelujah for the Cross!

HORATIUS BONAR, arr. JAMES McGRANAHAN

1. The cross it standeth fast, Hal - le - lu - jah, hal - le lu - jah! De - fy - ing
2. It is the old cross still, Hal - le - lu - jah, hal - le lu - jah! Its tri - umph
3. 'Twas here the debt was paid, Hal - le - lu - jah, hal - le - lu - jah! Our sins on

ev - 'ry blast, Hal - le - lu - jah, hal - le - lu - jah! The winds of hell have blown, The
let us tell, Hal - le - lu - jah, hal - le - lu - jah! The grace of God here shone Thro'
Je - sus laid, Hal - le - lu - jah, hal - le - lu - jah! So round the cross we sing Of

world its hate hath shown, Yet it is not o - ver-thrown, Hal-le-lu-jah for the cross!
Christ the blessed Son, Who did for sin a - tone, Hal-le-lu-jah for the cross!
Christ our of-fer - ing, Of Christ our liv-ing King, Hal-le-lu-jah for the cross!

SOLO SOP. OR TEN. OF DUET

Hal - le - lu - jah, hal - le - lu - jah, hal - le-

SOPRANO AND ALTO *

CHORUS. mp Hal - le - lu - jah, hal - le - lu - jah, hal - le-

TENOR AND BASS

*If desired, the Soprano and Alto may sing the upper Staff, omitting the middle Staff.
Copyright, 1910, by Mrs. A. McGranahan. Renewal. Hope Publishing Co., owner

Hallelujah for the Cross!

lu - - - jah for the cross! Hal - le - lu - jah,

lu - jah for the cross, hal - le - lu - jah for the cross! Hal - le - lu - jah,

hal - le - lu - jah, it shall nev - er suf - fer loss!

hal - le - lu - jah, it shall nev - er suf - fer, nev - er suf - fer loss!

FULL CHORUS

*Hal - le - lu - jah, hal - le - lu - jah, hal - le - lu - jah for the cross!

cres. *ff*

Hal - le - lu - jah, hal - le - lu - jah, it shall nev - er suf - fer loss!

*For a final ending, all the voices may sing the melody is unison through the last eight meas-
ures—the instrument playing the harmony.

148 All Hail, Immanuel!

D. R. Van Sickle

Chas. H. Gabriel

1. All hail to Thee, Im-man-u-el, We cast...... our crowns be-
2. All hail to Thee, Im-man-u-el, The ran-somed hosts sur-
3. All hail to Thee, Im-man-u-el, Our ris-en King and

fore Thee; Let ev-'ry heart o-bey Thy will, And ev-'ry voice a-
round Thee; And earthly monarchs clam-or forth Their Sov-'reign King to
Sav-ior! Thy foes are vanquished, and Thou art Om-nip-o-tent for-

dore Thee. In praise to Thee, our Sav-ior King, The vi-brant chords of
crown Thee. While those redeemed in a-ges gone, As-sem-bled round the
ev-er. Death, sin and hell no lon-ger reign, And Satan's pow'r is

Heav-en ring, And ech-o back the might-y strain: All
great white throne, Break forth in-to im-mor-tal song: All
burst in twain; E-ter-nal glo-ry to Thy Name: All

hail! all hail! All hail, all hail, Im-man-u-el!
All hail! all hail!

All Hail, Immanuel!

149 The Old Book and the Old Faith

G. H. C.

GEO. H. CARR

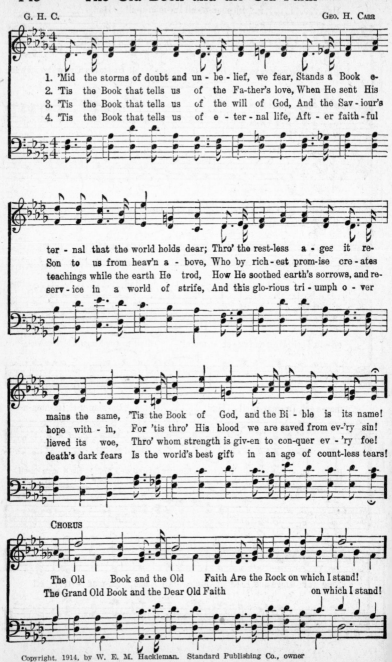

1. 'Mid the storms of doubt and un - be - lief, we fear, Stands a Book e-
2. 'Tis the Book that tells us of the Fa-ther's love, When He sent His
3. 'Tis the Book that tells us of the will of God, And the Sav-iour's
4. 'Tis the Book that tells us of e - ter - nal life, Aft - er faith-ful

ter - nal that the world holds dear; Thro' the rest-less a - ges it re-
Son to us from heav'n a - bove, Who by rich - est prom-ise cre - ates
teachings while the earth He trod, How He soothed earth's sorrows, and re-
serv - ice in a world of strife, And this glo-rious tri - umph o - ver

mains the same, 'Tis the Book of God, and the Bi - ble is its name!
hope with - in, For 'tis thro' His blood we are saved from ev - 'ry sin!
lieved its woe, Thro' whom strength is giv - en to con-quer ev - 'ry foe!
death's dark fears Is the world's best gift in an age of count-less tears!

CHORUS

The Old Book and the Old Faith Are the Rock on which I stand!
The Grand Old Book and the Dear Old Faith on which I stand!

The Old Book and the Old Faith

The Old Book and the Old Faith **Are** the bul-wark of the land!...
The Grand Old Book and the Dear Old Faith

Thro' storm and stress they stand the test, In ev-'ry clime and na-tion blest;

The Old Book and the Old Faith Are the hope of ev-'ry land!
The Grand Old Book and the Dear Old Faith

GRAND CHORUS AT CLOSE *(May be omitted)*

Oh, the Grand Old Book and the Dear Old Faith Are the Rock on which I stand!

rit.

Oh, the Grand Old Book and the Dear Old Faith Are the hope of ev-'ry land!

150　Wonderful Grace of Jesus

H. L.

HALDOR LILLENAS

1. Won - der- ful grace of Je - sus, Great - er than all my sin;
2. Won - der- ful grace of Je - sus, Reach- ing to all the lost,
3. Won - der- ful grace of Je - sus, Reach- ing the most de - filed,

How shall my tongue de-scribe it, Where shall its praise be - gin?.........
By it I have been par- doned, Saved to the ut - ter - most,......
By its transforming pow - er, Mak- ing him God's dear child,......

Tak - ing a- way my bur - den, Set - ting my spir - it free;
Chains have been torn a - sun - der, Giv- ing me lib - er - ty;
Pur - chas-ing peace and heav - en, For all e - ter - ni - ty;

For the won - der - ful grace of Je - sus reach - es me.
For the won - der - ful grace of Je - sus reach - es me.
And the won - der - ful grace of Je - sus reach - es me.

CHORUS

the matchless grace of Je - sus,
Won-der-ful the matchless grace of Je - - sus, Deep-er than the

Wonderful Grace of Jesus

151 One of the Sweet Old Chapters

Rev. E. P. Marvin
Chorus by J. M. G.

Guy C. Latchaw

1. One of the sweet old chap - ters, Aft - er a day like this, A
2. One of the sweet old chap - ters, That al-ways will a - vail, So
3. One of the sweet old chap - ters, When comes the lonely night, When

day of toil and sor - row, And eve-ning brings no kiss.
full of heav'n-ly com - fort, When earthly com-forts fail.
all things earth-ly fail us; And tears have dimmed our sight,

Bring out the fam-'ly Bi - ble That fa - ther used to read, The
A sweet and bless-ed mes - sage From God to His chil-dren dear, So
This on-ly can re - lieve us, A mes - sage from a - bove, Then

One of the Sweet Old Chapters

one that moth-er loved so well In ev - 'ry time of need.
rich in pre-cious prom - is - es, So full of love and cheer.
we can rest so sweet - ly, In faith and hope and love.

Chorus.

One of the sweet old chap - ters, From God to His children dear; O

gra-cious, heav'n-ly Fa - ther, Grant us the ear to hear.

"Whosoever Will"

P. P. B.

P. P. BLISS

1. "Who-so-ev-er hear-eth," shout, shout the sound! Spread the bless-ed ti-dings
2. Who-so-ev-er com-eth need not de-lay, Now the door is o-pen,
3. "Who-so-ev-er will!" the prom-ise is se-cure; "Who-so-ev-er will," for-

all the world a-round; Tell the joy-ful news wher-ev-er man is found:
en-ter while you may; Je-sus is the true, the on-ly Liv-ing Way:
ev-er must en-dure; "Who-so-ev-er will!" 'tis life for-ev-er-more:

CHORUS

"Who-so-ev-er will may come." "Who-so-ev-er will, who-so-ev-er will;"

Send the proc-la-ma-tion o-ver vale and hill; 'Tis a lov-ing

Fa-ther calls the wan-d'rer home: "Who-so-ev-er will may come."

153 Just As You Are

W. M. R.

WILLIAM M. RUNYAN

1. Just as you are there's a wel-come for you, Just as you are, come home; Turn-ing a-way from the old to the new,
2. You can-not heal your own soul if you try, Just as you are, come home; Je-sus must save you or else must you die,
3. Rag-ged and rent though your rai-ment has been, Just as you are, come home; Fam-ished in soul and pol-lu-ted by sin,
4. Come, for the Fa-ther has wait-ed so long, Just as you are, come home; Par-don a-waits you, and wel-com-ing song,

Just as you are, come home.

CHORUS

Je-sus will save you just as you are, Je-sus will wel-come you from a-far, Je-sus will heal sin's pit-i-ful scar; Just as you are, come home.

154   Jesus Is Calling

Fanny J. Crosby

Geo. C. Stebbins

1. Je - sus is ten- der- ly call-ing thee home— Call-ing to - day, call - ing to - day;
2. Je - sus is call-ing the wea - ry to rest— Call-ing to - day, call - ing to - day;
3. Je - sus is wait-ing, oh, come to Him now— Waiting to - day, wait - ing to - day;
4. Je - sus is pleading, oh, list to His voice— Hear Him to-day, hear Him to - day;

Why from the sun-shine of love wilt thou roam   Far - ther and far - ther a - way?
Bring Him thy bur-den, and thou shalt be blest;   He will not turn thee a - way.
Come with thy sins, at His feet low - ly bow;   Come, and no lon - ger de - lay.
They who be-lieve on His name shall re - joice;   Quick -ly a - rise and a - way.

Refrain

Call - ing to - day!........ Call - ing to - day!........
Call - ing, call - ing to - day, to - day! Call - ing, call - ing to - day, to - day!

Je - sus is call - ing, Is ten - der - ly call - ing to - day.
Je - sus is ten-der - ly call-ing to - day,

155 Open Wide the Door

W. KITCHING

J. H. BURKE

1. Je - sus knocks; He calls to thee; "Wea - ry one, O come to Me;"
2. Je - sus knocks; He comes to save, 'Twas for thee His life He gave;
3. Je - sus knocks; is knock-ing still; Yield to Him at once thy will;
4. Je - sus knocks; the mo-ments fly; While sal - va - tion yet is nigh;

He can save, and on - ly He;
He hath tri-umphed o'er the grave; O - - - pen wide the door.
He with joy thy heart can fill;
Ere the Sav - iour pass - eth by; O - pen, o - pen wide the door.

CHORUS

O - - - - pen wide the door,...............
O - pen, o - pen wide, O - pen wide the door,

O - - - pen wide the door;............... He can save, and
O - pen, o - pen wide, o - pen wide the door;

on - ly He;— O - - - pen wide the door...............
o - pen wide the door.
O - pen, o - pen wide the door...............

156   Softly and Tenderly

W. L. T.

WILL L. THOMPSON

1. Soft - ly and ten - der - ly Je - sus is call - ing, Call - ing for
2. Why should we tar - ry when Je - sus is plead - ing, Pleading for
3. Time is now fleet - ing, the moments are pass - ing, Pass - ing from
4. Oh! for the won - der - ful love He has promised, Promised for

you and for me, See on the por - tals He's waiting and watching,
you and for me? Why should we lin - ger and heed not His mercies,
you and from me; Shadows are gath - er - ing, death-beds are coming,
you and for me; Tho' we have sinn'd, He has mer - cy and par - don,

CHORUS

Watching for you and for me.
Mer - cies for you and for me.
Com - ing for you and for me.
Par - don for you and for me.

Come home, come home,
Come home, come home,

Ye who are wea - ry, come home, Earn - est - ly, ten - der - ly

Je - sus is call - ing, Call - ing, O sin - ner, come home!

Let Jesus Come Into Your Heart

C. H. M.

Mrs. C. H. MORRIS

1. If you are tired of the load of your sin, Let Je-sus come in-to your heart;
2. If 'tis for pu-ri-ty now that you sigh, Let Je-sus come in-to your heart;
3. If there's a tempest your voice cannot still, Let Je-sus come in-to your heart;
4. If you would join the glad song of the blest, Let Je-sus come in-to your heart;

If you de-sire a new life to be-gin, Let Jesus come in-to your heart.
Fountains for cleansing are flowing near by, Let Jesus come in-to your heart.
If there's a void this world nev-er can fill, Let Jesus come in-to your heart.
If you would en-ter the mansions of rest, Let Jesus come in-to your heart.

CHORUS.

Just now your doubtings give o'er; Just now, re-ject Him no more;
Last v.—Just now my doubtings are o'er; Just now, re-ject-ing no more;

Just now, throw o-pen the door; Let Je-sus come in-to your heart.
Just now I o-pen the door, And Je-sus comes in-to my heart.

I Am Praying for You

Samuel O'M. Cluff

Ira D. Sankey

1. I have a Sav-iour, He's plead-ing in glo-ry, A dear, lov-ing
2. I have a Fa-ther: to me He has giv-en A hope for e-
3. I have a robe: 'tis re-splen-dent in white-ness, A-wait-ing in
4. I have a peace: it is calm as a riv-er—A peace that the
5. When He has found you, tell oth-ers the sto-ry, That my lov-ing

Sav-iour, tho' earth-friends be few; And now He is watch-ing in
ter-ni-ty bless-ed and true: And soon He will call me to
glo-ry my wan-der-ing view; Oh, when I re-ceive it all
friends of this world nev-er knew: My Sav-iour a-lone is its
Sav-iour is your Sav-iour too; Then pray that your Sav-iour may

ten-der-ness o'er me, And oh, that my Sav-iour were your Sav-iour too!
meet Him in heav-en, But oh, that He'd let me bring you with me too!
shin-ing in brightness, Dear friend, could I see you re-ceiv-ing one too!
Au-thor and Giv-er, And oh, could I know it was giv-en to you!
bring them to glo-ry, And pray'r will be answered—'twas answered for you!

Chorus

For you I am pray-ing, For you I am pray-ing,

rall.

For you I am pray-ing, I'm pray-ing for you.

Battle Hymn of the Republic

JULIA WARD HOWE

Melody, "Glory, Hallelujah"

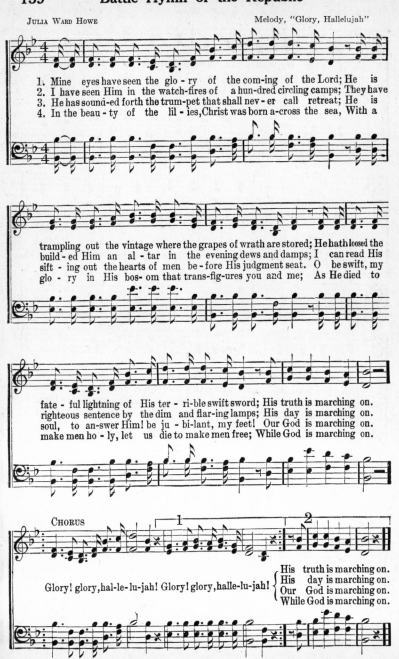

1. Mine eyes have seen the glo - ry of the com-ing of the Lord; He is
2. I have seen Him in the watch-fires of a hun-dred circling camps; They have
3. He has sound-ed forth the trum-pet that shall nev - er call retreat; He is
4. In the beau - ty of the lil - ies, Christ was born a-cross the sea, With a

trampling out the vintage where the grapes of wrath are stored; He hath loosed the
build - ed Him an al - tar in the evening dews and damps; I can read His
sift - ing out the hearts of men be - fore His judgment seat. O be swift, my
glo - ry in His bos - om that trans-fig-ures you and me; As He died to

fate - ful lightning of His ter - ri-ble swift sword; His truth is marching on.
righteous sentence by the dim and flar-ing lamps; His day is marching on.
soul, to an-swer Him! be ju - bi-lant, my feet! Our God is marching on.
make men ho - ly, let us die to make men free; While God is marching on.

CHORUS

Glory! glory, hal-le-lu-jah! Glory! glory, halle-lu-jah!

{ His truth is marching on.
His day is marching on.
Our God is marching on.
While God is marching on.

160 My Country, 'Tis of Thee

S. F. SMITH

AMERICA

HENRY CAREY

1. My coun-try, 'tis of thee, Sweet land of lib - er - ty,
2. My na - tive coun - try, thee, Land of the no - ble free,
3. Let mu - sic swell the breeze, And ring from all the trees
4. Our fa - thers' God! to Thee, Au - thor of lib - er - ty,

Of thee I sing: Land where my fa - thers died, Land of the
Thy name I love: I love thy rocks and rills, Thy woods and
Sweet free-dom's song: Let mor - tal tongues a-wake; Let all that
To Thee we sing: Long may our land be bright With free-dom's

pil-grims' pride, From ev - 'ry moun-tain side Let free-dom ring!
tem - pled hills; My heart with rap - ture thrills Like that a - bove.
breathe partake; Let rocks their si - lence break, The sound pro - long.
ho - ly light; Pro - tect us by Thy might, Great God, our King!

161 The Land We Love the Most

JOHN R. WREFORD

SERENITY. C. M.

WILLIAM V. WALLACE

1. Lord, while for all man-kind we pray, Of ev - 'ry clime and coast,
2. O guard our shores from ev - 'ry foe, With peace our bor-ders bless,
3. U - nite us in the sa - cred love Of knowl-edge, truth, and Thee;

The Land We Love the Most

O hear us for our na-tive land—The land we love the most.
Our cit-ies with pros-per-i-ty, Our fields with plenteousness.
And let our hills and val-leys shout The songs of lib-er-ty. A-MEN.

162   O God, Beneath Thy Guiding Hand

LEONARD BACON   DUKE STREET   JOHN HATTON

1. O God, be-neath Thy guid-ing hand, Our ex-iled
2. Thou heardst well pleased, the song, the prayer, Thy bless-ing
3. Laws, free-dom, truth, and faith in God Came with those
4. And here Thy name, O God of love, Their chil-dren's

fa-thers crossed the sea, And when they trod the win-try
came; and still its pow'r Shall on-ward thro' all a-ges
ex-iles o'er the waves, And where their pil-grim feet have
chil-dren shall a-dore, Till these e-ter-nal hills re-

strand, With prayer and psalm....they wor-shiped Thee.
bear The mem-'ry of...... that ho-ly hour.
trod, The God they trust-ed guards their graves.
move, And spring a-dorns... the earth no more. A-MEN.

The Star-Spangled Banner

Francis Scott Key

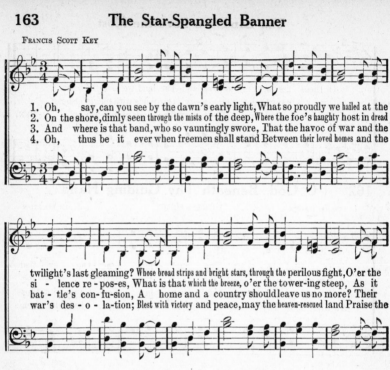

1. Oh,   say, can you see by the dawn's early light, What so proudly we hailed at the
2. On the shore, dimly seen through the mists of the deep, Where the foe's haughty host in dread
3. And   where is that band, who so vauntingly swore, That the havoc of war and the
4. Oh,   thus be it   ever when freemen shall stand Between their loved homes and the

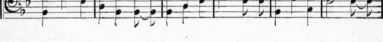

twilight's last gleaming? Whose broad strips and bright stars, through the perilous fight, O'er the
si - lence re - pos-es, What is that which the breeze, o'er the tower-ing steep, As it
bat - tle's con - fu-sion, A   home and a country should leave us no more? Their
war's des - o - la-tion; Blest with victory and peace, may the heaven-rescued land Praise the

ram-parts we watched, were so gallantly streaming? And the rockets' red glare, the bombs
fit - ful - ly blows, half conceals, half discloses? Now it catches the gleam of the
blood has washed out their foul footsteps' pollution; No   ref-uge could save the
power that hath made and preserved us a   na-tion. Then conquer we must, when the

Chorus
ff

bursting in air, Gave proof through the night that our flag was still there. Oh, say, does that
morning's first beam. In full glory reflected, now shines on the stream; 'Tis the star-spangled
hire-ling and slave From the ter-ror of flight or the gloom of the grave.   And the star-spangled
cause it is just, And   this be our motto: "In God is our trust!"   And the star-spangled

The Star-Spangled Banner

star-spangled banner yet wave O'er the land of the free, and the home of the brave?
ban- ner; oh, long may it wave O'er the land of the free, and the home of the brave.
ban- ner in triumph doth wave O'er the land of the free, and the home of the brave.
ban- ner in triumph shall wave O'er the land of the free, and the home of the brave.

164 O Beautiful for Spacious Skies

KATHERINE LEE BATES   MATERNA. C. M. D.   SAMUEL A. WARD

1. O beau - ti - ful for spacious skies, For am-ber waves of grain,   For pur-ple moun-tain
2. O beau - ti - ful for pil-grim feet, Whose stern, impassioned stress A thor-ough-fare for
3. O beau - ti - ful for he-roes proved In lib - er - at - ing strife,   Who more than self their
4. O beau - ti - ful for pa-triot dream That sees be-yond the years Thine al - a - bas - ter

maj - es - ties A - bove the fruit-ed plain!   A - mer - i - ca! A - mer - i - ca! God
free-dom beat A - cross the wil - der - ness!   A - mer - i - ca! A - mer - i - ca! God
country loved, And mer - cy more than life!   A - mer - i - ca! A - mer - i - ca! May
cit - ies gleam, Un-dimmed by hu - man tears!   A - mer - i - ca! A - mer - i - ca! God

shed His grace on thee, And crown thy good with brotherhood From sea to shin-ing sea!
mend thine ev-'ry flaw, Con - firm thy soul in self - con-trol, Thy lib - er - ty in law!
God thy gold re - fine, Till all suc-cess be no - ble-ness, And ev - 'ry gain di - vine!
shed His grace on thee, And crown thy good with brotherhood From sea to shin-ing sea!

165 Jesus Loves Even Me

P. P. B.

P. P. Bliss

1. I am so glad that our Fa-ther in heav'n Tells of His
2. Tho' I for-get Him and wan-der a-way, Still He doth
3. Oh, if there's on-ly one song I can sing, When in His

love in the Book He has giv'n; Won-der-ful things in the
love me wher-ev-er I stray; Back to His dear lov-ing
beau-ty I see the great King, This shall my song in e-

Bi-ble I see, This is the dear-est, that Je-sus loves me.
arms would I flee, When I re-mem-ber that Je-sus loves me.
ter-ni-ty be: "Oh, what a won-der that Je-sus loves me!"

Chorus

I am so glad that Je-sus loves me, Je-sus loves me, Je-sus loves me;

I am so glad that Je-sus loves me, Je-sus loves e-ven me.

166   If We Brightly Shine

William M. Runyan   Robert Beverly (D. B. T.)

1. If we bright-ly shine, if we sweet-ly smile, We will help to short-en
2. If we do kind deeds in a kind-ly way, Friends will glad-ly greet us
3. So we'll sweet-ly smile and we'll brightly shine, And the cross of Je - sus

each long mile; If we speak the words of love and cheer Hap-py
day by day, And our pres-ence, then, will wel-come be, All be-
be our sign; For we want this world to bet - ter be By our

rit.   Chorus

days will make a hap - py year.
cause our hap-pi-ness they see. If we bright - ly shine, if we
lov - ing serv - ice, glad and free.

sweet-ly smile, We will help to short-en the long, long mile; It will

rit.

help to make our lives di - vine, If, with Je - sus' love, we shine, shine, shine.

Wonderful Things to Know

H. H. L.   HELEN HOWARTH LEMMEL

VOICES IN UNISON
Simply, and not too fast

1. 'Tis won-der-ful to know that Je-sus Was once a child like me, And lived on earth and worked and played In His home in Gal-i-lee...... Won-der-ful, won-der-ful Je - - sus! Who was once a child like me;....
2. More won-der-ful it is to know.... That He has gone a-bove To pre-pare a place where I may live For-ev-er in His love.....

REFRAIN

Won-der-ful, won-der-ful Je - sus! Like Him I want to be....

168 His Banner Over Us

H. H. L.

HELEN HOWARTH LEMMEL

With martial spirit (*Voices in Unison*)

1. We are chil-dren of the King, And His prais-es we will
2. He, the glo-rious Son of God, Hath the way be-fore us
3. Fear-less in our Lead-er's might, Strong to do and dare the

sing, As we jour-ney to our home a-bove— His
trod; O-ver ev-'ry foe we'll con-qu'ror prove— His
right, We will jour-ney to our home a-bove— His

REFRAIN *With vigor*

Marked rhythm

ban-ner o-ver us is love!
ban-ner o-ver us is love! March-ing!
ban-ner o-ver us is love!

March-ing! With hap-py hearts we on-ward move, No foe we fear,

with our Cap-tain near— His ban-ner o-ver us is love!

169 **Do You Wonder Why?**

I. A. K.

Ida A. Koritz

Do you won-der why it is I *love Him, I *love Him, I *love Him?

Do you won-der why it is I *love Him? I will glad - ly tell you why.

D.S.—*This is why I can-not help but *love Him, Je - sus Christ, who died for me.*

Chorus

It's be-cause He left His home in glo - ry To die for me.

*Note. Additional verses: trust, serve, and praise Him.
Copyright, 1925, by Geo. S. Schuler. Used by permission

170 **Jewels**

Rev. Wm. O. Cushing

Geo. F. Root

1. When He com - eth, when He com - eth, To make up His jew - els,
2. He will gath - er, He will gath - er The gems for His king-dom,
3. Lit - tle chil - dren, lit - tle chil - dren, Who love their Re - deem - er,

All His jew - els, pre - cious jew - els, His loved and His own,—
All the pure ones, all the bright ones, His loved and His own.
Are the jew - els, pre - cious jew - els, His loved and His own.

Jewels

CHORUS

{ Like the stars of the morning, His bright crown adorning,
{ They shall shine in their beauty,(*Omit*............) His loved and His own.

171 Saviour, Like a Shepherd Lead Us

DOROTHY ANN THRUPP   W. B. BRADBURY

1. { Sav-iour, like a shep-herd lead us,   Much we need Thy tend'rest care;
    { In Thy pleas-ant pastures feed us,   For our use Thy folds prepare:

2. { We are Thine, do Thou be-friend us,   Be the guardian of our way;
    { Keep Thy flock, from sin de-fend us,   Seek us when we go a-stray:

3. { Thou hast promised to re-ceive us,   Poor and sin-ful tho' we be;
    { Thou hast mer-cy to re-lieve us,   Grace to cleanse, and pow'r to free:

4. { Ear-ly let us seek Thy fa-vor,   Ear-ly let us do Thy will;
    { Bless-ed Lord and on-ly Sav-iour,   With Thy love our bos-oms fill:

Bless-ed Je-sus! Bless-ed Je-sus! Thou hast bought us, Thine we are;
Bless-ed Je-sus! Bless-ed Je-sus! Hear, O hear us, when we pray;
Bless-ed Je-sus! Bless-ed Je-sus! We will ear-ly turn to Thee;
Bless-ed Je-sus! Bless-ed Je-sus! Thou hast loved us, love us still;

Bless-ed Je-sus! Bless-ed Je-sus! Thou hast bought us, Thine we are.
Bless-ed Je-sus! Bless-ed Je-sus! Hear, O hear us, when we pray.
Bless-ed Je-sus! Bless-ed Je-sus! We will ear-ly turn to Thee.
Bless-ed Je-sus! Bless-ed Je-sus! Thou hast loved us, love us still.

172 I Believe It!

H. H. L.

HELEN HOWARTH LEMMEL

Not too fast

1. I do not know how Ad - am's sin Lives on in you and me, Nor
2. I do not know how God could give Un - to a maid - en fair His
3. I do not know how God could lay My sins up - on His Son, Nor
4. I do not know how God could call His Son from out the grave, Nor
5. I do not know how Je - sus' blood Can cleanse my heart from sin, Nor
6. I do not know how one day He Can come to earth a - gain, Nor

REFRAIN *With decision*

how it caus - es all the wrong And sorrow that we see.
ho - ly Son, in Bethl'hem born, His bed a man - ger bare.
how, on Calv'ry's Cross, for me He per - fect par - don won. But I read it in God's
how that way to me His ev - er - last - ing life He gave.
how, by faith, in ev - 'ry fight The vic - t'ry I may win.
how like Him I shall be made, And ev - er with Him reign.

Word, and I be - lieve it— Yes, I be - lieve it, Ful - ly be - lieve it! I

Yes, I be - lieve it!

read it in God's Word, and I be - lieve it— And that is all I need to do.

be - lieve it,

NOTE.—Each verse is to be thoroughly studied before sung, and to aid in such de-
velopment, Bible references follow. After the song is so treated, sing through without
comment, with special emphasis on the Refrain.

1st verse—Origin of Satan and sin, Ez. 28, 11-18. Nature of his sin, Is. 14, 12-14. First
appearance on earth and result, Gen. 3.
2nd verse—The Redeemer promised, Gen. 3, 15. Manner and place of birth foretold, Is. 7, 14;
Micah, 5, 2. Prophecy fulfilled, Matt. 1; Matt. 2, 1.
3rd verse—Sacrifice, redemption and pardon, John 19; John 1, 29; Rom. 8, 1.
4th verse—Resurrection and Life, John 20; John 14, 19.
5th verse—Cleansing and victory, 1st John 1, 7; 1st John 5, 4-5.
6th verse—Second Coming, Matt. 24, 30; Acts 1, 11-12; Zech. 14, 1-5; Destiny of believers,
Phil. 3, 21; 2nd Tim. 2, 12; Rev. 5, 10.

173 ## The Sands of Time

A. R. Cousin   RUTHERFORD. 7, 6, D.   C. D'Urhan

1. The sands of time are sink - ing, The dawn of heav - en breaks;
2. Oh, Christ, He is the foun - tain, The deep, sweet well of love!
3. Oh, I am my Be - lov - ed's, And my Be - lov - ed's mine!
4. The Bride eyes not her gar - ment, But her dear Bridegroom's face;

The sum - mer morn I've sighed for, The fair, sweet morn a - wakes:
The streams on earth I've tast - ed, More deep I'll drink a - bove.
He brings a poor vile sin - ner In - to His "house of wine."
I will not gaze at glo - ry, But on my King of grace.

Dark, dark hath been the mid - night, But day - spring is at hand,
There, to an o - cean ful - ness, His mer - cy doth ex - pand,
I stand up - on His mer - it, I know no oth - er stand,
Not at the crown He giv - eth, But on His pierc - ed hand,

And glo - ry, glo - ry dwell - eth In Im - man - uel's land.
And glo - ry, glo - ry dwell - eth In Im - man - uel's land.
Not e'en where glo - ry dwell - eth In Im - man - uel's land.
The Lamb is all the glo - ry Of Im - man - uel's land.   A-MEN.

174 The Son of God Goes Forth to War

REGINALD HEBER

DR. H. S. CUTLER

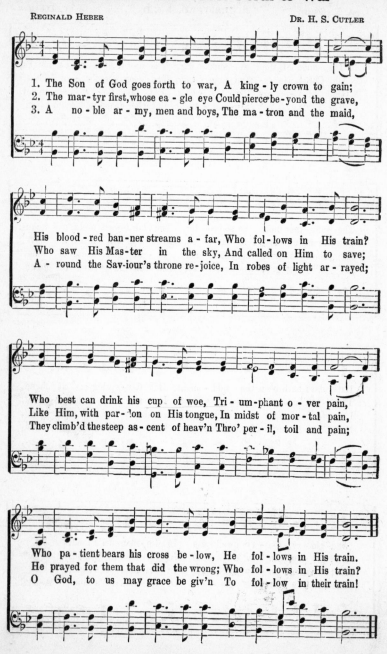

1. The Son of God goes forth to war, A king-ly crown to gain;
2. The mar-tyr first, whose ea-gle eye Could pierce be-yond the grave,
3. A no-ble ar-my, men and boys, The ma-tron and the maid,

His blood-red ban-ner streams a-far, Who fol-lows in His train?
Who saw His Mas-ter in the sky, And called on Him to save;
A-round the Sav-iour's throne re-joice, In robes of light ar-rayed;

Who best can drink his cup of woe, Tri-um-phant o-ver pain,
Like Him, with par-don on His tongue, In midst of mor-tal pain,
They climb'd the steep as-cent of heav'n Thro' per-il, toil and pain;

Who pa-tient bears his cross be-low, He fol-lows in His train.
He prayed for them that did the wrong; Who fol-lows in His train?
O God, to us may grace be giv'n To fol-low in their train!

A Mighty Fortress Is Our God

MARTIN LUTHER
Tr. F. H. HEDGE

LUTHER. P. M.

MARTIN LUTHER

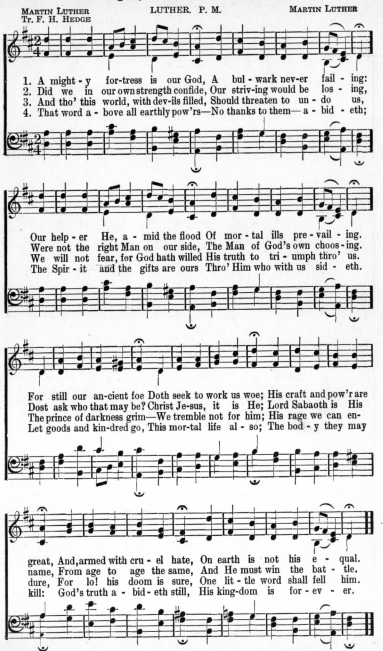

1. A might-y for-tress is our God, A bul-wark nev-er fail-ing:
2. Did we in our own strength confide, Our striv-ing would be los-ing,
3. And tho' this world, with dev-ils filled, Should threaten to un-do us,
4. That word a-bove all earthly pow'rs—No thanks to them—a-bid-eth;

Our help-er He, a-mid the flood Of mor-tal ills pre-vail-ing.
Were not the right Man on our side, The Man of God's own choos-ing.
We will not fear, for God hath willed His truth to tri-umph thro' us.
The Spir-it and the gifts are ours Thro' Him who with us sid-eth.

For still our an-cient foe Doth seek to work us woe; His craft and pow'r are
Dost ask who that may be? Christ Je-sus, it is He; Lord Sabaoth is His
The prince of darkness grim—We tremble not for him; His rage we can en-
Let goods and kin-dred go, This mor-tal life al-so; The bod-y they may

great, And, armed with cru-el hate, On earth is not his e-qual.
name, From age to age the same, And He must win the bat-tle.
dure, For lo! his doom is sure, One lit-tle word shall fell him.
kill: God's truth a-bid-eth still, His king-dom is for-ev-er.

176 The True Historic Jesus

EWING. 7s. 6s. D.

JAMES M. GRAY   ALEXANDER EWING, 1853

1. I know no oth-er Je-sus Than He who died for me;
2. That hu-man Christs could save me Is in-ad-mis-si-ble;
3. The In-fant of the man-ger, The vil-lage Car-pen-ter,

The Sav-iour of lost sin-ners, The Christ of Cal-va-ry.
My Je-sus is the im-age Of God in-vis-i-ble.
The Teach-er sent from heav-en To men to min-is-ter;

I know no "i-deal" Je-sus That hu-man minds in-vent;
My Christ be-came in-car-nate And of the Vir-gin born;
The true his-tor-ic Je-sus, Who died and rose a-gain,

The on-ly Christ I wor-ship Is whom the Fa-ther sent.
He left a crown of glo-ry To wear the plat-ted thorn.
He on-ly is the Je-sus That I pro-claim to men.

177 Arise, My Soul, Arise!

Charles Wesley · Har. by D. B. Towner

1. A - rise, my soul, a - rise! Shake off thy guilt - y fears;
2. He ev - er lives a - bove For me to in - ter - cede—
3. Five bleed - ing wounds He bears, Re - ceived on Cal - va - ry;
4. The Fa - ther hears Him pray, His dear a - noint - ed One;
5. My God is rec - on - ciled, His par - d'ning voice I hear;

The bleed - ing Sac - ri - fice In my be - half ap - pears.
His all - re - deem - ing love, His pre - cious blood to plead;
They pour ef - fec - tual prayers, They strong - ly plead for me.
He can - not turn a - way The pres - ence of His Son:
He owns me for His child— I can no lon - ger fear:

Be - fore the throne my Sure - ty stands; My name is writ - ten
His blood a - toned for all our race, And sprin - kles now the
"For - give him, O for - give!" they cry, "Nor let that ran - somed
His Spir - it an - swers to the blood, And tells me I am
With con - fi - dence I now draw nigh, And "Fa - ther, Ab - ba,

on His hands, My name is writ - ten on His hands.
throne of grace, And sprin - kles now the throne of grace.
sin - ner die, Nor let that ran - somed sin - ner die."
born of God, And tells me I am born of God.
Fa - ther!" cry, And "Fa - ther, Ab - ba, Fa - ther!" cry.

178   I'm Waiting for Thee, Lord

E. W. Bullinger

1. I'm wait-ing for Thee, Lord, Thy beau-ty to see, Lord;
2. Mid dan-ger and fear, Lord, I'm oft wea-ry here, Lord,
3. For those gone be-fore, Lord, Thy love we a-dore, Lord,
4. E'en now let my ways, Lord, Be bright with Thy praise, Lord,

I'm wait-ing for Thee, For Thy com-ing a-gain.
The day must be near, Of Thy com-ing a-gain.
We'll meet them once more, At Thy com-ing a-gain.
For brief are the days Ere Thy com-ing a-gain.

Thou'rt gone o-ver there, Lord, A place to pre-pare, Lord—
'Tis all sun-shine there, Lord, No sigh-ing or care, Lord,
Thy blood was the sign, Lord, Which marked them as Thine, Lord,
I'm wait-ing for Thee, Lord, Thy beau-ty to see, Lord,

Thy glo-ry I'll share At Thy com-ing a-gain.
But glo-ry so fair At Thy com-ing a-gain.
And bright-ly they'll shine At Thy com-ing a-gain.
No tri-umph for me Like Thy com-ing a-gain.

179 How Tedious and Tasteless the Hours

JOHN NEWTON
4th stanza alt. W. M. R.

CONTRAST. 8s. D.

LEWIS EDSON

1. How te-dious and tasteless the hours When Je-sus no lon-ger I see!
2. His name yields the rich-est perfume, And sweet-er than mu-sic His voice;
3. Con-tent with be-hold-ing His face, My all to His pleas-ure re-signed,
4. Then, Lord, since indeed I am Thine, Since Thou art my sun and my song,

Sweet prospects, sweet birds, and sweet flow'rs, Have all lost their sweetness to me;
His pres-ence dis-pers-es my gloom, And makes all with-in me re-joice:
No chang-es of sea-son or place Would make any change in my mind:
No more do I lan-guish and pine, E'en win-ter to me seems not long.

The mid-sum-mer sun shines but dim, The fields strive in vain to look gay;
I should, were He al-ways thus nigh, Have noth-ing to wish or to fear;
While blest with a sense of His love, A pal-ace a toy would ap-pear;
For clouds Thou hast driv'n from my sky, My hap-pi-ness Thou dost re-store;

But when I am hap-py in Him, De-cem-ber's as pleas-ant as May.
No mor-tal so hap-py as I, My sum-mer would last all the year.
And pris-ons would pal-a-ces prove, If Je-sus would dwell with me there.
Soon I shall be-hold Thee on high, Where wint-er and clouds are no more.

In Heavenly Love Abiding

ANNA L. WARING

FELIX MENDELSSOHN

1. In heav'nly love a-bid-ing, No change my heart shall fear; And safe is such con-
2. Wherev-er He may guide me, No want shall turn me back; My Shepherd is be-
3. Green pastures are before me, Which yet I have not seen; Bright skies will soon be

The storm may roar with-out me,

fid-ing, For nothing changes here. The storm may roar with-out me,
side me, And nothing can I lack. His wis-dom ev - er wak-eth,
o'er me, Where darkest clouds have been. My hope I can-not meas-ure,

The storm may roar with-out me.

My heart may low be laid, But God is round a-bout me, And can I be dis-
His sight is nev-er dim, He knows the way He tak-eth, And I will walk with
My path to life is free, My Sav-iour has my treas-ure, And He will walk with

a - bout me, And

And can I be dis-mayed?

mayed? But God is round a-bout me, And can........ I be dis-mayed?
Him; He knows the way He tak-eth, And I.......... will walk with Him.
me; My Sav-iour has my treasure, And He........ will walk with me.

can I be dis-mayed?..........

181 Rise, My Soul, and Stretch Thy Wings

AMSTERDAM

Rev. Robert Seagrave, 1742   "The Foundry Collection" 1742

1. Rise, my soul, and stretch thy wings, Thy bet-ter por-tion trace;
2. Riv-ers to the o-cean run, Nor stay in all their course;
3. Fly me rich-es, fly me cares, Whilst I that coast ex-plore;
4. Cease, ye pil-grims, cease to mourn, Press on-ward to the prize;

Rise from tran-si-to-ry things Toward heaven, thy na-tive place.
Fire as-cend-ing seeks the sun; Both speed them to their source:
Flatt'ring world, with all thy snares, So-lic-it me no more.
Soon our Sav-iour will re-turn Tri-um-phant in the skies:

Sun and moon and stars de-cay, Time shall soon this earth re-move;
So my soul, de-rived from God, Pants to view His glo-ri-ous face,
Pil-grims fix not here their home; Stran-gers tar-ry but a night;
Yet a sea-son, and you know Hap-py en-trance will be given,

Rise, my soul, and haste a-way To seats prepared a-bove.
For-ward tends to His a-bode, To rest in His em-brace.
When the last dear morn is come, They'll rise to joy-ful light.
All our sor-rows left be-low, And earth ex-changed for heav'n. A-men.

The Spacious Firmament

J. ADDISON

F. J. HAYDN

1. The spa-cious fir-ma-ment on high, With all the blue, e-
2. Soon as the eve-ning shades pre-vail, The moon takes up the
3. What tho' in sol-emn si-lence all Move round the dark ter-

the-real sky, And spangled heav'ns, a shin-ing frame, Their great O-
won-drous tale; And night-ly, to the lis-t'ning earth, Re-peats the
res-trial ball,—What tho' no re-al voice nor sound A-mid their

rig-i-nal pro-claim: Th'un-wea-ried sun, from day to day,
sto-ry of her birth; While all the stars that round her burn,
ra-diant orbs be found,—In rea-son's ear they all re-joice,

Does his Cre-a-tor's pow'r dis-play; And pub-lish-es to
And all the plan-ets in their turn, Con-firm the ti-dings
And ut-ter forth a glo-rious voice, For-ev-er sing-ing

ev-'ry land The work of an al-might-y hand.
as they roll, And spread the truth from pole to pole.
as they shine,—"The hand that made us is di-vine."

Great God of Wonders

HUDDERSFIELD. M. 8.

S. DAVIES   J. NEWTON

1. Great God of won - ders! all Thy ways Are match - less, god - like,
2. O may this strange, this match-less grace, This god - like mir - a-

and di - vine; But the fair glo - ries of Thy grace More god - like
cle of love, Fill the whole earth with grate-ful praise, And all th' an-

and un - ri - valed shine, More god - like and un - ri - valed shine.
gel - ic choirs a - bove, And all th' an-gel - ic choirs a - bove.

Who is a par - d'ning God like Thee? Or who has grace so
Who is a par - d'ning God like Thee? Or who has grace so

rich and free? Or who has grace so rich and free?
rich and free? Or who has grace so rich and free? A - MEN.

184   I Heard the Voice of Jesus Say

VOX DILECTI. C. M. D.

REV. HORATIUS BONAR, 1846   REV. JOHN B. DYKES, 1868

1. I heard the voice of Je-sus say, "Come un-to Me and rest;
2. I heard the voice of Je-sus say, "Be-hold, I free-ly give
3. I heard the voice of Je-sus say, "I am this dark world's Light;

Lay down, thou wea-ry one, lay down Thy head up-on My breast."
The liv-ing wa-ter; thirst-y one, Stoop down and drink, and live."
Look un-to Me, thy morn shall rise, And all thy day be bright."

I came to Je-sus as I was, Wea-ry and worn and sad,
I came to Je-sus, and I drank Of that life-giv-ing stream;
I looked to Je-sus, and I found In Him my Star, my Sun;

I found in Him a rest-ing-place, And He has made me glad.
My thirst was quenched, my soul revived, And now I live in Him.
And in that light of life I'll walk, Till traveling days are done. A-MEN.

Rejoicing In Jesus

EVELYN L. LAIRD

GEORGE S. SCHULER

1. Cour - age, ye pil - grims, and lift up your voice, Je - sus is
2. Cour - age, ye sol - diers, the bat - tle soon done, Je - sus is
3. Cour - age, ye saints, for the cross we'll lay down, Je - sus is

com - ing a - gain! The jour-ney's soon o - ver, re - joice, oh, re - joice!
com - ing a - gain! The dan - ger soon past and the vic - to - ry won,
com - ing a - gain! Then com-eth the crown and the sweet "wel-come home,"

Je - sus is com - ing a - gain! Soon, thro' the night, His voice we shall
Je - sus is com - ing a - gain! Then by His pres - ence, foes put to
Je - sus is com - ing a - gain! Com - ing, Him-self, our loved ones to

rit.　　*a tempo*

hear; Soon, thro' the dawn - ing, His face shall ap - pear; Soon, in the
flight, Dark-ness dis - pelled in His glo - ri - ous light, There at His
bring, Com - ing to call us, yea, swift on the wing, Then glo - rious

morn - ing, He'll dry ev - 'ry tear; Liv - ing for - ev - er in Him.
side, with our faith lost in sight, Ev - er re - joic - ing in Him.
man - sions, the home of the King, Reign-ing for - ev - er with Him.

186 Look, Ye Saints, the Sight is Glorious

CORONAE. 8. 7. 8. 7. 4. 7.

Thomas Kelly. 1809

William H. Monk

1. Look, ye saints; the sight is glo - rious; See the "Man of
2. Crown the Sav - iour, an - gels crown Him; Rich the tro - phies
3. Sin - ners in de - ri - sion crowned Him, Mock-ing thus Mes-
4. Hark! those bursts of ac - cla - ma - tion! Hark! those loud tri-

sor - rows" now; From the fight re - turned vic - to - rious,
Je - sus brings; On the seat of pow'r en - throne Him,
si - ah's claim; Saints and an - gels crowd a - round Him,
um - phant chords! Je - sus takes the high - est sta - tion;

Ev 'ry knee to Him shall bow; Crown Him!
While the vault of heav - en rings; Crown Him!
Own His ti - tle, praise His Name: Crown Him!
O what joy the sight af - fords! Crown Him!

Crown Him! Crowns be - come the Vic - tor's brow.
Crown Him! Crown the Sav - iour King of kings.
Crown Him! Spread a - broad the Vic - tor's fame!
Crown Him! King of kings and Lord of lords. A - MEN.

187 Love Divine, All Love Excelling

BEECHER. 8.7.8.7. D.

CHARLES WESLEY, 1747

JOHN ZUNDEL, 1870

1. Love Di - vine, all love ex - cell - ing, Joy of heaven, to earth come down;
2. Breathe, O breathe Thy lov - ing Spir - it In - to ev - 'ry troub - led breast;
3. Come, Al - might - y to de - liv - er, Let us all Thy life re - ceive;
4. Fin - ish, then, Thy new cre - a - tion; Pure and spot - less let us be:

Fix in us Thy hum - ble dwell - ing, All Thy faith - ful mer - cies crown:
Let us all in Thee in - her - it, Let us find the prom - ised rest;
Sud - den - ly re - turn, and nev - er, Nev - er more Thy tem - ples leave.
Let us see Thy great sal - va - tion Per - fect - ly re - stored in Thee;

Je - sus, Thou art all com - pas - sion, Pure, un - bound - ed love Thou art;
Take a - way the love of sin - ning; Al - pha and O - me - ga be;
Thee we would be al - ways bless - ing, Serve Thee as Thy hosts a - bove,
Changed from glo - ry in - to glo - ry Till in heaven we take our place,

Vis - it us with Thy sal - va - tion, En - ter ev - 'ry trem - bling heart.
End of faith, as its be - gin - ning, Set our hearts at lib - er - ty.
Pray, and praise Thee with - out ceas - ing, Glo - ry in Thy per - fect love.
Till we cast our crowns be - fore Thee, Lost in won - der, love and praise.

7

188   Lo, He Comes

AUTUMN. 8s. 7s. D.

CHARLES WESLEY, alt.   FRANCOIS H. BARTHELEMON

1. Lo, He comes, with clouds de-scend-ing, Once for fa-vored sinners slain;
2. Ev - 'ry eye shall now be-hold Him, Robed in dreadful maj-es - ty;
3. Yea, A-men; let all a - dore Thee, High on Thine e-ter-nal throne:

Thou-sand thou-sand saints at-tend - ing, Swell the tri-umph of His train:
Those who set at naught and sold Him, Pierced, and nailed Him to the tree,
Sav - iour, take the pow'r and glo - ry; Claim the kingdom for Thine own.

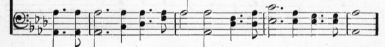

Hal - le - lu - jah! hal-le-lu - jah! God ap-pears on earth to reign;
Deep-ly wail - ing, deep-ly wail-ing, Shall the true Mes-si - ah see;
O come quick - ly, O come quick-ly, Hal - le - lu - jah! come, Lord, come;

Hal - le - lu - jah! hal-le - lu - jah! God appears on earth to reign.
Deep-ly wail-ing, deep-ly wail-ing, Shall the true Mes-si - ah see.
O come quick-ly, O come quickly, Hal le - lu-jah! come, Lord, come. A-MEN.

Hark, Hark, My Soul!

PILGRIMS. 11s. 10s.

FREDERICK W. FABER

HENRY SMART

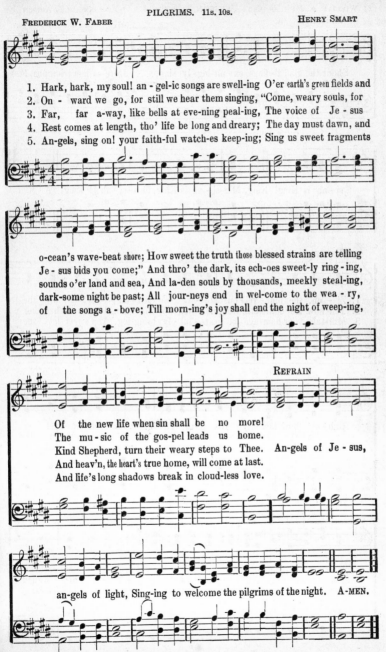

1. Hark, hark, my soul! an-gel-ic songs are swell-ing O'er earth's green fields and
2. On - ward we go, for still we hear them singing, "Come, weary souls, for
3. Far, far a-way, like bells at eve-ning peal-ing, The voice of Je - sus
4. Rest comes at length, tho' life be long and dreary; The day must dawn, and
5. An-gels, sing on! your faith-ful watch-es keep-ing; Sing us sweet fragments

o-cean's wave-beat shore; How sweet the truth those blessed strains are telling
Je - sus bids you come;" And thro' the dark, its ech-oes sweet-ly ring-ing,
sounds o'er land and sea, And la-den souls by thousands, meekly steal-ing,
dark-some night be past; All jour-neys end in wel-come to the wea - ry,
of the songs a - bove; Till morn-ing's joy shall end the night of weep-ing,

REFRAIN

Of the new life when sin shall be no more!
The mu - sic of the gos-pel leads us home.
Kind Shepherd, turn their weary steps to Thee. An-gels of Je - sus,
And heav'n, the heart's true home, will come at last.
And life's long shadows break in cloud-less love.

an-gels of light, Sing-ing to welcome the pilgrims of the night. A-MEN.

190 Shout the Glad Tidings

WILLIAM A. MUHLENBERG   AVISON. 11s. 12s.   CHARLES AVISON

REFRAIN

Shout the glad ti-dings, ex-ult-ing-ly sing,.... Je-ru-sa-lem triumphs, Mes-

1 & 2 | *After the last verse*   *rit.*

si - ah is King! King, Mes-si - ah is King, Mes - si - ah is King! A - MEN.

VERSE

1. Zi - on, the mar - vel - ous sto - ry be tell - ing, The Son of the
2. Tell how He com - eth; from na - tion to na - tion, The heart-cheer-ing
3. Mor-tals, your hom-age be grate - ful-ly bring-ing, And sweet let the

High - est, how low - ly His birth! The bright-est arch - an - gel in
news let the earth ech - o round; How free to the faith - ful He
glad - some ho - san - na a - rise; Ye an - gels, the full hal - le-

Repeat Refrain

glo - ry ex-cel-ling, He stoops to re-deem thee, He reigns up - on earth!
of - fers sal-va-tion, How His people with joy ev - er - last - ing are crowned.
lu - jah be singing; Our cho-rus re-sound thro' the earth and the skies.

191 The Homeland!

Rev. R. W. Haweis   Geo. C. Stebbins

1. The Homeland! O the Homeland! The land of the free-born! There's no night in the Homeland, But aye the fade-less morn; I'm sigh-ing for the Homeland, My heart is ach-ing here; There is no pain in the Homeland To which I'm draw-ing near; There is no pain in the Homeland To which I'm drawing near.

2. My Lord is in the Homeland, With an-gels bright and fair; There's no sin in the Homeland, And no temp-ta-tion there; The mu-sic of the Homeland, Is ring-ing in my ears. And when I think of the Homeland My eyes are fill'd with tears; And when I think of the Homeland My eyes are fill'd with tears.

3. My loved ones in the Homeland Are wait-ing me to come, Where neither death nor sor-row Invades their ho-ly home; O dear, dear na-tive Coun-try! O rest and peace above! Christ bring us all to the Homeland Of thy re-deem-ing love; Christ bring us all to the Homeland Of thy re-deem-ing love!

192 Onward, Christian Soldiers!

S. BARING GOULD

Sir ARTHUR SULLIVAN

1. Onward, Chris-tian sol-diers! March-ing as to war; With the cross of
2. Like a might-y ar - my Moves the Church of God; Broth-ers, we are
3. Crowns and thrones may per - ish, King-doms rise and wane; But the Church of
4. On-ward, then, ye faith-ful, Join our hap-py throng; Blend with ours your

Je - sus Go-ing on be-fore; Christ, the Roy - al Mas-ter, Leads a-
tread - ing Where the saints have trod; We are not di - vid-ed, All one
Je - sus Con-stant will re-main: Gates of hell can nev-er 'Gainst that
voic - es, In the tri-umph song: Glo - ry, laud, and hon - or, Un - to

gainst the foe; For-ward in - to bat - tle, See His ban-ners go.
bod - y we— One in hope and doc - trine, One in char - i - ty.
Church pre-vail; We have Christ's own prom - ise— And that can-not fail.
Christ the King; This thro' countless a - ges Men and an-gels sing.

CHORUS

On - ward, Chris - tian sol - diers! March - ing as to war,

With the

With the cross of Je - sus, Go - ing on be - fore.
cross of

193 All Hail the Power of Jesus' Name!

E. Perronet   DIADEM   James Ellor

1. All hail the power of Je - sus' name! Let an - gels prostrate fall,
2. Ye cho - sen seed of Is - rael's race, Ye ran-somed from the fall,
3. Let ev - 'ry kin - dred, ev - 'ry tribe On this ter - res - trial ball,
4. O that with yon - der sa - cred throng We at His feet may fall,

Let an - gels pros-trate fall; Bring forth the roy - al di - a - dem,
Ye ran-somed from the fall, Hail Him who saves you by His grace,
On this ter - res - trial ball, To Him all maj - es - ty as - cribe,
We at His feet may fall! We'll join the ev - er - last - ing song,

And crown . . . . Him, crown Him,

And crown Him, crown Him, crown Him, crown Him And crown Him Lord of
And crown . . . . Him, crown Him,

And crown Him, crown Him, crown Him, crown . . . .

crown Him, crown Him,

all, crown Him, And crown Him Lord of all!
crown . . . . Him,

. . . . Him, And crown Him Lord of all.

194 Thou Didst Leave Thy Throne

EMILY E. S. ELLIOTT. ARR.   T. R. MATTHEWS

1. Thou didst leave Thy throne and Thy king - ly crown, When Thou
2. Heav - en's arch - es rang when the an - gels sang, In pro -
3. Thou didst come, O Lord, with the liv - ing word, That should
4. Heav - en's arch shall ring, and her choirs shall sing, At Thy

cam - est to earth for me; But in Beth-le'm's home was there
claim - ing Thy high de - gree; But in low - ly birth didst Thou
set all Thy peo - ple free; But with mock-ing scorn, and with
com - ing to vic - to - ry, Call-ing, "Come—come home," say-ing,

found no room For Thy ho - ly na - tiv - i - ty:
come to earth, And in deep - est hu - mil - i - ty:
crown of thorn, They bore Thee to Cal - va - ry.
"There is room, There is room at My side for thee:"

REFRAIN

1-3. O come to my heart, Lord Je - sus, There is room in my heart for Thee.
4. My heart shall re-joice, Lord Je - sus, When Thou comest in vic - to - ry.

195 Spirit of God, Descend Upon My Heart

GEORGE CROLY

FREDERICK C. ATKINSON

1. Spir - it of God, de - scend up - on my heart;
2. Hast Thou not bid us love Thee, God and King?
3. Teach me to feel that Thou art al - ways nigh;
4. Teach me to love Thee as Thine an - gels love,

Wean it from earth; through all its puls - es move;
All, all Thine own, soul, heart, and strength, and mind;
Teach me the strug - gles of the soul to bear,
One ho - ly pas - sion fill - ing all my frame;

Stoop to my weak - ness, might - y as Thou art,
I see Thy cross— there teach my heart to cling:
To check the ris - ing doubt, the reb - el sigh;
The bap - tism of the heav'n - de - scend - ed Dove,

And make me love Thee as I ought to love.
O let me seek Thee, and O let me find.
Teach me the pa - tience of un - an - swered prayer.
My heart an al - tar, and Thy love the flame.

196 O Thou God of My Salvation

THOMAS OLIVERS

D. B. TOWNER

1. O Thou God of my sal - va - tion, My Re - deem - er from all sin;
2. Tho' un - seen, I love the Sav - iour, He hath bro't sal - va - tion near;
3. While the an - gel choirs are cry - ing, "Glo - ry to the great I Am,"
4. An - gels now are hov - 'ring round us, Un - perceived a - mong the throng;

Moved by Thy di - vine com - pas - sion, Who hast died my heart to win,
Man - i - fests His par - d'ning fa - vor; And when Je - sus doth ap - pear,
I with them will still be vy - ing— Glo - ry, glo - ry to the Lamb!
Won - d'ring at the love that crowned us, Glad to sing the ho - ly song;

I will praise Thee, I will praise Thee, Where shall I Thy praise be - gin?
Soul and bod - y, soul and bod - y, Shall His glo - rious im - age bear,
O how pre - cious, O how pre - cious, Is the sound of Je - sus' name!
Hal - le - lu - jah, hal - le - lu - jah, Love and praise to Christ be - long!

I will praise Thee, I will praise Thee, Where shall I Thy praise be - gin?
Soul and bod - y, soul and bod - y, Shall His glo - rious im - age bear.
O how pre - cious, O how pre - cious, Is the sound of Je - sus' name!
Hal - le - lu - jah, hal - le - lu - jah, Love and praise to Christ be - long!

O Jesus, I Have Promised

JOHN E. BODE

ARTHUR H. MANN

1. O Je - sus, I have prom - ised To serve Thee to the end;
2. O let me feel Thee near me: The world is ev - er near;
3. O let me hear Thee speak - ing, In ac - cents clear and still,
4. O Je - sus, Thou hast prom - ised To all who fol - low Thee,

Be Thou for - ev - er near me, My Mas - ter and my Friend;
I see the sights that daz - zle, The tempt - ing sounds I hear;
A - bove the storms of pas - sion, The mur - murs of self - will;
That where Thou art in glo - ry There shall Thy serv - ant be;

I shall not fear the bat - tle If Thou art by my side,
My foes are ev - er near me, A - round me and with - in;
O speak to re - as - sure me, To has - ten or con - trol;
And, Je - sus, I have prom - ised To serve Thee to the end;

Nor wan - der from the path - way If Thou wilt be my Guide.
But, Je - sus, draw Thou near - er, And shield my soul from sin.
O speak, and make me lis - ten, Thou Guard-ian of my soul.
O give me grace to fol - low, My Mas - ter and my Friend.

O Word of God Incarnate

MUNICH. 7. 6. 7. 6. D.

Bishop WILLIAM W. HOW   Würtemberg Gesangbuch

1. O Word of God In - car - nate, O Wis - dom from on high,
2. The Church from her dear Mas - ter, Re-ceived the gift di - vine,
3. It float - eth like a ban - ner Be - fore God's host un-furled;
4. O make Thy Church, dear Sav - iour, A lamp of pur - est gold,

O Truth unchanged, un-chang - ing, O Light of our dark sky;
And still that light she lift - eth O'er all the earth to shine.
It shin - eth like a bea - con A - bove the dark-ling world.
To bear be - fore the na - tions Thy true light, as of old.

We praise Thee for the ra - diance That from the hal - lowed page,
It is the gold - en cas - ket, Where gems of truth are stored;
It is the chart and com - pass That o'er life's surg - ing sea,
O teach Thy wan - d'ring pil - grims By this their path to trace,

A lan - tern to our foot-steps, Shines on from age to age.
It is the heav'n-drawn picture Of Christ, the liv-ing Word.
'Mid mists and rocks and quicksands, Still guides, O Christ, to Thee.
Till, clouds and dark-ness end - ed, They see Thee face to face. A-MEN.

O Little Town of Bethlehem

ST. LOUIS. 8. 6. 7.

PHILLIPS BROOKS

LEWIS H. REDNER

1. O lit-tle town of Beth-le-hem, How still we see thee lie!
2. For Christ is born of Ma - ry, And gath-ered all a - bove,
3. How si - lent-ly, how si - lent-ly, The won-drous gift is given!
4. O ho - ly Child of Beth-le-hem! De-scend to us, we pray;

A - bove thy deep and dream-less sleep The si - lent stars go by;
While mor-tals sleep, the an - gels keep Their watch of wond'ring love.
So God im-parts to hu - man hearts The bless-ings of His heaven.
Cast out our sin, and en - ter in; Be born in us to - day.

Yet in thy dark streets shin - eth The ev - er - last-ing Light;
O morn-ing stars, to - geth - er Pro-claim the ho - ly birth!
No ear may hear His com - ing, But in this world of sin,
We hear the Christ-mas an - gels The great glad ti - dings tell;

The hopes and fears of all the years Are met in thee to - night.
And prais - es sing to God the King, And peace to men on earth.
Where meek souls will re - ceive Him still, The dear Christ en - ters in.
O come to us, a - bide with us, Our Lord Em - man - u - el.

Come to the Morning Prayer

James Montgomery   MORNINGTON. S. M.   Mornington

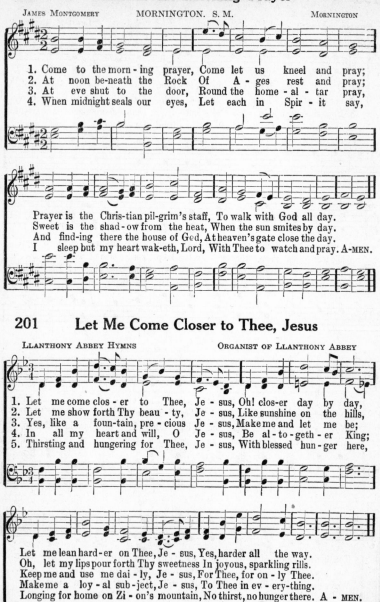

1. Come to the morn-ing prayer, Come let us kneel and pray;
2. At noon be-neath the Rock Of A-ges rest and pray;
3. At eve shut to the door, Round the home-al-tar pray,
4. When midnight seals our eyes, Let each in Spir-it say,

Prayer is the Chris-tian pil-grim's staff, To walk with God all day.
Sweet is the shad-ow from the heat, When the sun smites by day.
And find-ing there the house of God, At heaven's gate close the day.
I sleep but my heart wak-eth, Lord, With Thee to watch and pray. A-men.

201   Let Me Come Closer to Thee, Jesus

Llanthony Abbey Hymns   Organist of Llanthony Abbey

1. Let me come clos-er to Thee, Je-sus, Oh! clos-er day by day,
2. Let me show forth Thy beau-ty, Je-sus, Like sunshine on the hills,
3. Yes, like a foun-tain, pre-cious Je-sus, Make me and let me be;
4. In all my heart and will, O Je-sus, Be al-to-geth-er King;
5. Thirsting and hungering for Thee, Je-sus, With blessed hun-ger here,

Let me lean hard-er on Thee, Je-sus, Yes, harder all the way.
Oh, let my lips pour forth Thy sweetness In joyous, sparkling rills.
Keep me and use me dai-ly, Je-sus, For Thee, for on-ly Thee.
Make me a loy-al sub-ject, Je-sus, To Thee in ev-ery-thing.
Longing for home on Zi-on's mountain, No thirst, no hunger there. A-men.

202 The Holy Ghost Is Here

CHAS. H. SPURGEON   ST. THOMAS. S. M.   AARON WILLIAMS, Coll.

1. The Ho - ly Ghost is here, Where saints in prayer a - gree;
2. Not far a - way is He, To be by prayer bro't nigh,
3. He dwells with - in our soul, An ev - er wel - come guest;
4. Our bod - ies are His shrine, And He th' in-dwell-ing Lord;
5. O - be - dient to Thy will, We wait to feel Thy pow'r;

As Je - sus' part-ing gift—is near Each plead-ing com-pa - ny.
But here in pres-ent maj - es - ty, As in His courts on high.
He reigns with ab - so-lute con-trol, As mon-arch in the breast.
All hail, Thou Com-fort-er di-vine, Be ev - er - more a - dored!
O Lord of life, our hopes ful-fil, And bless this hal-lowed hour. A - MEN.

203 Fling Out the Banner!

G. W. DOANE   WALTHAM   J. B. CALKIN

1. Fling out the ban-ner! let it float Skyward and seaward, high and wide; The
2. Fling out the ban-ner! an-gels bend In anx-ious si-lence o'er the sign, And
3. Fling out the ban-ner! heathen lands Shall see from far the glorious sight, And
4. Fling out the ban-ner! sin-sick souls, That think and per-ish in the strife, Shall
5. Fling out the ban-ner! let it float Skyward and seaward, high and wide, Our

sun that lights its shin-ing folds, The cross on which the Saviour died.
vain - ly seek to com-pre-hend The won-der of the love di-vine.
na-tions, crowding to be born, Bap-tize their spir-its in its light.
touch in faith its ra-diant hem, And spring im-mor-tal in - to life.
glo - ry, on - ly in the cross; Our on - ly hope the Cru - ci-fied! A - MEN.

204 What Grace, O Lord

Sir Edward Denny, 1839   DOWNS. C. M.   Lowell Mason

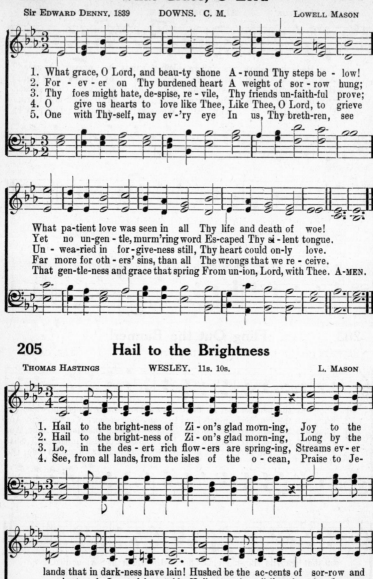

1. What grace, O Lord, and beau-ty shone A - round Thy steps be - low!
2. For - ev - er on Thy burdened heart A weight of sor - row hung;
3. Thy foes might hate, de-spise, re - vile, Thy friends un-faith-ful prove;
4. O give us hearts to love like Thee, Like Thee, O Lord, to grieve
5. One with Thy-self, may ev -'ry eye In us, Thy breth-ren, see

What pa-tient love was seen in all Thy life and death of woe!
Yet no un-gen - tle, murm'ring word Es-caped Thy si - lent tongue.
Un - wea-ried in for-give-ness still, Thy heart could on-ly love.
Far more for oth - ers' sins, than all The wrongs that we re - ceive.
That gen-tle-ness and grace that spring From un-ion, Lord, with Thee. A-men.

205 Hail to the Brightness

Thomas Hastings   WESLEY. 11s. 10s.   L. Mason

1. Hail to the bright-ness of Zi - on's glad morn-ing, Joy to the
2. Hail to the bright-ness of Zi - on's glad morn-ing, Long by the
3. Lo, in the des - ert rich flow-ers are spring-ing, Streams ev - er
4. See, from all lands, from the isles of the o - cean, Praise to Je-

lands that in dark-ness have lain! Hushed be the ac-cents of sor-row and
proph-ets of Is - rael fore-told; Hail to the mil-lions from bond-age re-
co - pious are glid-ing a - long; Loud from the mountain-tops ech-oes are
ho - vah as-cend-ing on high; Fallen are the en-gines of war and com-

Hail to the Brightness

mourn-ing, Zi - on in tri - umph be - gins her mild reign.
turn - ing! Gen-tiles and Jews the blest vi - sion be - hold.
ring - ing, Wastes rise in ver - dure and min - gle in song.
mo - tion, Shouts of sal - va - tion are rend-ing the sky. A - MEN.

206 Watchman, Tell Us of the Night

JOHN BOWRING   WATCHMAN 7s. D.   LOWELL MASON

1. Watch-man, tell us of the night, What its signs of prom - ise are.
2. Watch-man, tell us of the night, High - er yet the star as - cends.
3. Watch-man, tell us of the night, For the morn-ing seems to dawn.

Trav -'ler, o'er yon mountain's height See that glo - ry-beam-ing star!
Trav -'ler, bless - ed - ness and light, Peace and truth, its course por-tends.
Trav -'ler, dark-ness takes its flight; Doubt and ter - ror are with-drawn.

Watch-man, does its beau-teous ray Aught of hope or joy fore - tell?
Watch-man, will its beams a - lone Gild the spot that gave them birth?
Watch-man, let thy wan-d'ring cease; Hie thee to thy qui - et home!

Trav -'ler, yes; it brings the day, Prom-ised day of Is - ra - el.
Trav -'ler, a - ges are its own, See, it bursts o'er all the earth.
Trav -'ler, lo, the Prince of Peace, Lo, the Son of God is come! A - MEN.

207 The King of Love

HENRY W. BAKER   DOMINUS REGIT ME. 8s. 7s.   JOHN B. DYKES

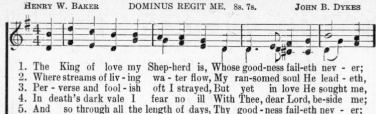

1. The King of love my Shep-herd is, Whose good-ness fail-eth nev - er;
2. Where streams of liv-ing wa - ter flow, My ran-somed soul He lead - eth,
3. Per - verse and fool-ish oft I strayed, But yet in love He sought me,
4. In death's dark vale I fear no ill With Thee, dear Lord, be-side me;
5. And so through all the length of days, Thy good-ness fail-eth nev - er;

I noth-ing lack if I am His, And He is mine for - ev - er.
And, where the verdant pastures grow, With food ce-les - tial feed - eth.
And on His shoulder gen - tly laid, And home, re-joic-ing, bro't me.
Thy rod and staff my com-fort still, Thy cross be-fore to guide me.
Good Shepherd, may I sing Thy praise With-in Thy house for-ev - er. A-MEN.

208 O Worship the King

ROBERT GRANT   LYONS. 10. 10. 11. 11.   FRANCIS J. HAYDN

1. O wor - ship the King, all - glo - rious a - bove, O grate-ful - ly
2. O tell of His might, O sing of His grace, Whose robe is the
3. Thy boun - ti - ful care what tongue can re - cite? It breathes in the
4. Frail chil-dren of dust, and fee - ble as frail, In Thee do we

sing His won-der-ful love; Our Shield and De-fend-er, the An-cient of
light, whose can-o - py space; His char-iots of wrath the deep thunderclouds
air, it shines in the light, It streams from the hills, it de-scends to the
trust, nor find Thee to fail; Thy mer-cies how ten-der! how firm to the

O Worship the King

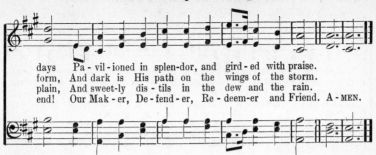

days Pa - vil - ioned in splen - dor, and gird - ed with praise.
form, And dark is His path on the wings of the storm.
plain, And sweet - ly dis - tils in the dew and the rain.
end! Our Mak - er, De - fend - er, Re - deem - er and Friend. A - MEN.

209 Saviour, Again to Thy Dear Name

JOHN ELLERTON   ELLERS. 10s.   EDWARD J. HOPKINS

1. Sav - iour, a - gain to Thy dear name we raise With one ac - cord our
2. Grant us Thy peace up - on our homeward way; With Thee be - gan, with
3. Grant us Thy peace, Lord, thro' the coming night, Turn Thou for us its
4. Grant us Thy peace thro' - out our earth - ly life, Our balm in sor - row,

part - ing hymn of praise; We stand to bless Thee ere our wor - ship
Thee shall end the day; Guard Thou the lips from sin, the hearts from
dark - ness in - to light; From harm and dan - ger keep Thy chil - dren
and our stay in strife; Then, when Thy voice shall bid our con - flict

cease, Then, low - ly kneel - ing, wait Thy word of peace.
shame, That in this house have called up - on Thy name.
free, For dark and light are both a - like to Thee.
cease, Call us, O Lord, to Thine e - ter - nal peace. A - MEN.

210 Jesus, Where'er Thy People Meet

WILLIAM COWPER   MALVERN. L. M.   LOWELL MASON

1. Je - sus, wher-e'er Thy peo-ple meet, There they be-hold Thy mer - cy - seat;
2. For Thou, with-in no walls confined, Dost dwell with those of hum-ble mind;
3. Great Shepherd of Thy cho - sen few, Thy for-mer mer-cies here re - new;
4. Here may we prove the pow'r of prayer To strengthen faith and sweet-en care;

Wher-e'er they seek Thee, Thou art found, And ev-'ry place is hal-lowed ground.
Such ev - er bring Thee where they come, And, go-ing, take Thee to their home.
Here, to our waiting hearts, proclaim The sweetness of Thy sav-ing name.
To teach our faint de-sires to rise, And bring all heav'n be-fore our eyes. A-MEN.

211 Still, Still With Thee

CONSOLATION. 11s. 10s.

HARRIET B. STOWE   FELIX MENDELSSOHN-BARTHOLDY

1. Still, still with Thee, when pur-ple morn-ing break-eth, When the bird
2. A - lone with Thee, a - mid the mys - tic shad-ows, The sol-emn
3. As in the dawn-ing o'er the wave-less o - cean, The im - age
4. When sinks the soul, sub-dued by toil, to slum - ber, Its clos - ing
5. So shall it be at last, in that bright morn-ing, When the soul

wak - eth, and the shad-ows flee; Fair - er than morn-ing, love-li - er than
hush of na-ture new-ly born; A - lone with Thee in breathless ad - o-
of the morning-star doth rest, So in this still-ness, Thou be-hold-est
eyes look up to Thee in prayer; Sweet the re-pose beneath Thy wings o'er-
wak - eth, and life's shadows flee; O in that hour, fair-er than day-light

Still, Still With Thee

day - light, Dawns the sweet con-scious-ness, I am with Thee.
ra - tion, In the calm dew and fresh-ness of the morn.
on - ly Thine im - age in the wa - ters of my breast.
shad - ing, But sweet-er still, to wake and find Thee there.
dawn - ing, Shall rise the glo - rious tho't—I am with Thee. A-MEN.

212 ## For All the Saints

Bishop WILLIAM W. HOW   SARUM. 10. 10. 10. 4.   Sir JOSEPH BARNBY

1. For all the saints who from their la - bors rest, Who Thee by
2. Thou wast their Rock, their For-tress, and their Might; Thou, Lord, their
3. O may Thy sol - diers, faith-ful, true, and bold, Fight as the
4. O blest com-mun - ion, fel - low-ship di - vine! We fee - bly
5. And when the strife is fierce, the war-fare long, Steals on the

faith be - fore the world con - fessed, Thy name, O Je - sus,
Cap - tain in the well - fought fight; Thou, in the dark - ness
saints who no - bly fought of old, And win with them the
strug - gle, they in glo - ry shine; Yet all are one in
ear the dis - tant tri - umph - song, And hearts are brave a-

be for - ev - er blest. Al - le - lu - ia! Al - le - lu - ia!
drear, their one true Light. Al - le - lu - ia! Al - le - lu - ia!
vic - tor's crown of gold. Al - le - lu - ia! Al - le - lu - ia!
Thee, for all are Thine. Al - le - lu - ia! Al - le - lu - ia!
gain, and arms are strong. Al - le - lu - ia! Al - le - lu - ia! A-MEN.

213 Come, Thou Fount

ROBERT ROBINSON NETTLETON. 8s. 7s. D. JOHN WYETH

1. { Come, Thou Fount of ev-'ry bless-ing, Tune my heart to sing Thy grace; }
   { Streams of mer-cy, nev-er ceas-ing, Call for songs of loud-est praise. }

2. { Here I raise my Eb-en-e-zer; Hith-er by Thy help I'm come; }
   { And I hope, by Thy good pleas-ure, Safe-ly to ar-rive at home. }

3. { O to grace how great a debt-or Dai-ly I'm constrained to be! }
   { Let Thy good-ness, like a fet-ter, Bind my wand'ring heart to Thee }

Teach me some me-lo-dious son-net, Sung by flam-ing tongues a-bove:
Je-sus sought me when a stran-ger, Wand'ring from the fold of God;
Prone to wan-der, Lord, I feel it, Prone to leave the God I love;

Praise the mount, I'm fixed up-on it; Mount of Thy redeeming love.
He, to res-cue me from dan-ger, In-ter-posed His precious blood.
Here's my heart, O take and seal it; Seal it for Thy courts a-bove. A-MEN.

214 Take My Life, and Let It Be

FRANCES R. HAVERGAL CÆSAR MALAN

1. Take my life, and let it be Con-se-cra-ted, Lord, to Thee; Take my hands, and
2. Take my feet, and let them be Swift and beau-ti-ful for Thee; Take my voice, and
3. Take my lips, and let them be Filled with mes-sa-ges for Thee; Take my sil-ver
4. Take my moments and my days, Let them flow in ceaseless praise; Take my in-tel-
5. Take my will and make it Thine, It shall be no lon-ger mine; Take my heart, it
6. Take my love, my God, I pour At Thy feet its treasure store; Take myself, and

Take My Life, and Let It Be

let them move At the im-pulse of Thy love, At the im-pulse of Thy love.
let me sing Always, on-ly for my King, Always, on-ly, for my King.
and my gold, Not a mite would I with-hold, Not a mite would I with-hold.
lect, and use Ev'ry pow'r as Thou shalt choose, Ev'ry pow'r as Thou shalt choose.
is Thine own, It shall be Thy roy-al throne, It shall be Thy roy-al throne.
I will be Ev-er, on-ly, all for Thee, Ev-er, on-ly, all for Thee.

215 On the Mountain's Top Appearing

THOMAS KELLEY   ZION. 8. 7. 8. 7. 4. 7.   THOMAS HASTINGS

1. On the mountain's top appearing, Lo! the sa-cred her-ald stands, Wel-come
2. Has thy night been long and mournful? Have thy friends unfaithful proved? Have thy
3. God, thy God, will now restore thee; He Himself appears thy Friend; All thy

news to Zi-on bear-ing, Zi-on, long in hostile lands: Mourning captive, God Him-
foes been proud and scornful, By thy sighs and tears unmoved? Cease thy mourning; Zi-on
foes shall flee before thee; Here their boasts and triumphs end: Great deliv'rance Zi-on's

self shall loose thy bands. Mourning captive, God Himself shall loose thy bands.
still is well be-loved. Cease thy mourning; Zi-on still is well be-loved.
King will sure-ly send. Great deliv'rance Zion's King will sure-ly send. A-MEN.

216 Awake, My Soul

Samuel Medley   LOVING-KINDNESS. L. M.   Composer Unknown

1. A-wake, my soul, in joy-ful lays, And sing thy great Re-deem-er's praise;
2. He saw me ru-ined by the fall, Yet loved me not-with-stand-ing all;
3. When trouble, like a gloom-y cloud, Has gathered thick and thundered loud,
4. Soon shall I pass the gloom-y vale; Soon all my mor-tal pow'rs must fail:

He just-ly claims a song from me: His lov-ing-kind-ness, O how free!
He saved me from my lost es-tate: His lov-ing-kind-ness, O how great!
He near my soul has al-ways stood: His lov-ing-kind-ness, O how good!
O may my last ex-pir-ing breath His lov-ing-kind-ness sing in death!

Lov-ing-kind-ness, lov-ing-kind-ness, His lov-ing-kind-ness, O how free!
Lov-ing-kind-ness, lov-ing-kind-ness, His lov-ing-kind-ness, O how great!
Lov-ing-kind-ness, lov-ing-kind-ness, His lov-ing-kind-ness, O how good!
Lov-ing-kind-ness, lov-ing-kind-ness, His lov-ing-kind-ness sing in death! Amen.

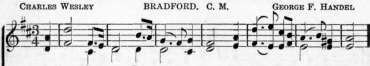

217 I Know That My Redeemer Lives

Charles Wesley   BRADFORD. C. M.   George F. Handel

1. I know that my Re-deem-er lives, And ev-er prays for me;
2. I find Him lift-ing up my head; He brings sal-va-tion near:
3. He wills that I should ho-ly be; Who can with-stand His will?
4. Je-sus, I hang up-on Thy word, I stead-fast-ly be-lieve

I Know That My Redeemer Lives

A to-ken of His love He gives, A pledge of lib-er-ty.
His pres-ence makes me free in-deed, And He will soon ap-pear.
The coun-sel of His grace in me He sure-ly shall ful-fill.
Thou wilt re-turn, and claim me, Lord, And to Thy-self re-ceive. A-MEN.

218   O Love That Wilt Not Let Me Go

GEORGE MATHESON   MARGARET. 8. 8. 8. 8. 6   A. L. PEACE

p

1. O Love that wilt not let me go, I rest my
2. O Light that fol-l'west all my way, I yield my
3. O Joy that seek-est me thro' pain, I can-not
4. O Cross that lift-est up my head, I dare not

wea-ry soul in Thee; I give Thee back the life I owe, That
flick-'ring torch to Thee; My heart re-stores its bor-rowed ray, That
close my heart to Thee; I trace the rain-bow thro' the rain, And
ask to hide from Thee; I lay in dust life's glo-ry dead, And

in Thine o-cean depths its flow May rich-er, full-er be.
in Thy sunshine's blaze its day May bright-er, fair-er be.
feel the prom-ise is not vain That morn shall tear-less be.
from the ground there blossoms red Life that shall end-less be. A-MEN.

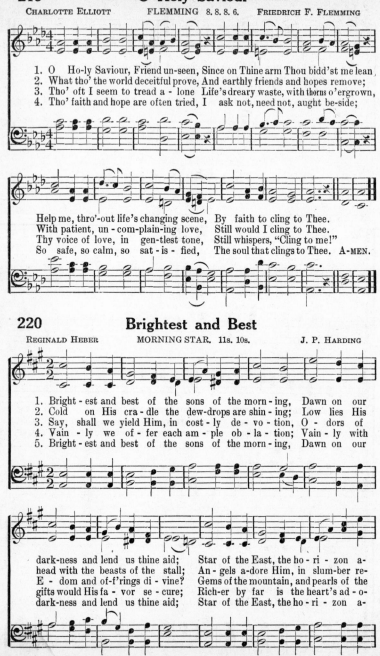

219 O Holy Saviour

CHARLOTTE ELLIOTT   FLEMMING 8. 8. 8. 6.   FRIEDRICH F. FLEMMING

1. O Ho-ly Saviour, Friend un-seen, Since on Thine arm Thou bidd'st me lean,
2. What tho' the world deceitful prove, And earthly friends and hopes remove;
3. Tho' oft I seem to tread a - lone Life's dreary waste, with thorns o'ergrown,
4. Tho' faith and hope are often tried, I ask not, need not, aught be-side;

Help me, thro'-out life's changing scene, By faith to cling to Thee.
With patient, un - com-plain-ing love, Still would I cling to Thee.
Thy voice of love, in gen-tlest tone, Still whispers, "Cling to me!"
So safe, so calm, so sat - is - fied, The soul that clings to Thee. A-MEN.

220 Brightest and Best

REGINALD HEBER   MORNING STAR. 11s. 10s.   J. P. HARDING

1. Bright - est and best of the sons of the morn - ing, Dawn on our
2. Cold on His cra - dle the dew-drops are shin - ing; Low lies His
3. Say, shall we yield Him, in cost - ly de - vo - tion, O - dors of
4. Vain - ly we of - fer each am - ple ob - la - tion; Vain - ly with
5. Bright - est and best of the sons of the morn - ing, Dawn on our

dark-ness and lend us thine aid; Star of the East, the ho - ri - zon a-
head with the beasts of the stall; An - gels a-dore Him, in slum-ber re-
E - dom and of-f'rings di - vine? Gems of the mountain, and pearls of the
gifts would His fa - vor se - cure; Rich-er by far is the heart's ad - o-
dark-ness and lend us thine aid; Star of the East, the ho - ri - zon a-

Brightest and Best

dorn - ing, Guide where our in - fant Re - deem-er is laid.
clin - ing, Mak - er, and Mon-arch, and Sav - iour of all.
o - cean, Myrrh from the for - est, and gold from the mine?
ra - tion; Dear - er to God are the prayers of the poor.
dorn - ing, Guide where our in - fant Re - deem-er is laid. A - MEN.

221 Ten Thousand Times Ten Thousand

HENRY ALFORD ALFORD. 7. 6. 8. 6. D. JOHN B. DYKES

1. Ten thou - sand times ten thou - sand, In spar - kling rai - ment bright,
2. O then what rap-tured greet - ings On Ca-naan's hap - py shore,
3. Bring near Thy great sal - va - tion, Thou Lamb for sin - ners slain;

The ar - mies of the ran-somed saints Throng up the steeps of light:
What knit-ting sev-ered friend-ships up, Where part-ings are no more!
Fill up the roll of Thine e - lect, Then take Thy pow'r and reign;

'Tis fin - ished, all is fin - ished, Their fight with death and sin:
Then eyes with joy shall spar - kle, That brimmed with tears of late,
Ap - pear, De - sire of na - tions! Thine ex - iles long for home;

Fling o - pen wide the gold-en gates, And let the vic - tors in!
Or-phans no lon - ger fa - ther-less, Nor wid-ows des - o - late.
Show in the heav'ns Thy promised sign, Thou Prince and Saviour, come! A-MEN.

222 The Saint's Inheritance

James M. Gray   *(An effective solo)*   Suggestion from a Mendelssohn theme
George S. Schuler

Slowly

1. My Fa-ther, I give thanks, Thy praises I re-peat, That with the saints in light,
2. Thy ful-ness dwells in Him, Thy ver-y im-age He, And yet on Calv'ry's cross
3. By faith complete in Christ My sin is put a-way; By faith in Him I died

Thy grace hath made me meet To share the her-it-age, The kingdom of Thy Son,
His blood was shed for me; Estranged in sin was I, Nor tho't, nor way, was right,
And rose to live al-way; And now the things above Grow dearer, and more dear,

By whose re-deem-ing love That boon for me was won! me was won!
But now in Christ I stand Un-blem-ished in Thy sight! in Thy sight!
And glo-ry on-ly waits Till Je-sus shall ap-pear! shall ap-pear!

223 My Soul, Be On Thy Guard

George Heath   LABAN. S. M.   Lowell Mason

1. My soul, be on thy guard, Ten thou-sand foes a-rise; The
2. O watch, and fight, and pray! The bat-tle ne'er give o'er; Re-
3. Ne'er think the vic-t'ry won, Nor lay thine ar-mor down; The
4. Fight on, my soul, till death Shall bring thee to thy God! He'll

My Soul, Be On Thy Guard

hosts of sin are press-ing hard To draw thee from the skies.
new it bold-ly ev-'ry day, And help di-vine im-plore.
work of faith will not be done Till thou ob-tain thy crown.
take thee at thy part-ing breath, Up to His blest a-bode. A-MEN.

224   The Lord Jehovah Reigns

ISAAC WATTS

D. B. TOWNER

1. The Lord Je-ho-vah reigns, His throne is built on high; The
2. The thun-ders of His hand Keep the wide world in awe; His
3. Thro' all His might-y works A-maz-ing wis-dom shines; Con-
4. And will this sovereign King Of glo-ry con-de-scend; And

gar-ments He as-sumes Are light and maj-es-ty; His glo-ries
wrath and jus-tice stand To guard His ho-ly law; And where His
founds the pow'rs of hell, And all their dark de-signs; Strong is His
will He write His name, My Fa-ther and my Friend? I love His

shine with beams so bright, No mor-tal eye can bear the sight.
love re-solves to bless, His truth con-firms and seals the grace.
arm and shall ful-fill His great de-crees and sover-eign will.
name, I love His word; Join all my pow'rs to praise the Lord.

225 O Thou, In Whose Presence

JOSEPH SWAIN   MEDITATION   FREEMAN LEWIS

1. O Thou, in whose presence my soul takes delight, On whom in af-flic-tion I call,
2. Where dost Thou, dear Shepherd, resort with Thy sheep, To feed them in pastures of love?
3. O why should I wan-der, an alien from Thee, Or cry in the des-ert for bread?
4. He looks! and the thousands of angels rejoice, And myr-i-ads wait for His word;
5. Dear Shepherd! I hear, and will follow Thy call; I know the sweet sound of Thy voice;

My comfort by day and my song in the night, My hope, my sal-va-tion, my all!
Say, why in the val-ley of death should I weep, Or a-lone in this wil-der-ness rove?
Thy foes will rejoice when my sorrows they see, And smile at the tears I have shed.
He speaks, and eternity, filled with His voice, Re - ech - oes the praise of the Lord.
Restore and defend me, for Thou art my all, And in Thee I will ev-er re - joice.

226 "Thou Shalt Call His Name Jesus"

Author unknown   HANFORD. 8. 8. 8. 4.   ARTHUR S. SULLIVAN

1. Sweet Name come down from heav'n above To win our heart's deep, tender love,
2. Mys - te-rious Name! Lies hid in Thee A balm for ev - 'ry mal - a - dy,
3. Thy Name to me is true de - light, My rest and heal-ing, food and light
4. For man-kind all, Thy love is shown, Yet seem'st to be for me a - lone;
5. Oh! grant my dy - ing prayer may be What oft thro' life I whis-pered Thee

As Beth - le - hem and Cal - v'ry prove, My Je - sus!
For deep - est wound a rem - e - dy, My Je - sus!
To guide my fal-t'ring steps a - right, My Je - sus!
I claim Thee for my ver - y own, My Je - sus!
And hope to sing e - ter - nal - ly, My Je - sus! A - MEN.

227 At Even, Ere the Sun Was Set

HENRY TWELLS   ANGELUS. L. M.   Alt. from GEORGE JOSEPHI

1, At e - ven, ere the sun was set, The sick, O Lord, a-round Thee lay :
2. Once more 'tis e-ven-tide, and we, Oppressed with various ills draw near:
3. O Sav-iour Christ, our woes dis-pel: For some are sick, and some are sad,
4. And none, O Lord, have perfect rest, For none are wholly free from sin ;
5. O Saviour Christ, Thou too art man, Thou hast been troubled, tempted, tried ;
6. Thy touch has still its ancient power ; No word from Thee can fruitless fall ;

O in what div - ers pains they met ! O with what joy they went a - way !
What if Thy form we can - not see ? We know and feel that Thou art here.
And some have nev - er loved Thee well, And some have lost the love they had ;
And they who fain would serve Thee best Are concious most of wrong with-in.
Thy kind but searching glance can scan The very wounds that shame would hide.
Hear in this sol-emn eve-ning hour, And in Thy mer - cy heal us all.

228 Saviour, Breathe an Evening Blessing

JAMES EDMESTON   GEO. C. STEBBINS

1. Sav-iour, breathe an evening blessing, Ere re - pose our spir - its seal:
2. Though de-struc-tion walk around us, Though the ar-rows past us fly ;
3. Though the night be dark and drear-y, Dark-ness can - not hide from Thee ;
4. Should swift death this night o'er-take us, And our couch be-come our tomb,

rit.

Sin and want we come con - fess - ing, Thou canst save and Thou canst heal.
An-gel-guards from Thee surround us, We are safe if Thou art nigh.
Thou art He who, nev - er wear - y, Watch-est where Thy peo - ple be.
May the morn in heaven a - wake us, Clad in bright and death-less bloom.

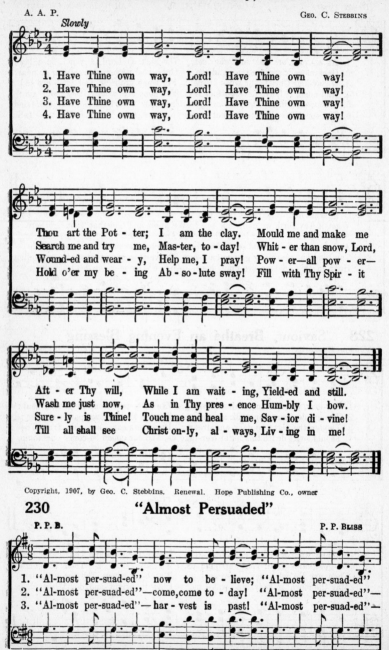

229 Have Thine Own Way, Lord!

A. A. P.   GEO. C. STEBBINS

Slowly

1. Have Thine own way, Lord! Have Thine own way!
2. Have Thine own way, Lord! Have Thine own way!
3. Have Thine own way, Lord! Have Thine own way!
4. Have Thine own way, Lord! Have Thine own way!

Thou art the Pot - ter; I am the clay. Mould me and make me
Search me and try me, Mas-ter, to - day! Whit - er than snow, Lord,
Wound-ed and wear - y, Help me, I pray! Pow - er—all pow - er—
Hold o'er my be - ing Ab - so - lute sway! Fill with Thy Spir - it

Aft - er Thy will, While I am wait - ing, Yield-ed and still.
Wash me just now, As in Thy pres - ence Hum-bly I bow.
Sure - ly is Thine! Touch me and heal me, Sav - ior di - vine!
Till all shall see Christ on-ly, al - ways, Liv - ing in me!

230 "Almost Persuaded"

P. P. B.   P. P. BLISS

1. "Al-most per-suad-ed" now to be - lieve; "Al-most per-suad-ed"
2. "Al-most per-suad-ed"—come, come to - day! "Al-most per-suad-ed"—
3. "Al-most per-suad-ed"—har - vest is past! "Al-most per-suad-ed"—

"Almost Persuaded"

Christ to re - ceive; Seems now some soul to say: "Go, Spir - it,
turn not a - way! Je - sus in - vites you here, An - gels are
doom comes at last! "Al-most" can - not a - vail, "Al - most" is

go Thy way; Some more con-ven - ient day On Thee I'll call."
lingering near, Prayers rise from hearts so dear; O wanderer, come!
but to fail; Sad, sad, that bit - ter wail: "Al-most—but lost!"

231   Jesus, Thou Joy of Loving Hearts

Tr. by RAY PALMER   J. B. TROWBRIDGE

1. Je - sus, Thou joy of lov - ing hearts, Thou Fount of life, Thou Light of men!
2. Thy truth unchanged hath ev - er stood; Thou savest those that on Thee call;
3. We taste Thee, O Thou liv - ing Bread, And long to feast up - on Thee still;
4. Our rest-less spir - its yearn for Thee, Wher-e'er our changeful lot is cast;
5. O Je - sus, ev - er with us stay; Make all our mo - ments calm and bright;

From the best bliss that earth im-parts, We turn un - filled to Thee a - gain.
To them that seek Thee, Thou art good, To them that find Thee, All in All!
We drink of Thee, the Fountain Head, And thirst our souls from Thee to fill.
Glad when Thy gra - cious smile we see, Blest, when our faith can hold Thee fast.
Chase the dark night of sin a - way, Shed o'er the world Thy ho - ly light.

232 Help Me to be Holy

Adoniram J. Gordon

D. B. Towner

1. Help me to be ho - ly, O Fa - ther of light; Guilt-burdened and low - ly, I bow in thy sight; How shall a stained conscience Dare gaze on Thy face, E'en tho' in Thy pres - ence Thou grant me a place?

2. Help me to be ho - ly, O Sav - iour di - vine; Why con-quer so slow - ly This na - ture of mine? Stamp deeply Thy like-ness Where Satan's hath been; Ex - pel with Thy bright-ness My dark-ness and sin!

3. Help me to be ho - ly, O Spir - it di - vine; Come, sanc - ti - fy who - ly This tem - ple of Thine; Now cast out each i - dol, Here set up Thy throne, Reign, reign with-out ri - val, Su-preme and a - lone!

233 We Praise Thee, O God!

Wm. P. Mackay

J. J. Husband

1. We praise Thee, O God, for the Son of Thy love,

2. We praise Thee, O God, for Thy Spir - it of light,

3. All glo - ry and praise to the Lamb that was slain,

4. Re - vive us a - gain, fill each heart with Thy love,

We Praise Thee, O God!

For Je-sus who died and is now gone a-bove!
Who has shown us our Sav-iour and scat-tered our night!
Who has borne all our sins and has cleansed ev-'ry stain!
May each soul be re-kin-dled with fire from a-bove!

CHORUS

Hal-le-lu-jah, Thine the glo-ry! Hal-le-lu-jah, A-men! Re-vive us a-gain!

234   Jesus Paid It All

Mrs. E. M. HALL   JOHN T. GRAPE

1. I hear the Saviour say: "Thy strength indeed is small; Child of weakness,
2. Lord, now in-deed I find Thy power, and Thine a-lone, Can change the
3. For noth-ing good have I Where-by Thy grace to claim; I'll wash my

watch and pray, Find in Me thine all in all."
lep-er's spots, And melt the heart of stone. Je-sus paid it all,
gar-ments white In the blood of Cal-v'ry's Lamb.

CHORUS

All to Him I owe; Sin had left a crimson stain, He washed it white as snow!

235 Jesus Loves Me!

ANNA WARNER

WM. B. BRADBURY

1. Je-sus loves me! this I know, For the Bi-ble tell me so;
2. Je-sus loves me! He who died, Heav-en's gate to o-pen wide;
3. Je-sus loves me! loves me still, When I'm sad or weak and ill;
4. Je-sus loves me! He will stay, Close be-side me all the way,

Lit-tle ones to Him be-long, They are weak, but He is strong.
He will wash a-way my sin, Let His lit-tle child come in.
From His shin-ing throne on high, Comes to watch me where I lie.
If I love Him, by and by He will take me home on high.

CHORUS

{ Yes, Je-sus loves me, Yes, Je-sus loves me; }
{ Yes, Je-sus loves me, (Omit.)........... } The Bi-ble tells me so.

236 We May Not Climb the Heavenly Steeps

JOHN G. WHITTIER

EVAN. C. M.

WILLIAM H. HAVERGAL

1. We may not climb the heav'nly steeps To bring the Lord Christ down;
2. But warm, sweet, ten-der, e-ven yet A pres-ent help is He;
3. The heal-ing of the seamless dress Is by our beds of pain;
4. Thro' Him the first fond prayers are said Our lips of child-hood frame;
5. O Lord and Mas-ter of us all, What-e'er our name or sign,

We May Not Climb the Heavenly Steeps

In vain we search the low-est deeps, For Him no depths can drown.
And faith has still its Ol - i - vet, And love its Gal - i - lee.
We touch Him in life's throng and press, And we are whole a - gain.
The last low whis-pers of our dead Are burdened with His name.
We own Thy sway, we hear Thy call, We test our lives by Thine. A - MEN.

237 Therefore Give Us Love

Bishop CHRISTOPHER WORDSWORTH   "Scots Wha' Hae"

1. Gra-cious Spir - it, Ho - ly Ghost, Taught by Thee we cov - et most,
2. Faith and hope and love we see, Join - ing hand and hand, a - gree;
3. From the o - ver-shad-ow - ing Of Thy gold and sil - ver wing,

Of Thy gifts at Pen - te - cost, Ho - ly, heav'n - ly love.
But the great-est of the three, And the best, is love.
Shed on us who to Thee sing, Ho - ly, heav'n - ly love.

Love is kind, and suf - fers long; Love is meek and thinks no wrong;
Faith will van - ish in - to sight; Hope be emp - tied in de - light;
Proph - e - cy will fade a - way, Melt - ing in the light of day;

Love than death it - self more strong; There-fore give us love.
Love in heav'n will shine more bright; There-fore give us love.
Love will ev - er with us stay; There-fore give us love.

238 Lord, I'm Coming Home

W. J. K.

WM. J. KIRKPATRICK

1. I've wan-dered far a-way from God, Now I'm com-ing home;
2. I've wast-ed man-y pre-cious years, Now I'm com-ing home;
3. I'm tired of sin and stray-ing, Lord, Now I'm com-ing home;
4. My soul is sick, my heart is sore, Now I'm com-ing home;

FINE

The paths of sin too long I've trod, Lord, I'm com-ing home.
I now re-pent with bit-ter tears, Lord, I'm com-ing home.
I'll trust Thy love, be-lieve Thy word, Lord, I'm com-ing home.
My strength re-new, my hope re-store, Lord, I'm com-ing home.

D.S.—O - pen wide Thine arms of love, Lord, I'm com-ing home.

CHORUS

D. S.

Com-ing home, com-ing home, Nev-er more to roam;

5 My only hope, my only plea,
  Now I'm coming home;
That Jesus died, and died for me,
  Lord, I'm coming home.

6 I need His cleansing blood, I know,
  Now I'm coming home;
O wash me whiter than the snow,
  Lord, I'm coming home.

239 The Way of the Cross

E. W. BLANDLY

Arr. from P. P. BLISS

1. I can hear my Sav-iour call-ing, I can hear my Sav-iour call-ing,
2. I'll go with Him thro' the gar-den, I'll go with Him thro' the gar-den,
3. I'll go with Him thro' the judgment, I'll go with Him thro' the judgment,
4. He will give me grace and glo-ry, He will give me grace and glo-ry,

D.C.—Where He leads me I will fol-low, Where He leads me I will fol-low.

The Way of the Cross

ad lib.   *D.C. for Chorus*

I can hear my Sav-iour call-ing, "Take thy cross and fol-low, fol-low Me."
I'll go with Him thro' the gar-den, I'll go with Him, with Him all the way.
I'll go with Him thro' the judgment, I'll go with Him, with Him all the way.
He will give me grace and glo-ry, And go with me, with me all the way.

Where He leads me I will fol-low, I'll go with Him, with Him all the way.

240   Pass Me Not

FANNY J. CROSBY   W. H. DOANE

1. Pass me not, O gen-tle Sav-iour, Hear my num-ble cry; While on
2. Let me at a throne of mer-cy Find a sweet re-lief; Kneel-ing
3. Trust-ing on-ly in Thy mer-it, Would I seek Thy face; Heal my
4. Thou the Spring of all my com-fort, More than life to me; Whom have

oth-ers Thou art call-ing, Do not pass me by.
there in deep con-tri-tion, Help my un-be-lief.   Sav-iour, Sav-iour,
wound-ed, bro-ken spir-it, Save me by Thy grace?
I on earth be-side Thee! Whom in heav'n but Thee?

CHORUS

Hear my humble cry; While on oth-ers Thou art call-ing, Do not pass me by.

He Will Answer Every Prayer

MARY BERNSTECHER

D. B. TOWNER

1. God has giv-en you His prom-ise, That He hears and answers prayer;
2. He will not with-hold one bless-ing, He will give you what is best;
3. He can hear the great pe-ti-tion, And the small-est, o-ver there;
4. Take to God your plans and fail-ures, An-y time and an-y-where;

He will heed your sup-pli-ca-tion, If you cast on Him your care.
God will an-swer by His Spir-it, Ev-'ry one who makes re-quest.
Un-to God pray with-out ceas-ing, He will an-swer ev-'ry prayer.
No one e'er has gone un-answered, For He an-swers ev-'ry prayer.

CHORUS

He will an-swer ev-'ry prayer, He will answer ev-'ry prayer,
He will an-swer, an-swer ev'ry prayer, He will answer, answer ev-'ry prayer.

Go to Him in faith be-liev-ing, He will an-swer ev-'ry prayer.

242

Bringing In the Sheaves

KNOWLES SHAW

GEORGE A. MINOR

1. Sow-ing in the morn-ing, sowing seeds of kindness, Sowing in the noon-tide
2. Sow-ing in the sun-shine, sowing in the shadows, Fearing neither clouds nor
3. Go then, ev-er weep-ing, sow-ing for the Mas-ter, Tho' the loss sustained our

Bringing In the Sheaves

and the dew - y eve; Wait-ing for the har-vest, and the time of reap-ing,
winter's chilling breeze; By and by the har-vest and the la-bor end-ed,
spir - it often grieves; When our weeping's o - ver He will bid us wel-come,

FINE. CHORUS

We shall come re-joic-ing, bring-ing in the sheaves. Bringing in the sheaves,

D.S.— *We shall come re-joic-ing, bringing in the sheaves.*

After repeat D. S. to Fine.

bring-ing in the sheaves, We shall come re-joic-ing, bringing in the sheaves!

243   Old-Time Power

C. D. T.   CHARLIE D. TILLMAN

1. { They were in an up - per cham-ber, They were all with one ac-cord, }
   { When the Ho-ly Ghost de-scend-ed, As was promised by our Lord. }
2. { Yes, this pow'r from heav'n descend-ed With the sound of rush-ing wind; }
   { Tongues of fire came down up-on them, As the Lord said He would send. }
3. { Yes, this "old-time" pow'r was giv-en To our fa-thers who were true; }
   { This is prom-ised to be-liev-ers, And we all may have it, too. }

CHORUS

O Lord, send the pow'r just now; O Lord, send the pow'r just now, And baptize ev'ry one.

244 Thank God For the Bible

JAMES M. GRAY   M. PORTOGALLO

1. O how can we thank Thee, our God, for the Bible, Whose truth doth each century
2. O here thou revealest that Thou art our Father, The hand that hath fashioned and
3. O how can we thank Thee, our God, for the Bible, The gospel's glad sto-ry nor
4. Then glory and hon-or, do-min-ion and power As-cribe to the Trinity a-

clear-er reveal; The fountain of wisdom and source of all knowledge, The court of hu-
caused us to be; O "resident forces," "electrons," and "atoms" Could never have
else had we known Of sin-ners redeemed and made meet for Thy glory, Of sin-ners re-
gain and again, To Father, and Son and the blest Holy Spirit, For-ev - er and

man - i-ty's fi - nal ap-peal, The court of hu-man - i-ty's fi - nal ap-peal.
made or have loved us like Thee! Could never have made or have loved us like Thee!
deemed who shall sit on Thy throne! Of sin-ners redeemed who shall sit on Thy throne!
ev - er, and ev -er, A-men! For-ev - er and ev - er, and ev-er, A-men!

245 I Was a Wandering Sheep

H BONAR   LEBANON. S. M. D.   JOHN ZUNDEL

1. I was a wan-d'ring sheep, I did not love the fold,
2. The Shepherd sought His sheep, The Fa - ther sought His child;
3. No more a wan-d'ring sheep, I love to be con - trolled,

I Was a Wandering Sheep

FINE.

I did not love my Shepherd's voice, I would not be con - trolled:
He fol - lowed me o'er vale and hill, O'er des-erts waste and wild:
I love my ten - der Shepherd's voice, I love the peace-ful fold;

D.S.—I did not love my Fa - ther's voice, I loved a - far to roam.
D.S.—He bound me with the bands of love, He saved the wan-d'ring one.
D.S.—I love my heav'n-ly Fa - ther's voice, I love, I love His home!

D.S.

I was a way-ward child, I did not love my home,
He found me nigh to death, Famished, and faint, and lone;
No more a way-ward child, I seek no more to roam; A - MEN.

246 I'll Live for Him

R. E. HUDSON   C. C. DUNBAR

1. My life, my love I give to Thee, Thou Lamb of God, who died for me;
2. I now be-lieve Thou dost re-ceive, For Thou hast died that I might live;
3. O Thou, who died on Cal - va - ry To save my soul and make me free,

CHO.—*I'll live for Him who died for me; How hap-py then my soul shall be!*

D. C. for Chorus

O may I ev - er faith-ful be, My Sav-iour and my God!
And now hence-forth I'll trust in Thee, My Sav-iour and my God!
I con - se-crate my life to Thee, My Sav-iour and my God!

I'll live for Him who died for me, My Sav-iour and my God!

Rev. Francis Pott   Arthur Sullivan

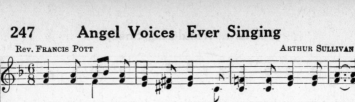

1. An - gel voi - ces ev - er sing - ing Round Thy throne of light,
2. Thou who art be-yond the far - thest Mor - tal eye can scan,
3. Yea, we know Thy love re - joi - ces O'er each work of Thine;
4. Here, great God, to - day we of - fer Of Thine own to Thee;

An - gel harps, for - ev - er ring - ing, Rest not day nor night;
Can it be that Thou re-gard-est Songs of sin - ful man?
Thou didst ears and hands and voi - ces For Thy praise com - bine;
And for Thine ac - cept-ance prof - fer, All un - wor - thi - ly,

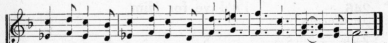

Thou-sands on-ly live to bless Thee, And con - fess Thee Lord of might.
Can we feel that Thou art near us, And wilt hear us? Yea, we can.
Crafts-man's art and music's measure For Thy pleas-ure Didst de - sign.
Hearts and minds, and hands and voices, In our choic-est Mel - o - dy.

248 **O Where Are Kings and Empires Now?**

A. Cleveland Coxe   ST. ANNE   William Croft

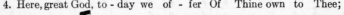

1. O where are kings and em-pires now Of old that went and came?
2. We mark her good - ly bat - tle-ments And her foun - da - tions strong;
3. For not like king-doms of the world Thy ho - ly Church, O God;
4. Un-shak - en as e - ter - nal hills, Im - mov - a - ble she stands;

O Where Are Kings and Empires Now?

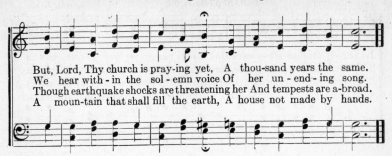

But, Lord, Thy church is pray-ing yet, A thou-sand years the same.
We hear with-in the sol-emn voice Of her un-end-ing song.
Though earthquake shocks are threatening her And tempests are a-broad.
A moun-tain that shall fill the earth, A house not made by hands.

249   ### Break Thou the Bread of Life

MARY A. LATHBURY   W. F. SHERWIN

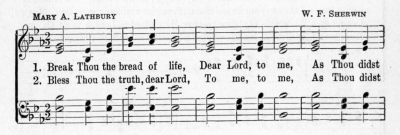

1. Break Thou the bread of life, Dear Lord, to me, As Thou didst
2. Bless Thou the truth, dear Lord, To me, to me, As Thou didst

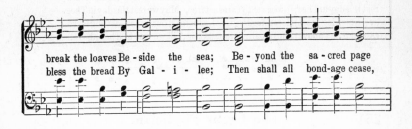

break the loaves Be-side the sea; Be-yond the sa-cred page
bless the bread By Gal-i-lee; Then shall all bond-age cease,

I seek Thee, Lord; My spir-it pants for Thee, O liv-ing Word!
All fet-ters fall, And I shall find my Peace, My All in All!

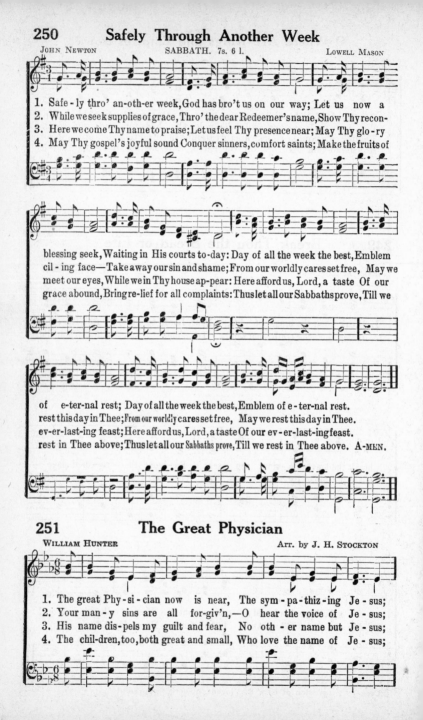

250 Safely Through Another Week

JOHN NEWTON   SABBATH. 7s. 6 l.   LOWELL MASON

1. Safe - ly thro' an-oth-er week, God has bro't us on our way; Let us now a
2. While we seek supplies of grace, Thro' the dear Redeemer's name, Show Thy recon-
3. Here we come Thy name to praise; Let us feel Thy presence near; May Thy glo - ry
4. May Thy gospel's joyful sound Conquer sinners, comfort saints; Make the fruits of

blessing seek, Waiting in His courts to-day: Day of all the week the best, Emblem
cil - ing face—Take away our sin and shame; From our worldly cares set free, May we
meet our eyes, While we in Thy house ap-pear: Here afford us, Lord, a taste Of our
grace abound, Bring re-lief for all complaints: Thus let all our Sabbaths prove, Till we

of e-ter-nal rest; Day of all the week the best, Emblem of e-ter-nal rest.
rest this day in Thee; From our worldly cares set free, May we rest this day in Thee.
ev-er-last-ing feast; Here afford us, Lord, a taste Of our ev-er-last-ing feast.
rest in Thee above; Thus let all our Sabbaths prove, Till we rest in Thee above. A-MEN.

251 The Great Physician

WILLIAM HUNTER   Arr. by J. H. STOCKTON

1. The great Phy-si-cian now is near, The sym-pa-thiz-ing Je - sus;
2. Your man-y sins are all for-giv'n,—O hear the voice of Je - sus;
3. His name dis-pels my guilt and fear, No oth-er name but Je - sus;
4. The chil-dren, too, both great and small, Who love the name of Je - sus;

The Great Physician

FINE.

He speaks, the drooping heart to cheer; O hear the voice of Je - sus.
Go on your way in peace to heav'n, And wear a crown with Je - sus.
O how my soul de - lights to hear The charming name of Je - sus.
May now ac - cept the gra - cious call To work and live for Je - sus.

D.S.— *Sweet-est car - ol ev - er sung,* } *Je - sus, bless-ed Je - sus.*

D. S.

CHORUS

Sweet-est note in ser - aph song, Sweet-est name on mor - tal tongue,

252   Nicaea

REGINALD HEBER

J. B. DYKES

1. Ho - ly, ho - ly, ho - ly!   Lord   God Al - might - y! Ear - ly in the
2. Ho - ly, ho - ly, ho - ly!   all the saints a - dore Thee, Casting down their
3. Ho - ly, ho - ly, ho - ly!   tho' the darkness hide Thee, Tho' the eye of
4. Ho - ly, ho - ly, ho - ly!   Lord   God Al - might - y! All Thy works shall

morn - ing our song shall rise to Thee; Ho - ly, ho - ly, ho - ly!
gold-en crowns a-round the glass-y sea; Cher-u - bim and ser-a - phim,
sin - ful man Thy glo - ry may not see; On - ly Thou art ho - ly,
praise Thy name in earth, and sky, and sea; Ho - ly, ho - ly, ho - ly!

Mer - ci-ful and Might - y, God in three per - sons, blessed Trin - i - ty!
fall-ing down be-fore Thee, Which wert, and art, and ev-er-more shalt be.
there is none be-side Thee, Per-fect in pow'r, in love, and pu - ri - ty.
Mer - ci-ful and Might - y, God in three per - sons, blessed Trin - i - ty! A - MEN.

253 — In the Waves

Translated by Rev. Elvet Lewis   EBENEZER. 8s, 7s, D.   D. Williams

1. { In the waves and might-y wa-ters No one will sup - port my head }
   { But my Sav - iour, my Be - lov - ed, Who was strick-en in my stead; }

2. { O the grace no will can con-quer! The om - nip - o - tence of love! }
   { Changeless is my Fa - ther's prom-ise, It will nev - er, nev - er move! }

He's a Friend in death's dark riv - er, He will hold my head a - bove;
In the storm this is my an-chor—God will nev - er change His mind;

I shall thro' the waves go sing-ing, For one look of Him I love!
In the wounds of Christ He promised Life to me; and He is kind.

254 — Take Time to Be Holy

W. D. Longstaff   Geo. C. Stebbins

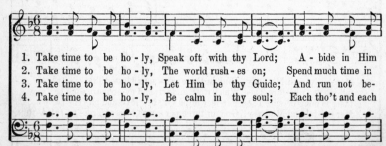

1. Take time to be ho - ly, Speak oft with thy Lord;   A - bide in Him
2. Take time to be ho - ly, The world rush - es on;   Spend much time in
3. Take time to be ho - ly, Let Him be thy Guide;   And run not be-
4. Take time to be ho - ly, Be calm in thy soul;   Each tho't and each

Take Time to Be Holy

al - ways, And feed on His Word. Make friends of God's chil - dren;
se - cret With Je - sus a - lone— By look-ing to Je - sus,
fore Him, What-ev - er be - tide; In joy or in sor - row,
mo - tive Be - neath His con - trol; Thus led by His Spir - it

Help those who are weak; For-get-ting in noth-ing His blessing to seek.
Like Him thou shalt be; Thy friends in thy conduct His likeness shall see.
Still fol - low thy Lord, And, looking to Je-sus, Still trust in His Word.
To foun-tains of love, Thou soon shalt be fit - ted For serv-ice a - bove.

255 Sing to Me of Heaven

Author unknown   Composer unknown

1. O sing to me of heav'n When I'm a - bout to die;
2. Then to my rap-tured soul Let one sweet song be giv'n;
3. Then, round my sense-less clay As - sem-ble those I love,

CHO.—There'll be no sor - row there, There'll be no sor - row there;

D. C.

Sing songs of ho - ly ec - sta - sy To waft my soul on high!
Let mu - sic cheer me last on earth, And greet me first in heav'n.
And sing of heav'n, de-light-ful heav'n, My glo-rious home a - bove.

In heav'n a - bove, where all is love, There'll be no sor - row there.

256 O for a Thousand Tongues to Sing

CHARLES WESLEY   AZMON. C. M.   CARL GLASER

1. O for a thou-sand tongues to sing My great Re-deem-er's praise,
2. My gracious Mas-ter and my God, As-sist me to pro-claim,
3. Je - sus! the name that charms our fears, That bids our sor-rows cease,
4. He breaks the pow'r of can-celed sin, He sets the pris-'ner free;

The glo-ries of my God and King, The triumphs of His grace!
To spread thro' all the earth abroad, The hon-ors of Thy name.
'Tis mu-sic in the sinner's ears, 'Tis life, and health, and peace.
His blood can make the foul-est clean; His blood a-vailed for me. A - MEN.

257 Sun of My Soul

JOHN KEBLE   HURSLEY L. M.   PETER RITTER

1. Sun of my soul! Thou Saviour dear, It is not night if Thou be near;
2. When the soft dews of kind-ly sleep My wearied eye-lids gen-tly steep,
3. A - bide with me from morn till eve, For with-out Thee I can-not live;
4. If some poor wand'ring child of Thine Have spurned, to-day, the voice di - vine,

O may no earth-born cloud a-rise To hide Thee from Thy servant's eyes.
Be my last tho't—how sweet to rest For-ev-er on my Sav-iour's' breast!
Abide with me when night is nigh, For without Thee I dare not die.
Now, Lord, the gra-cious work be-gin; Let him no more lie down in sin. A - MEN.

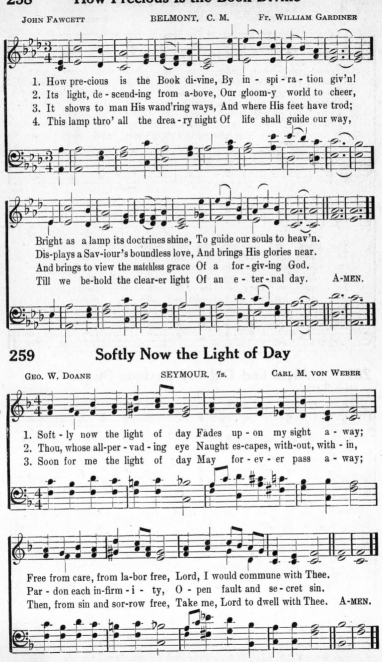

258 How Precious Is the Book Divine

JOHN FAWCETT   BELMONT, C. M.   FR. WILLIAM GARDINER

1. How pre-cious is the Book di-vine, By in-spi-ra-tion giv'n!
2. Its light, de-scend-ing from a-bove, Our gloom-y world to cheer,
3. It shows to man His wand'ring ways, And where His feet have trod;
4. This lamp thro' all the drea-ry night Of life shall guide our way,

Bright as a lamp its doctrines shine, To guide our souls to heav'n.
Dis-plays a Sav-iour's boundless love, And brings His glories near.
And brings to view the matchless grace Of a for-giv-ing God.
Till we be-hold the clear-er light Of an e-ter-nal day. A-MEN.

259 Softly Now the Light of Day

GEO. W. DOANE   SEYMOUR. 7s.   CARL M. VON WEBER

1. Soft-ly now the light of day Fades up-on my sight a-way;
2. Thou, whose all-per-vad-ing eye Naught es-capes, with-out, with-in,
3. Soon for me the light of day May for-ev-er pass a-way;

Free from care, from la-bor free, Lord, I would commune with Thee.
Par-don each in-firm-i-ty, O-pen fault and se-cret sin.
Then, from sin and sor-row free, Take me, Lord to dwell with Thee. A-MEN.

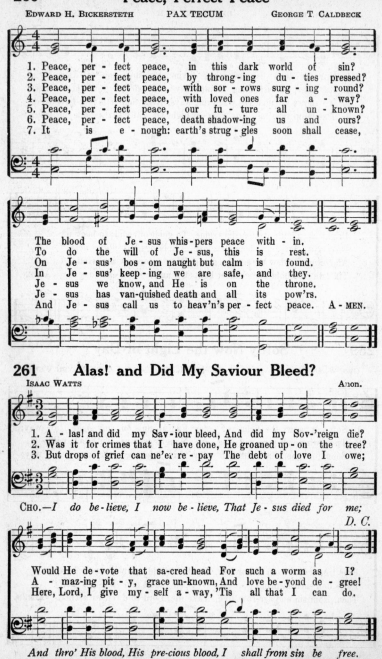

260 Peace, Perfect Peace

EDWARD H. BICKERSTETH   PAX TECUM   GEORGE T. CALDBECK

1. Peace, per - fect peace, in this dark world of sin?
2. Peace, per - fect peace, by throng - ing du - ties pressed?
3. Peace, per - fect peace, with sor - rows surg - ing round?
4. Peace, per - fect peace, with loved ones far a - way?
5. Peace, per - fect peace, our fu - ture all un - known?
6. Peace, per - fect peace, death shadow-ing us and ours?
7. It is e - nough: earth's strug - gles soon shall cease,

The blood of Je - sus whis - pers peace with - in.
To do the will of Je - sus, this is rest.
On Je - sus' bos - om naught but calm is found.
In Je - sus' keep - ing we are safe, and they.
Je - sus we know, and He is on the throne.
Je - sus has van-quished death and all its pow'rs.
And Je - sus call us to heav'n's per - fect peace. A - MEN.

261 Alas! and Did My Saviour Bleed?

ISAAC WATTS   Anon.

1. A - las! and did my Sav - iour bleed, And did my Sov - 'reign die?
2. Was it for crimes that I have done, He groaned up - on the tree?
3. But drops of grief can ne'er re - pay The debt of love I owe;

CHO.—*I do be - lieve, I now be - lieve, That Je - sus died for me;*

D. C.

Would He de - vote that sa - cred head For such a worm as I?
A - maz - ing pit - y, grace un-known, And love be - yond de - gree!
Here, Lord, I give my - self a - way, 'Tis all that I can do.

And thro' His blood, His pre-cious blood, I shall from sin be free.

Jesus Calls Us

CECIL F. ALEXANDER

WILLIAM H. JUDE

1. Je-sus calls us o'er the tu-mult Of our life's wild, rest-less sea;
2. Je-sus calls us from the wor-ship Of the vain world's golden store;
3. In our joys and in our sor-rows, Days of toil and hours of ease,
4. Je-sus calls us! by Thy mer-cies, Sav-iour, may we hear Thy call;

Day by day His sweet voice soundeth, Say-ing, Chris-tian, fol-low Me!
From each i-dol that would keep us, Say-ing, Chris-tian, love Me more!
Still He calls, in cares and pleas-ures, Christian, love Me more than these!
Give our hearts to Thine o-be-dience, Serve and love Thee best of all!

263

Jesus, Saviour, Pilot Me

EDWARD HOPPER

JOHN E. GOULD

FINE.

1. Je-sus, Sav-iour, pi-lot me O-ver life's tem-pest-uous sea;
2. As a moth-er stills her child, Thou canst hush the o-cean wild;
3. When at last I near the shore, And the fear-ful break-ers roar

D.C.—Chart and com-pass came from Thee: Je-sus, Sav-iour, pi-lot me.
D.C.—Wondrous Sov'reign of the sea, Je-sus, Sav-iour, pi-lot me.
D.C.—May I hear Thee say to me, "Fear not, I will pi-lot thee!"

D. C.

Unknown waves be-fore me roll, Hid-ing rock and treach'rous shoal;
Boist'rous waves o-bey Thy will When Thou say'st to them, "Be still!"
'Twixt me and the peaceful rest, Then, while leaning on Thy breast, A-MEN.

264   All Hail the Power

EDWARD PERRONET   MILES LANE   WILLIAM SHRUBSOLE

1. All hail the pow'r of Je-sus' name! Let an-gels prostrate fall; Bring forth the
2. Crown Him, ye morning stars of light, Who fixed this earthly ball; Now hail the
3. Sin-ners, whose love can ne'er for-get The worm-wood and the gall, Go, spread your
4. Ye chos-en seed of Is-rael's race, Ye ransomed from the fall, Hail Him who
5. Let ev-'ry kin-dred, ev-'ry tribe, On this ter-res-trial ball, To Him all
6. O that with yon-der sa-cred throng We at His feet may fall, We'll join the

roy - al di - a - dem, And crown Him, crown Him, crown Him, Crown Him Lord of all.
strength of Israel's might, And crown Him, crown Him, crown Him, Crown Him Lord of all.
tro - phies at His feet, And crown Him, crown Him, crown Him, Crown Him Lord of all.
saves you by His grace, And crown Him, crown Him, crown Him, Crown Him Lord of all.
maj - es - ty as-cribe, And crown Him, crown Him, crown Him, Crown Him Lord of all.
ov - er-lasting song, And crown Him, crown Him, crown Him, Crown Him Lord of all.

265   All Hail the Power of Jesus' Name

EDWARD PERRONET   CORONATION. Second Tune   OLIVER HOLDEN

1. All hail the pow'r of Je-sus' name, Let an-gels pros-trate fall;

Bring forth the roy - al di - a - dem, And crown Him Lord of all.

Bring forth the roy - al di - a - dem, And crown Him Lord of all.

How Beauteous Were the Marks

ROCKINGHAM. L. M.

LOWELL MASON

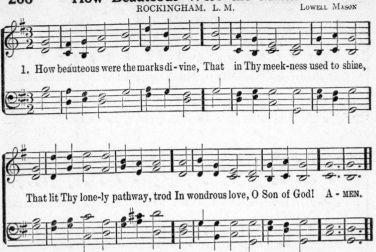

1. How beauteous were the marks di-vine, That in Thy meek-ness used to shine,

That lit Thy lone-ly pathway, trod In wondrous love, O Son of God! A - MEN.

2 O who like Thee, so calm, so bright,
So pure, so made to live in light?
O who like Thee did ever go
So patient through a world of woe?

3 O who like Thee so humbly bore
The scorn, the scoffs of men, before?
So meek, forgiving, godlike, high,
So glorious in humility?

4 The bending angels stooped to see
The lisping infant clasp Thy knee,

And smile as in a father's eye,
Upon Thy mild divinity.

5 And death, which sets the prisoner free,
Was pang, and scoff, and scorn to Thee;
Yet love through all Thy torture glowed;
And mercy with Thy life-blood flowed.

6 O in Thy light be mine to go,
Illuming all my way of woe;
And give me ever on the road
To trace Thy footsteps, Son of God!

Arthur C. Coxe.

267 All Hail the Coming Son

Tune:—CORONATION. No. 265

1 All hail the coming Son of God,
 He's coming back again;
 ‖:He's coming in the clouds of heaven,
 He's coming back to reign! :‖

2 Sinners whose sins are washed away,
 Nor left a single stain,
 ‖:Go, hail the advent of your Lord;
 He's coming back to reign! :‖

3 Let every kindred, every tribe,
 Free of creation's pain,
 ‖:Aloud acclaim His welcome back,—
 He's coming back to reign! :‖

4 Ah! soon with all the ransomed throng,
 Beholding Him once slain,
 ‖:We'll see the rolling cloud, and shout,
 He's coming back to reign! :‖

James M. Gray

268 O Wondrous Type

1 O wondrous type, O vision fair,
 Of glory that the Church shall share,
 Which Christ upon the mountain shows,
 Where brighter than the sun He glows!

2 With shining face and bright array,
 Christ deigns to manifest to-day
 What glory shall be theirs above,
 Who joy in God with perfect love.

3 And faithful hearts are raised on high,
 By this great vision's mystery;
 For which in joyful strains we raise
 The voice of prayer, the hymn of praise.

4 O Father, with the Eternal Son,
 And Holy Spirit, ever One,
 Vouchsafe to bring us by Thy grace
 To see Thy glory face to face.

John M. Neale, tr.

269   Come, Holy Spirit, Heavenly Dove

ORTONVILLE. C. M.   Thomas Hastings

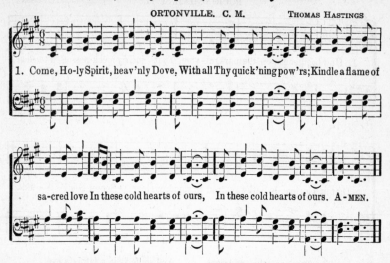

1. Come, Ho-ly Spirit, heav'nly Dove, With all Thy quick'ning pow'rs; Kindle a flame of

sa-cred love In these cold hearts of ours, In these cold hearts of ours. A-MEN.

2 Look—how we grovel here below,
    Fond of these earthly toys;
Our souls, how heavily they go,
    To reach eternal joys.

3 In vain we tune our formal songs,
    In vain we strive to rise;
Hosannas languish on our tongues
    And our devotion dies.

4 Father, and shall we ever live
    At this poor dying rate,
Our love so faint, so cold to Thee,
    And Thine to us so great?

5 Come, Holy Spirit, heavenly Dove,
    With all Thy quickening powers;
Come, shed abroad a Saviour's love,
    And that shall kindle ours.

Isaac Watts.

270   Spirit Divine!

1 Spirit Divine! attend our prayer,
    And make our hearts Thy home;
Descend with all Thy gracious power:
    Come, Holy Spirit, come!

2 Come as the light: to us reveal
    Our sinfulness and woe;
And lead us in those paths of life
    Where all the righteous go.

3 Come as the fire, and purge our hearts
    Like sacrificial flame:
Let our whole soul an offering be
    To our Redeemer's name.

4 Come as the dew and sweetly bless
    This consecrated hour;
Shed richly on our fruitless souls
    Thy fertilizing power.

5 Come as the wind, with rushing sound,
    With Pentecostal grace;
And make the great salvation known
    Wide as the human race.

Andrew Reed

271   Majestic Sweetness

1 Majestic sweetness sits enthroned
    Upon the Saviour's brow;
His head with radiant glories crowned,
    His lips with grace o'erflow.

2 No mortal can with Him compare,
    Among the sons of men;
Fairer is He than all the fair
    That fill the heavenly train.

3 He saw me plunged in deep distress,
    And flew to my relief;
For me He bore the shameful cross,
    And carried all my grief.

4 To Him I owe my life and breath,
    And all the joys I have;
He makes me triumph over death,
    And saves me from the grave.

5 Since from His bounty I receive
    Such proofs of love divine,
Had I a thousand hearts to give,
    Lord, they should all be Thine.

Samuel Siennett

Joy to the World!

272

ANTIOCH. C. M.   Fr. GEORGE F. HANDEL

1. Joy to the world; the Lord is come! Let earth re-ceive her King;

Let ev-'ry heart pre-pare Him room, And heav'n and nature sing, And

And heav'n and na-ture

heav'n and nature sing, And heav'n, and heav'n and nature sing. A-MEN.

sing, And heav'n and na - ture sing.

2 Joy to the world; the Saviour reigns;
Let men their songs employ;
While fields and floods, rocks, hills, and 4
Repeat the sounding joy.   [plains,

3 No more let sin and sorrow grow,
Nor thorns infest the ground;

He comes to make His blessings flow
Far as the curse is found.

He rules the world with truth and grace,
And makes the nations prove
The glories of His righteousness,
And wonders of His love.

Isaac Watts

273   Hark, the Glad Sound!

1 Hark, the glad sound! the Saviour comes,
The Saviour promised long;
Let every heart prepare a throne,
And every voice a song.

2 He comes the prisoners to release,
In Satan's bondage held;
The gates of brass before Him burst,
The iron fetters yield.

3 He comes the broken heart to bind;
The bleeding soul to cure;
And, with the treasures of His grace,
To enrich the humble poor.

4 Our glad hosannas, Prince of Peace,
Thy welcome shall proclaim,
And heav'ns eternal arches ring
With Thy beloved name.

Philip Doddridge, 1735

274   Tune: Ortonville, 269

1 Jesus, thine all victorious love
Shed in my heart abroad:
Then shall my feet no longer rove,
Rooted and fixed in God.

2 O that in me the sacred fire
Might now begin to glow,
Burn up the dross of base desire
And make the mountains flow!

3 O that it now from heaven might fall,
And all my sins consume!
Come, Holy Ghost, for thee I call;
Spirit of burning, come!

4 Refining fire, go through my heart;
Illuminate my soul;
Scatter thy life through every part,
And sanctify the whole.

5 No longer then my heart shall mourn,
While, purified by grace,
I only for His glory burn,
And always see His face.

6 My steadfast soul, from falling free,
Shall then no longer move,
While Christ is all the world to me,
And all my heart is love.

Charles Wesley

AURELIA. 7s, 6s. D.   S. S. WESLEY

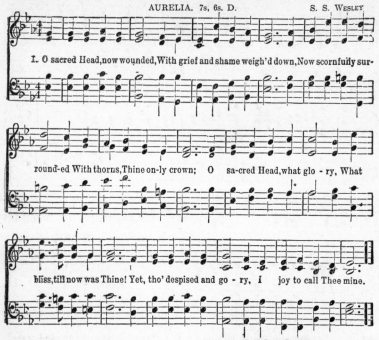

1. O sacred Head, now wounded, With grief and shame weigh'd down, Now scornfully sur-round-ed With thorns, Thine on-ly crown; O sa-cred Head, what glo - ry, What bliss, till now was Thine! Yet, tho' despised and go - ry, I joy to call Thee mine.

276 I Need Thee

2 What Thou, my Lord, hast suffered
  Was all for sinners' gain:
Mine, mine was the transgression,
  But Thine the deadly pain:
Lo, here I fall, my Saviour!
  'Tis I deserved Thy place;
Look on me with Thy favor,
  Vouchsafe to me Thy grace.

3 What language shall I borrow
  To thank Thee, dearest Friend,
For this, Thy dying sorrow,
  Thy pity without end?
Lord, make me Thine forever,
  Nor let me faithless prove:
O let me never, never,
  Abuse such dying love.

4 Be near when I am dying,
  O show Thy cross to me!
And for my succor flying,
  Come, Lord, and set me free!
These eyes, new faith receiving,
  From Jesus shall not move;
For he who dies believing,
  Dies safely—through Thy love.

James W. Alexander, tr.

1 I need Thee, precious Jesus!
  For I am full of sin;
My soul is dark and guilty,
  My heart is dead within.
I need the cleansing fountain,
  Where I can always flee,
The blood of Christ most precious,
  The sinner's perfect plea.

2 I need Thee, blessed Jesus!
  For I am very poor;
A stranger and a pilgrim,
  I have no earthly store;
I need the love of Jesus
  To cheer me on my way,
To guide my doubting footsteps,
  To be my strength and stay.

3 I need Thee, blessed Jesus!
  And hope to see Thee soon,
Encircled with the rainbow,
  And seated on Thy throne:
There, with Thy blood-bought children,
  My joy shall ever be
To sing Thy praise, Lord Jesus,
  To gaze, my Lord, on Thee!

Frederick Whitfield

Christ, the Lord, Is Risen

NUREMBURG. 7s.

JOHANN R. AHLE

1. Christ, the Lord, is ris'n to-day, Sons of men, and an-gels say;

Raise your joys and tri-umphs high; Sing, ye heav'ns —and earth reply! A-MEN.

2 Love's redeeming work is done,
Fought the fight, the battle won:
Lo! the sun's eclipse is o'er;
Lo! he sets in blood no more.

3 Vain the stone, the watch, the seal!
Christ hath burst the gates of hell!
Death in vain forbids His rise;
Christ hath opened Paradise!

4 Lives again our glorious King:
Where, O Death, is now thy sting?
Once He died, our souls to save:
Where thy victory, boasting Grave?

5 Soar we now where Christ has led,
Follow our exalted Head;
Made like Him, like Him we rise;
Ours the cross, the grave, the skies.

Charles Wesley

278   **Tune: Aurelia, 275**

1 The Church's one foundation
  Is Jesus Christ her Lord;
She is His new creation
  By water and the word:
From heaven He came and sought her,
  To be His holy bride;
With His own blood He bought her,
  And for her life He died.

2 Elect from every nation
  Yet one o'er all the earth,
Her charter of salvation
  One Lord, one faith, one birth;
One holy name she blesses,
  Partakes one holy food,
And to one hope she presses,
  With every grace endued.

3 'Mid toil and tribulation,
  And tumult of her war,
She waits the consummation
  Of peace forevermore;
Till with the vision glorious
  Her longing eyes are blest,
And the great Church victorious
  Shall be the Church at rest.

4 Yet she on earth hath union
  With God the Three in One,
And mystic sweet communion
  With those whose rest is won:
Oh, happy ones and holy!
  Lord, give us grace that we
Like them, the meek and lowly,
  On high may dwell with Thee.

Samuel J. Stone. 1865

Behold, a Stranger!

FEDERAL STREET. L. M.

HENRY K. OLIVER

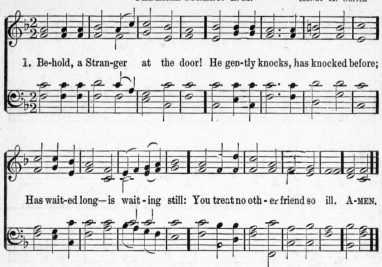

1. Be-hold, a Stran-ger at the door! He gen-tly knocks, has knocked before;

Has wait-ed long—is wait-ing still: You treat no oth-er friend so ill. A-MEN.

2 O lovely attitude! He stands
With melting heart and laden hands:
O matchless kindness! and He shows
This matchless kindness to His foes.

3 But will He prove a friend indeed?
He will; the very friend you need:
The friend of sinners—yes, 't is He,
With garments dyed on Calvary.

4 Admit Him, ere His anger burn;
His feet, departed, ne'er return;
Admit Him, or the hour's at hand
You'll at His door rejected stand.

Joseph Grigg

280 God Calling Yet!

1 God calling yet! shall I not hear?
Earth's pleasures shall I still hold dear?
Shall life's swift passing years all fly.
And still my soul in slumber lie?

2 God calling yet! shall I not rise?
Can I His loving voice despise,
And basely His kind care repay?
He calls me still; can I delay?

3 God calling yet! and shall He knock,
And I my heart the closer lock?

He still is waiting to receive,
And shall I dare His Spirit grieve?

4 God calling yet! I cannot stay;
My heart I yield without delay:
Vain world, farewell! from thee I part;
The voice of God hath reached my heart.

Jane Borthwick, tr.

281 Ashamed of Jesus!

1 Jesus, and shall it ever be,
A mortal man ashamed of Thee?
Ashamed of Thee, whom angels praise,
Whose glories shine thro' endless days?

2 Ashamed of Jesus! sooner far
Let evening blush to own a star;
He sheds the beams of light divine
O'er this benighted soul of mine.

3 Ashamed of Jesus! yes, I may,
When I've no guilt to wash away,
No tear to wipe, no good to crave,
No fear to quell, no soul to save.

4 Till then, nor is my boasting vain,
Till then I boast a Saviour slain;
And O may this my glory be,
That Christ is not ashamed of me.

Joseph Grigg

The Prayer of a Saint

MERCY. 7s.

JAMES M. GRAY

Arr. from LOUIS M. GOTTSCHALK

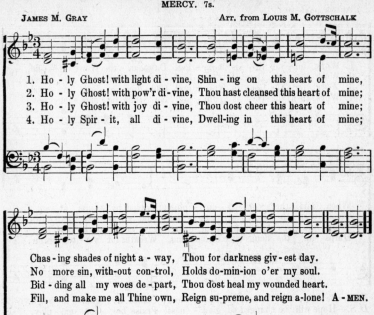

1. Ho - ly Ghost! with light di - vine, Shin - ing on this heart of mine,
2. Ho - ly Ghost! with pow'r di - vine, Thou hast cleansed this heart of mine;
3. Ho - ly Ghost! with joy di - vine, Thou dost cheer this heart of mine;
4. Ho - ly Spir - it, all di - vine, Dwell-ing in this heart of mine;

Chas - ing shades of night a - way, Thou for darkness giv - est day.
No more sin, with-out con-trol, Holds do-min-ion o'er my soul.
Bid - ding all my woes de - part, Thou dost heal my wounded heart.
Fill, and make me all Thine own, Reign su-preme, and reign a-lone! A - MEN.

283 The Prayer of a Sinner

1 Holy Ghost! with light divine,
  Shine upon this heart of mine;
  Chase the shades of night away,
  Turn my darkness into day.

2 Holy Ghost! with power divine,
  Cleanse this guilty heart of mine;
  Long hath sin, without control,
  Held dominion o'er my soul.

3 Holy Ghost! with joy divine,
  Cheer this saddened heart of mine;
  Bid my many woes depart,
  Heal my wounded, bleeding heart.

4 Holy Spirit! all divine,
  Dwell within this heart of mine;
  Cast down every idol-throne,
  Reign supreme—and reign alone.
                        Andrew Reed

284 Christ Gone Before

1 Christ to heaven is gone before
  In the body here He wore;
  He that as our Brother died,
  Is our Brother glorified.

2 All the angels wondering own,
  'Tis our nature on the throne;
  "How He lovèd them, behold!"
  Trembles on the harps of gold.

3 Fear not, ye of little faith,
  For He hath abolished death;
  And no longer now we die,
  We but follow Christ on high.

4 As our Shepherd He is there,
  With the comfort of His care;
  Fear no evil, doubt no more,
  Christ to heaven is gone before.
                        George Rawson, 1857

Work, For the Day is Coming

Author unknown

LOWELL MASON

1. Work, for the Day is com-ing! Day in the Word fore-told,
2. Work, for the Day is com-ing! Dark-ness will soon be gone;
3. Work, for the Lord is com-ing! Chil-dren of light are we;
4. Work, then, the Day is com-ing! No time for sigh-ing now!

FINE.

When, 'mid the scenes tri-um-phant, Craved by saints of old,
Then o'er the night of weep-ing End-less day shall dawn.
From Je-sus' bright ap-pear-ing Pow'rs of dark-ness flee.
Harps for the hands once droop-ing, Wreaths for vic-tor's brow.

D.S.—Je-sus, the Prince, the Sav-iour, Comes a-gain to reign.
D.S.—Hope will be changed to glad-ness, Praise be our em-ploy.
D.S.—O'er all the East are spread-ing Tints of ros-y morn.
D.S.—Night shades ap-pal no lon-ger, Je-sus Christ is near.

D. S.

He, who on earth a stran-ger Trav-ersed its paths of pain,
What now we sow in sad-ness Then we shall reap in joy;
As from the mist a-ris-ing Souls like the dew are born;
Now morn-ing Light is break-ing, Soon will the Day ap-pear;

286 Work, For the Night is Coming

1 Work, for the night is coming,
   Work through the morning hours;
Work while the dew is sparkling,
   Work 'mid springing flow'rs;
Work when the day grows brighter,
   Work in the glowing sun;
Work, for the night is coming,
   When man's work is done.

2 Work, for the night is coming,
   Work through the sunny noon;
Fill brightest hours with labor,
   Rest comes sure and soon.

Give every flying minute
   Something to keep in store;
Work, for the night is coming,
   When man works no more.

3 Work, for the night is coming,
   Under the sunset skies;
While their bright tints are glowing,
   Work, for daylight flies.
Work till the last beam fadeth,
   Fadeth to shine no more;
Work while the night is darkening,
   When man's work is o'er.

Annie L. Coghil.

"By His Stripes We Are Healed"

FEDERAL STREET. L. M.

JAMES M. GRAY   HENRY K. OLIVER

1. My sins laid o - pen to the rod The back which
2. No beam was in His eye, nor mote, Nor laid to
3. I pierced those sa - cred hands and feet That nev - er
4. That sponge of vin - e - gar and gall Was placed by
5. And yet His blood was shed for me, To be of

from the law was free; And the E - ter - nal Son of
Him was an - y blame; And yet His cheeks for me were
touched or walked in sin; I broke the heart that on - ly
me up - on His tongue; And when de - ri - sion mocked His
sin the dou - ble cure; And balm there flows from Cal - v'ry's

God Re - ceived the stripes once due to me.
smote— The cheeks that nev - er blushed for shame.
beat The souls of sin - ful men to win.
call, I stood that mock - ing crowd a - mong.
tree That heals my guilt and makes me pure. A - MEN.

288   **Come, Gracious Spirit**

FEDERAL STREET

1 Come, gracious Spirit, heavenly Dove,
With light and comfort from above:
Be Thou our guardian, Thou our guide,
O'er every thought and step preside.

2 To us the light of truth display,
And make us know and choose Thy way;
Plant holy fear in every heart,
That we from God may ne'er depart.

3 Lead us to holiness—the road
That we must take to dwell with God;
Lead us to Christ, the Living Way,
Nor let us from His precepts stray.

4 Lead us to God, our final rest,
To be with Him forever blest.
Lead us to heaven, its bliss to share—
Fullness of joy forever there!

Simon Browne

289 Nearer, Our God, to Thee *

E. E.
BETHANY
Lowell Mason

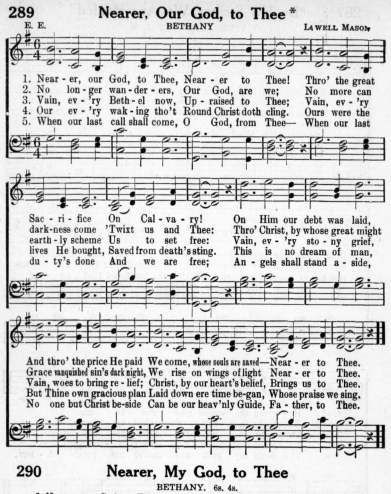

1. Near-er, our God, to Thee, Near-er to Thee! Thro' the great
2. No lon-ger wan-der-ers, Our God, are we; No more can
3. Vain, ev-'ry Beth-el now, Up-raised to Thee; Vain, ev-'ry
4. Our ev-'ry wak-ing tho't Round Christ doth cling. Ours were the
5. When our last call shall come, O God, from Thee— When our last

Sac-ri-fice On Cal-va-ry! On Him our debt was laid,
dark-ness come 'Twixt us and Thee; Thro' Christ, by whose great might
earth-ly scheme Us to set free: Vain, ev-'ry sto-ny grief,
lives He bought, Saved from death's sting. This is no dream of man,
du-ty's done And we are free; An-gels shall stand a-side,

And thro' the price He paid We come, whose souls are saved—Near-er to Thee.
Grace vanquished sin's dark night, We rise on wings of light Near-er to Thee.
Vain, woes to bring re-lief; Christ, by our heart's belief, Brings us to Thee.
But Thine own gracious plan Laid down ere time be-gan, Whose praise we sing.
No one but Christ be-side Can be our heav'nly Guide, Fa-ther, to Thee.

290 Nearer, My God, to Thee
BETHANY. 6s. 4s.

1 Nearer, my God, to Thee,
Nearer to Thee,
E'en though it be a cross
That raiseth me;
Still all my song shall be,
Nearer, my God, to Thee,
Nearer to Thee!

2 Though like a wanderer,
The sun gone down,
Darkness be over me,
My rest a stone,
Yet in my dreams I'd be
Nearer, my God, to Thee,
Nearer to Thee!

3 Then, with my waking thoughts
Bright with Thy praise,
Out of my stony griefs
Bethel I'll raise;
So by my woes to be
Nearer, my God, to Thee,
Nearer to Thee!

4 Or if, on joyful wing
Cleaving the sky,
Sun, moon, and stars forgot,
Upward I fly,
Still all my song shall be,
Nearer, my God, to Thee,
Nearer to Thee.

Mrs. Sarah F. Adams

*The author of this poem is an English woman, born in Asia, a correspondent for the *London Times* for more than thirty years, under whose auspices she traveled to the four corners of the earth. The hymn is not intended to serve as a paraphrase of the famous "Nearer, My God, to Thee," but it emphasizes in a beautiful and scriptural way the believer's means of approach to God-the merits of our Lord and Saviour, Jesus Christ.-Editors

291　Jesus, the Very Thought of Thee

ST. AGNES.　C. M.

BERNARD OF CLAIRVAUX, tr.

JOHN B. DYKES

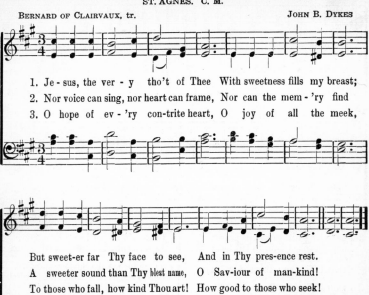

1. Je - sus, the ver - y tho't of Thee With sweetness fills my breast;
2. Nor voice can sing, nor heart can frame, Nor can the mem - 'ry find
3. O hope of ev - 'ry con - trite heart, O joy of all the meek,

But sweet-er far Thy face to see, And in Thy pres-ence rest.
A sweeter sound than Thy blest name, O Sav-iour of man-kind!
To those who fall, how kind Thou art! How good to those who seek!

4 But what to those who find? Ah! this
　Nor tongue, nor pen can show;
　The love of Jesus, what it is,
　None but His loved ones know.

5 Jesus, our only joy be Thou,
　As Thou our prize wilt be;
　Jesus, be Thou our glory now,
　And through eternity.

292　Light of the Lonely Pilgrim's Heart

Tune: ST. AGNES

1 Light of the lonely pilgrim's heart!
　Star of the coming day!
　Arise, and with Thy morning beams
　Chase all my griefs a-way.

2 Come, blessed Lord! let every shore
　And answering island sing
　The praises of Thy royal name,
　And own Thee as their King.

3 Hope of our hearts, O Lord, appear,
　Thou glorious Star of day!
　Shine forth and chase the dreary night,
　With all our tears away.

4 No resting-place we seek on earth,
　No loveliness we see;
　Our eye is on the royal crown,
　Prepared for us—and Thee!

Sir Edward Denny

Depth of Mercy!

ALETTA 7s.

WILLIAM B. BRADBURY

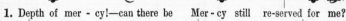

1. Depth of mer - cy!—can there be Mer - cy still re-served for me?

Can my God His wrath for-bear? Me, the chief of sin-ners, spare? A - MEN.

2 I have long withstood His grace;
Long provoked Him to His face;
Would not hearken to His calls;
Grieved Him by a thousand falls.

3 Kindled His relentings are;
Me He now delights to spare;

Cries, How shall I give thee up?—
Lets the lifted thunder drop!

4 There for me the Saviour stands;
Shows His wounds and spreads His hands!
God is love! I know, I feel;
Jesus weeps, and loves me still.

Charles Wesley

Not All the Blood

BOYLSTON. S. M.

LOWELL MASON

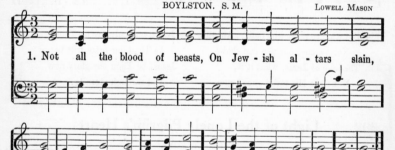

1. Not all the blood of beasts, On Jew - ish al - tars slain,

Could give the guilt - y conscience peace, Or wash a - way the stain. A - MEN.

2 But Christ, the heavenly Lamb,
Takes all our sins away—
A sacrifice of nobler name,
And richer blood than they.

3 My faith would lay her hand
On that dear head of Thine,

While like a penitent I stand,
And there confess my sin.

4 Believing, we rejoice
To see the curse remove;
We bless the Lamb with cheerful voice,
And sing His bleeding love.

Isaac Watts

295 O Happy Day

Fr. Edward F. Rimbault

1. { O hap-py day that fixed my choice On Thee, my Sav-iour and my God!
Well may this glow-ing heart re-joice, And tell its rap-tures all a-broad. }

CHORUS.

FINE.

Hap-py day, hap-py day, When Je-sus washed my sins a-way!

D. S.

He taught me how to watch and pray, And live re-joic-ing ev-'ry day; A-MEN.

2 O happy bond, that seals my vows
To Him who merits all my love!
Let cheerful anthems fill His house,
While to that sacred shrine I move.

3 'T is done; the great transaction's done;
I am my Lord's, and He is mine;
He drew me, and I followed on,
Charmed to confess the voice divine.

Philip Doddridge.

296 Take My Heart

TALMAR. 8s, 7s.

Isaac B. Woodbury

1. Take my heart, O Fa-ther, take it; Make and keep it all Thine own;

Let thy Spir-it melt and break it—This proud heart of sin and stone. A-MEN.

2 Father, make me pure and lowly,
Fond of peace and far from strife;
Turning from the paths unholy
Of this vain and sinful life.

3 May the blood of Jesus heal me,
And my sins be all forgiven;
Holy Spirit, take and seal me,
Guide me in the path to heaven.

Abide with Me!

EVENTIDE. 10s.

WILLIAM H. MONK

1. Abide with me! Fast falls the eventide, The darkness deepens—Lord, with me abide!

When other helpers fail, and comforts flee, Help of the helpless, O, abide with me! AMEN.

2 Swift to its close ebbs out life's little day;
Earth's joys grow dim, its glories pass away;
Change and decay in all around I see;
O Thou, who changest not, abide with me!

3 I need Thy presence every passing hour;
What but Thy grace can foil the tempter's power?
Who, like Thyself, my guide and stay can be?
Through cloud and sunshine, O, abide with me!

4 Hold Thou Thy cross before my closing eyes;
Shine through the gloom, and point me to the skies;
Heaven's morning breaks, and earth's vain shadows flee;
In life, in death, O Lord, abide with me!

Henry F. Lyte

298

Now the Day Is Over

JOSEPH BARNBY

1. Now the day is o - ver, Night is draw-ing nigh, Shad-ows of the
2. Je - sus, give the wear - y Calm and sweet re-pose; With Thy tend'rest

eve - ning Steal a-cross the sky.
bless - ing May our eye-lids close.

3 Through the long night-watches,
May Thine angels spread
Their white wings above me,
Watching round my bed.

4 When the morning wakens,
Then may I arise,
Pure, and fresh, and sinless,
In Thy holy eyes.

Sabine Baring-Gould

evening Steal a - cross the sky.

299 ## When I Survey the Wondrous Cross

HAMBURG. L. M. Ad. by Lowell Mason

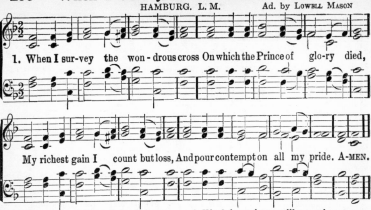

1. When I sur-vey the won-drous cross On which the Prince of glo-ry died,

My richest gain I count but loss, And pour contempt on all my pride. A-MEN.

2 Forbid it, Lord, that I should boast,
  Save in the death of Christ, my God;
All the vain things that charm me most,
  I sacrifice them to His blood.

3 See, from His head, His hands, His feet,
  Sorrow and love flow mingled down;
Did e'er such love and sorrow meet,
  Or thorns compose so rich a crown?

4 His dying crimson, like a robe,
  Spreads o'er His body on the tree;
Then I am dead to all the globe,
  And all the globe is dead to me.

5 Were the whole realm of nature mine,
  That were a present far too small;
Love so amazing, so divine,
  Demands my soul, my life, my all.

Isaac Watts

300 ## Jesus! Jesus! Jesus!

Slowly

1. Je - sus! Je - sus! Je - sus! Sing a - loud the Name;

Till it soft - ly, slow - ly, Sets all hearts a - flame A-MEN.

2 Jesus! Name of cleansing,
  Washing all our stains;
Jesus! Name of healing,
  Balm for all our pains.

3 Jesus! Name of boldness,—
  Making cowards brave;
Name! that in the battle,
  Certainly must save.

4 Jesus! Name of victory,
  Stretching far away,

Right across earth's war-fields,
  To the plains of day.

5 Jesus! Name of beauty,
  Beauty far too bright
For our earth-bound fancy,
  For our mortal sight.

6 Jesus! be our joy-note
  In this vale of tears;
Till we reach the home-land,
  And th'eternal years.

Llanthony Abbey Hymns

301 Lord, Speak to Me, That I May Speak

CANONBURY. L. M.

Arr. from Robert A. Schumann, 1839

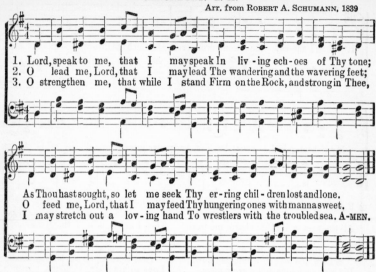

1. Lord, speak to me, that I may speak In liv-ing ech-oes of Thy tone;
2. O lead me, Lord, that I may lead The wandering and the wavering feet;
3. O strengthen me, that while I stand Firm on the Rock, and strong in Thee,

As Thou hast sought, so let me seek Thy er-ring chil-dren lost and lone.
O feed me, Lord, that I may feed Thy hungering ones with manna sweet.
I may stretch out a lov-ing hand To wrestlers with the troubled sea. A-MEN.

4 O teach me, Lord, that I may teach
   The precious things Thou dost impart;
   And wing my words, that they may reach
   The hidden depths of many a heart.

5 O give Thine own sweet rest to me,
   That I may speak with soothing power
   A word in season, as from Thee,
   To weary ones in needful hour.

6 O fill me with Thy fulness, Lord,
   Until my very heart o'erflow
   In kindling thought and glowing word,
   Thy love to tell, Thy praise to show.

7 O use me, Lord, use even me,
   Just as Thou wilt, and when, and where;
   Until Thy blessed face I see,
   Thy rest, Thy joy, Thy glory share.

Frances R. Havergal, 1872

302 Come, Ye Thankful People

Tune 303

1 Come, ye thankful people, come,
   Raise the song of harvest-home:
   All is safely gathered in,
   Ere the winter storms begin;
   God, our Maker, doth provide
   For our wants to be supplied:
   Come to God's own temple, come,
   Raise the song of the harvest-home.

2 All the world is God's own field,
   Fruit unto His praise to yield;
   Wheat and tares together sown,
   Unto joy or sorrow grown;
   First the blade, and then the ear,
   Then the full corn shall appear:
   Lord of harvest, grant that we
   Wholesome grain and pure may be.

3 For the Lord our God shall come,
   And shall take His harvest-home,
   From His field shall in that day
   All offenses purge away;
   Give His angels charge at last
   In the fire the tares to cast;
   But the fruitful ears to store
   In His garner evermore.

4 Even so, Lord, quickly come
   To Thy final harvest-home;
   Gather Thou Thy people in,
   Free from sorrow, free from sin;
   There, forever purified,
   In Thy presence to abide:
   Come, with all Thine angels, come,
   Raise the glorious harvest-home.

Henry Alford

Hark! the Herald Angels Sing

CHARLES WESLEY   FELIX MENDELSSOHN-BARTHOLDY

1. Hark! the herald an-gels sing, "Glo-ry to the newborn King; Peace on earth, and

mer-cy mild, God and sin-ners rec-on-ciled!" Joy-ful, all ye na-tions, rise,

Join the tri-umph of the skies; With the an-gel host proclaim, "Christ is born in

Beth-le-hem!" With the angel host proclaim, "Christ is born in Bethlehem!" A-MEN.

2 Christ, by highest heaven adored,
Christ, the everlasting Lord;
In the manger born a King,
While adoring angels sing,
"Peace on earth, to men good-will;"
Bid the trembling soul be still,
Christ on earth has come to dwell,
Jesus, our Immanuel!

3 Hail! the heaven-born Prince of peace!
Hail the Sun of righteousness!
Life and light to all He brings,
Risen with healing in His wings.
Mild He lays His glory by,
Born that man no more may die,
Born to raise the sons of earth,
Born to give them second birth.

304 . It Came Upon the Midnight Clear

CAROL. C. M. D.

RICHARD S. WILLIS

1. It came upon the midnight clear, That glorious song of old, From angels bending near the earth,

To touch their harps of gold; "Peace to the earth, good-will to men, From heav'n's all-gracious

King:" The earth in sol-emn stillness lay, To hear the an-gels sing. A-MEN.

2 Still through the cloven skies they come,
   With peaceful wings unfurled;
And still celestial music floats
   O'er all the weary world;
Above its sad and lonely plains
   They bend on heavenly wing,
And ever o'er its Babel sounds,
   The blessed angels sing.

3 O ye, beneath life's crushing load,
   Whose forms are bending low,
Who toil along the climbing way,
   With painful steps and slow;—

Look up! for glad and golden hours
   Come swiftly on the wing;
O rest beside the weary road,
   And hear the angels sing!

4 For lo! the days are hastening on,
   By prophet-bards foretold,
When with the ever-circling years
   Comes round the age of gold!
When peace shall over all the earth
   Its final splendors fling,
And the whole world send back the song
   Which now the angels sing!

Edmund H. Sears

305　Calm On the Listening Ear of Night

1 Calm on the listening ear of night
   Come heaven's melodious strains,
Where wild Judea stretches far
   Her silver-mantled plains.
Celestial choirs, from courts above,
   Shed sacred glories there,
And angels, with their sparkling lyres,
   Make music on the air.

2 "Glory to God!" the lofty strain
   The realms of ether fills;
How sweeps the song of solemn joy
   O'er Judah's sacred hills!
"Glory to God!" the sounding skies
   Loud with their anthems ring:
"Peace on the earth; good-will to men,
   From heaven's eternal King."

Edmund H. Sears

306   Come, Thou Almighty King

CHARLES WESLEY   ITALIAN HYMN. 6s, 4s.   FELICE GIARDINI

1. Come, Thou Al-might-y King, Help us Thy name to sing,
2. Come, Thou In-car-nate Word, Gird on Thy might-y sword,
3. Come, Ho-ly Com-fort-er, Thy sa-cred wit-ness bear
4. To the great One in Three, The high-est prais-es be

Help us to praise; Fa-ther all-glo-ri-ous, O'er all vic-
Our prayer at-tend; Come, and Thy peo-ple bless, And give Thy
In this glad hour: Thou who al-might-y art, Now rule in
Hence, ev-er-more! His sov-'reign maj-es-ty May we in

to-ri-ous, Come and reign o-ver us, An-cient of days.
word suc-cess: Spir-it of ho-li-ness, On us de-scend.
ev-'ry heart, And ne'er from us de-part, Spir-it of pow'r!
glo-ry see, And to e-ter-ni-ty Love and a-dore. A-MEN.

307   Glory to God On High!

1 Glory to God on high!
  Let heaven and earth reply,
    "Praise ye His name!"
  His love and grace adore,
  Who all our sorrows bore;
  Sing loud for evermore,
    "Worthy the Lamb!"

2 While they around the throne
  Cheerfully join in one,
    Praising His name,—
  Ye who have felt His blood
  Sealing your peace with God,
  Sound His dear name abroad,
    "Worthy the Lamb!"

3 Join, all ye ransomed race,
  Our Lord and God to bless;
    Praise ye His name!
  In Him we will rejoice,
  And make a joyful noise,
  Shouting with heart and voice,
    "Worthy the Lamb!"

4 Soon must we change our place,
  Yet will we never cease
    Praising His name;
  To Him our songs we bring,
  Hail Him our gracious King;
  And through all ages sing,
    "Worthy the Lamb!"

James Allen

Blest Be the Tie

JOHN FAWCETT   DENNIS. S. M.   HANS G. NAEGELI

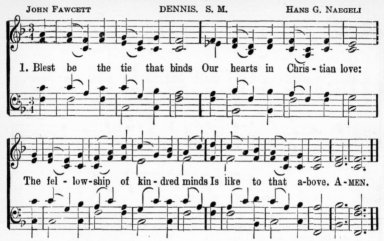

1. Blest be the tie that binds Our hearts in Chris-tian love:

The fel-low-ship of kin-dred minds Is like to that a-bove. A-MEN.

2 Before our Father's throne
  We pour our ardent prayers;
Our fears, our hopes, our aims are one,
  Our comforts and our cares.

3 We share our mutual woes,
  Our mutual burdens bear;

And often for each other flows
  The sympathizing tear.

4 When we asunder part,
  It gives us inward pain;
But we shall still be joined in heart,
  And hope to meet again.

309   O Son of Man

JOSEPH ANSTICE   RAPHAEL. C. M.   From G. DONNIZETTI

1. O Son of Man, Thy-self hath proved Our tri - als and our tears;

Life's thankless toil and scant re-pose, Death's ag - o - nies and fears. A-MEN.

2 In all things like Thy brethren Thou
  Wast made, yet free from sin;
Yet how unlike to us, O Lord;
  Replies the voice within.

3 O Son of God, in glory raised,
  Thou sittest on Thy throne:

There by Thy pleadings and Thy grace
  Still succoring Thine own.

4 Brother and Saviour, Friend and Judge:
  To Thee, O Christ, be given,
To bind upon Thy crown the names
  Elect in earth and heaven.

310 O God, Our Help

ISSAC WATTS   DUNDEE. C. M.   ANDRO HART's Psalter

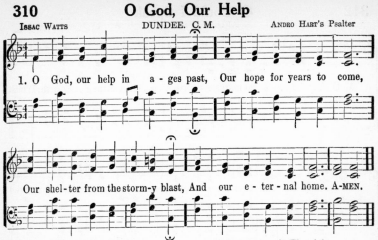

1. O God, our help in a-ges past, Our hope for years to come,

Our shel-ter from the storm-y blast, And our e-ter-nal home. A-MEN.

2 Under the shadow of Thy throne
  Thy saints have dwelt secure;
Sufficient is Thine arm alone,
  And our defense is sure.

3 Before the hills in order stood,
  Or earth received her frame,
From everlasting Thou art God,
  To endless years the same.

4 A thousand ages, in Thy sight,
  Are like an evening gone;
Short as the watch that ends the night,
  Before the rising sun.

5 Time, like an ever-rolling stream,
  Bears all its sons away;
They fly, forgotten, as a dream
  Dies at the opening day.

311 In the Cross of Christ I Glory

JOHN BOWRING   RATHBUN. 8s, 7s.   ITHAMAR CONKEY

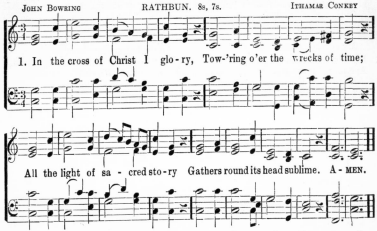

1. In the cross of Christ I glo-ry, Tow-'ring o'er the wrecks of time;

All the light of sa-cred sto-ry Gathers round its head sublime. A-MEN.

2 When the woes of life o'ertake me,
  Hopes deceive, and fears annoy,
Never shall the cross forsake me:
  Lo! it glows with peace and joy.

3 When the sun of bliss is beaming
  Light and love upon my way,

From the cross the radiance streaming,
  Adds more luster to the day.

4 Bane and blessing, pain and pleasure,
  By the cross are sanctified;
Peace is there that knows no measure,
  Joys that through all time abide.

312 O Could I Speak

SAMUEL MEDLEY

ARIEL. C. P. M.

Arr. by LOWELL MASON

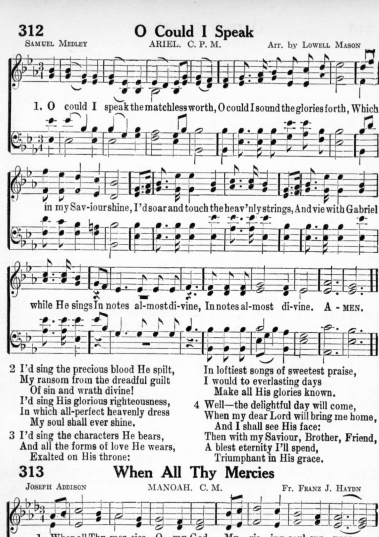

1. O could I speak the matchless worth, O could I sound the glories forth, Which in my Sav-iour shine, I'd soar and touch the heav'nly strings, And vie with Gabriel while He sings In notes al-most di-vine, In notes al-most di-vine. A - MEN.

2 I'd sing the precious blood He spilt,
My ransom from the dreadful guilt
Of sin and wrath divine!
I'd sing His glorious righteousness,
In which all-perfect heavenly dress
My soul shall ever shine.

3 I'd sing the characters He bears,
And all the forms of love He wears,
Exalted on His throne:

In loftiest songs of sweetest praise,
I would to everlasting days
Make all His glories known.

4 Well—the delightful day will come,
When my dear Lord will bring me home,
And I shall see His face:
Then with my Saviour, Brother, Friend,
A blest eternity I'll spend,
Triumphant in His grace.

313 When All Thy Mercies

JOSEPH ADDISON

MANOAH. C. M.

Fr. FRANZ J. HAYDN

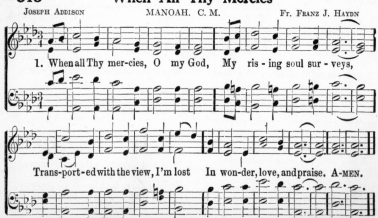

1. When all Thy mer-cies, O my God, My ris-ing soul sur-veys, Trans-port-ed with the view, I'm lost In won-der, love, and praise. A-MEN.

314 There Is a Fountain

WILLIAM COWPER

Ad. Fr. LOWELL MASON

1. There is a foun-tain filled with blood Drawn from Im-man-uel's veins;

And sin-ners, plunged be-neath that flood, Lose all their guilt-y stains.

Lose all their guilt-y stains, Lose all their guilt-y stains; A-MEN.

2 The dying thief rejoiced to see
   That fountain in his day;
And there may I, though vile as he,
   Wash all my sins away.

3 Dear dying Lamb, Thy precious blood
   Shall never lose its power,
Till all the ransomed Church of God
   Be saved to sin no more.

4 E'er since, by faith, I saw the stream
   Thy flowing wounds supply,
Redeeming love has been my theme,
   And shall be till I die.

5 Then in a nobler, sweeter song,
   I'll sing Thy power to save,
When this poor lisping, stammering
   Lies silent in the grave.   [tongue

Tune: Manoah

2 Unnumbered comforts to my soul,
   Thy tender care bestowed,
Before my infant heart conceived
   From whom those comforts flowed.

3 When, in the slippery paths of youth,
   With heedless steps, I ran,
Thine arm, unseen, conveyed me safe,
   And led me up to man.

4 Ten thousand thousand precious gifts
   My daily thanks employ;

Nor is the least a cheerful heart,
   That tastes those gifts with joy.

5 Through every period of my life
   Thy goodness I'll pursue;
And after death, in distant worlds,
   The glorious theme renew.

6 Through all eternity, to Thee
   A joyful song I'll raise;
For O, eternity's too short
   To utter all Thy praise!

Joseph Addison

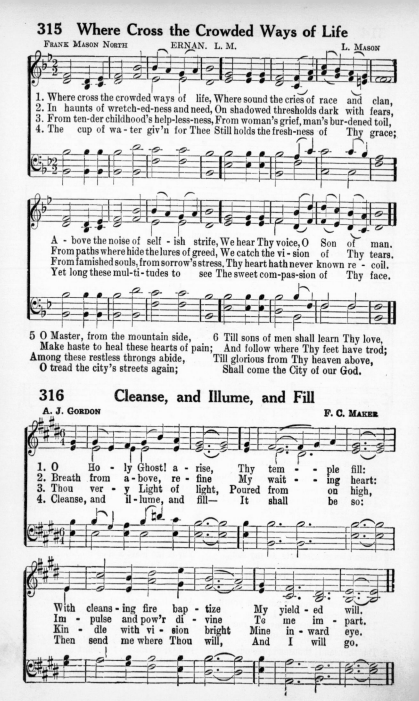

315 Where Cross the Crowded Ways of Life

FRANK MASON NORTH ERNAN. L. M. L. MASON

1. Where cross the crowded ways of life, Where sound the cries of race and clan,
2. In haunts of wretch-ed-ness and need, On shadowed thresholds dark with fears,
3. From ten-der childhood's help-less-ness, From woman's grief, man's bur-dened toil,
4. The cup of wa-ter giv'n for Thee Still holds the fresh-ness of Thy grace;

A - bove the noise of self - ish strife, We hear Thy voice, O Son of man.
From paths where hide the lures of greed, We catch the vi - sion of Thy tears.
From famished souls, from sorrow's stress, Thy heart hath never known re - coil.
Yet long these mul-ti-tudes to see The sweet com-pas-sion of Thy face.

5 O Master, from the mountain side,
  Make haste to heal these hearts of pain;
Among these restless throngs abide,
  O tread the city's streets again;

6 Till sons of men shall learn Thy love,
  And follow where Thy feet have trod;
Till glorious from Thy heaven above,
  Shall come the City of our God.

316 Cleanse, and Illume, and Fill

A. J. GORDON F. C. MAKER

1. O Ho - ly Ghost! a - rise, Thy tem - - ple fill:
2. Breath from a - bove, re - fine My wait - - ing heart:
3. Thou ver - y Light of light, Poured from on high,
4. Cleanse, and il - lume, and fill— It shall be so:

With cleans - ing fire bap - tize My yield - ed will.
Im - pulse and pow'r di - vine To me im - part.
Kin - dle with vi - sion bright Mine in - ward eye.
Then send me where Thou will, And I will go.

317 My Faith Looks Up to Thee

OLIVET. 6s, 4s.

RAY PALMER

LOWELL MASON

1. My faith looks up to Thee, Thou Lamb of Calvary, Sav-iour divine! Now hear me while I pray, Take all my guilt away, O let me from this day Be whol-ly Thine.

2 May Thy rich grace impart
Strength to my fainting heart,
My zeal inspire;
As Thou hast died for me,
O may my love to Thee
Pure, warm, and changeless be,
A living fire!

3 While life's dark maze I tread,
And griefs around me spread,
Be Thou my Guide;
Bid darkness turn to day,

Wipe sorrow's tears away,
Nor let me ever stray
From Thee aside.

4 When ends life's transient dream,
When death's cold, sullen stream
Shall o'er me roll,
Blest Saviour! then, in love,
Fear and distrust remove;
O bear me safe above,
A ransomed soul!

318 The Solid Rock

EDWARD MOTE

WILLIAM B. BRADBURY

REFRAIN

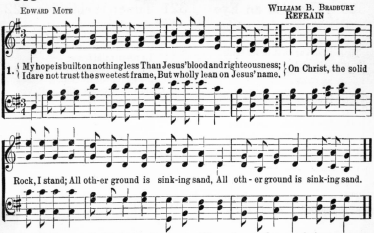

1. My hope is built on nothing less Than Jesus' blood and righteousness;
I dare not trust the sweetest frame, But wholly lean on Jesus' name. On Christ, the solid Rock, I stand; All oth-er ground is sink-ing sand, All oth-er ground is sink-ing sand.

2 When darkness veils His lovely face,
I rest on His unchanging grace;
In every high and stormy gale,
My anchor holds within the veil.

3 His oath, His covenant, His blood,
Support me in the whelming flood;

When all around my soul gives way,
He then is all my hope and stay.

4 When He shall come with trumpet sound,
O may I then in Him be found;
Drest in His righteousness alone,
Faultless to stand before the throne.

319 Father, Whate'er of Earthly Bliss

ANNE STEEL NAOMI. C. M. Arr. from HANS G. NAEGELI, by LOWELL MASON

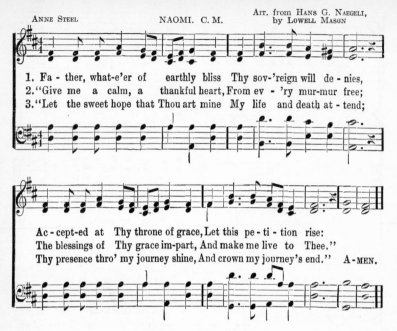

1. Fa - ther, what-e'er of   earthly bliss Thy sov-'reign will de - nies,
2. "Give me a calm, a   thankful heart, From ev - 'ry mur-mur free;
3. "Let the sweet hope that Thou art mine My life and death at - tend;

Ac - cept-ed at Thy throne of grace, Let this pe - ti - tion rise:
The blessings of Thy grace im-part, And make me live to Thee."
Thy presence thro' my journey shine, And crown my journey's end." A-MEN.

320 There Is an Eye

1 There is an eye that never sleeps
   Beneath the wing of night;
   There is an ear that never shuts,
   When sink the beams of light.

2 There is an arm that never tires,
   When human strength gives way;
   There is a love that never fails,
   When earthly loves decay.

3 But there's a power which man can wield
   When mortal aid is vain,
   That eye, that arm, that love to reach,
   That listening ear to gain.

4 That power is prayer, which soars on high
   Through Jesus to the throne;
   And moves the hand which moves the world,
   To bring salvation down.

James E. Wallace

321 Tune: Webb. No. 322

1 The morning light is breaking;
   The darkness disappears;
   The sons of earth are waking
   To penitential tears;
   Each breeze that sweeps the ocean
   Brings tidings from afar,
   Of nations in commotion,
   Prepared for Zion's war.

2 See heathen nations bending
   Before the God we love,
   And thousand hearts ascending
   In gratitude above;
   While sinners, now confessing,
   The gospel call obey,
   And seek the Saviour's blessing—
   A nation in a day.

3 Blest river of salvation!
   Pursue thine onward way;
   Flow thou to every nation,
   Nor in thy richness stay:
   Stay not till all the lowly
   Triumphant reach their home:
   Stay not till all the holy
   Proclaim—"The Lord is come!"

Samuel F. Smith, 1832

Stand Up, Stand Up for Jesus

GEORGE DUFFIELD

G. J. WEBB

1. Stand up, stand up for Je - sus! Ye sol-diers of the cross, Lift high His
2. Stand up, stand up for Je - sus! The trum-pet call o - bey; Forth to the
3. Stand up, stand up for Je - sus! Stand in His strength alone; The arm of
4. Stand up, stand up for Je - sus! The strife will not be long; This day the

roy - al ban - ner, It must not suf-fer loss; From vic-t'ry un - to vic-t'ry, His
might-y con-flict, In this His glorious day. Ye that are men now serve Him, A-
flesh will fail you, Ye dare not trust your own; Put on the gos-pel ar-mor, Each
noise of bat - tle, The next the victor's song: To him that o - ver-com-eth A

ar - my shall He lead. Till ev - 'ry foe is vanquished And Christ is Lord indeed.
gainst unnumbered foes; Let courage rise with danger, And strength to strength oppose.
piece put on with prayer; Where duty calls, or dan-ger, Be nev-er wanting there.
crown of life shall be; He with the King of glo - ry Shall reign e-ter-nal-ly.

323   Hail, to the Lord's Anointed

Above Tune

1 Hail, to the Lord's Anointed,
   Great David's greater Son!
Hail, in the time appointed,
   His reign on earth begun!
He comes to break oppression,
   To set the captive free,
To take away transgression,
   And rule in equity.

2 He comes with succor speedy
   To those who suffer wrong;
To help the poor and needy,
   And bid the weak be strong:
To give them songs for sighing,
   Their darkness turn to light,
Whose souls, condemned and dying,
   Were precious in His sight.

3 He shall descend like showers
   Upon the fruitful earth,
And love and joy, like flowers,
   Spring in His path to birth:
Before Him, on the mountains,
   Shall peace, the herald, go,
And righteousness, in fountains,
   From hill to valley flow.

4 To Him shall prayer unceasing,
   And daily vows ascend;
His kingdom still increasing,
   A kingdom without end.
The tide of time shall never
   His covenant remove;
His name shall stand forever;
   That name to us is Love.

James Montgomery

How Firm a Foundation

GEORGE KEITH PORTUGUESE HYMN. 11s. MARCANTOINE PORTOGALLO

1 How firm a foun-da-tion, ye saints of the Lord, Is laid for your faith in His ex-cel-lent word! What more can He say, than to you He hath said,— To you, who for ref-uge to Je-sus have fled? To you, who for ref-uge to Je-sus have fled? A-MEN.

2 "Fear not, I am with thee, O be not dismayed,
For I am thy God, I will still give thee aid;
I'll strengthen thee, help thee, and cause thee to stand,
Upheld by My gracious, omnipotent hand.

3 "When through the deep waters I call thee to go,
The rivers of sorrow shall not overflow;
For I will be with thee thy trouble to bless,
And sanctify to thee thy deepest distress.

4 "When through fiery trials thy pathway shall lie,
My grace, all-sufficient, shall be thy supply;
The flame shall not hurt thee; I only design
Thy dross to consume, and thy gold to refine.

5 "E'en down to old age all My people shall prove,
My sovereign, eternal, unchangeable love,
And then, when gray hairs shall their temples adorn,
Like lambs they shall still in My bosom be borne.

6 "The soul that on Jesus hath leaned for repose,
I will not—I will not desert to his foes;
That soul—though all hell should endeavor to shake,
I'll never—no never, no never forsake!"

O Day of Rest and Gladness

MENDEBRAS. 7s, 6s. D.   Arr. by LOWELL MASON

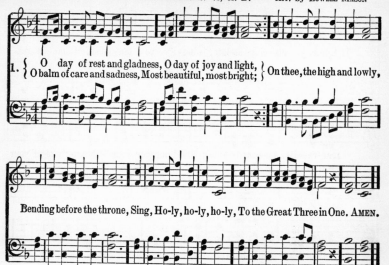

1. { O day of rest and gladness, O day of joy and light, }
   { O balm of care and sadness, Most beautiful, most bright; } On thee, the high and lowly,

Bending before the throne, Sing, Ho-ly, ho-ly, ho-ly, To the Great Three in One. AMEN.

2 To-day on weary nations
  The heavenly manna falls;
To holy convocations
  The silver trumpet calls,
Where gospel light is glowing
  With pure and radiant beams,
And living water flowing
  With soul-refreshing streams.

3 New graces ever gaining
  From this our day of rest,
We reach the rest remaining
  To spirits of the blest.
To Holy Ghost be praises,
  To Father and to Son;
The Church her voice upraises
  To Thee, blest Three in One.

Christopher Wordsworth

326   Tune: Portuguese Hymn.   No. 324

1 O come, all ye faithful, triumphantly sing!
  Come, see in the manger, the angels' dread King!
  To Bethlehem hasten, with joyful accord:
  O hasten! O hasten! to worship the Lord.

2 True Son of the Father, He comes from the skies:
  The womb of the Virgin He doth not despise;
  To Bethlehem hasten, with joyful accord:
  O hasten! O hasten! to worship the Lord.

3 O hark to the angels, all singing in heaven,
  "To God in the highest, all glory be given!"
  To Bethlehem hasten, with joyful accord:
  O hasten! O hasten! to worship the Lord.

4 To Thee, then, O Jesus, this day of Thy birth,
  Be glory and honor through heaven and earth;
  True Godhead Incarnate, Omnipotent Word!
  O hasten! O hasten! to worship the Lord.

Tr. by Edward Caswall, 1848

327

Come, Ye Disconsolate

Samuel Webbe

1. Come, ye dis-con-so-late, wher-e'er ye lan-guish; Come to the mer-cy-seat, fer-vent-ly kneel; Here bring your wounded hearts, here tell your an-guish, Earth hath no sor-row that heav'n can-not heal. A-MEN.

2 Joy of the comfortless, light of the straying,
Hope of the penitent, fadeless and pure;
Here speaks the Comforter, tenderly saying—
Earth has no sorrow that heaven cannot cure.

3 Here see the Bread of Life; see waters flowing
Forth from the throne of God, pure from above;
Come to the feast of love; come, ever knowing
Earth has no sorrow but heaven can remove.

Thomas Moore

328

Why Will Ye Waste

BERA. L. M.

John E. Gould

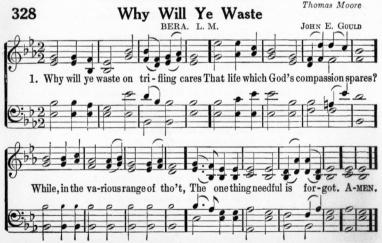

1. Why will ye waste on tri-fling cares That life which God's compassion spares? While, in the va-rious range of tho't, The one thing needful is for-got. A-MEN.

Just As I Am

WOODWORTH. L. M.　　WILLIAM B. BRADBURY

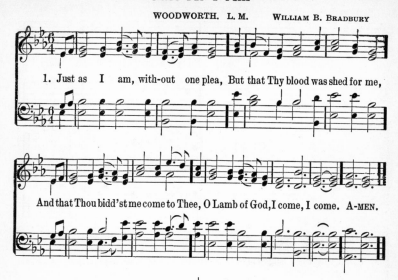

1. Just as I am, with-out one plea, But that Thy blood was shed for me,

And that Thou bidd'st me come to Thee, O Lamb of God, I come, I come. A-MEN.

2 Just as I am, and waiting not
To rid my soul of one dark blot, [spot,
To Thee, whose blood can cleanse each
O Lamb of God, I come.

3 Just as I am, though tossed about
With many a conflict, many a doubt,
Fightings and fears, within, without,
O Lamb of God, I come.

4 Just as I am, poor, wretched, blind;
Sight, riches, healing of the mind,
Yea, all I need, in Thee to find,
O Lamb of God, I come.

5 Just as I am! Thou wilt receive,
Wilt welcome, pardon, cleanse, relieve;
Because Thy promise I believe,
O Lamb of God, I come.

Charlotte Elliott

330 Return, O Wanderer

1 Return, O wanderer, return,
　And seek an injured Father's face;
Those warm desires that in thee burn
　Were kindled by reclaiming grace.

2 Return, O wanderer, return,
　And seek a Father's melting heart;
His pitying eyes thy grief discern,
　His hand shall heal thine inward smart.

3 Return, O wanderer, return;
　Thy Saviour bids thy spirit live;
Go to His bleeding feet, and learn
　How freely Jesus can forgive.

4 Return, O wanderer, return,
　And wipe away the falling tear;
'Tis God who says, "No longer mourn";
　'Tis mercy's voice invites thee near.

William B. Collyer

Tune:—BERA

2 Shall God invite you from above?
Shall Jesus urge His dying love?
Shall troubled conscience give you pain?
And all these pleas unite in vain?

3 Not so your eyes will always view
Those objects which you now pursue;

Not so will heaven and hell appear,
When death's decisive hour is near.

4 Almighty God! Thy grace impart;
Fix deep conviction on each heart:
Nor let us waste on trifling cares
That life which Thy compassion spares.

Philip Doddridge

331 Come, Lord, and Tarry Not

HORATIUS BONAR   GREENWOOD. S. M.   JOSEPH SWEETSER

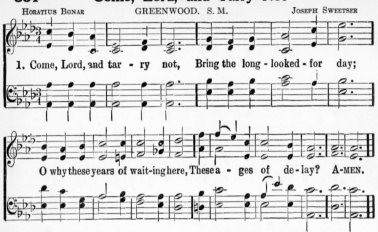

1. Come, Lord, and tar - ry not, Bring the long - looked - for day;

O why these years of wait-ing here, These a - ges of de - lay? A-MEN.

2 Come! for creation groans,
   Impatient of Thy stay,
  Worn out with these long years of ill,
   These ages of delay.

3 Come, and make all things new;
   Build up this ruined earth,

Restore our faded Paradise,
   Creation's second birth!

4 Come, and begin Thy reign
   Of everlasting peace,
  Come, take the kingdom to Thyself,
   Great King of Righteousness!

332 From Greenland's Icy Mountains

REGINALD HEBER   MISSIONARY HYMN   LOWELL MASON

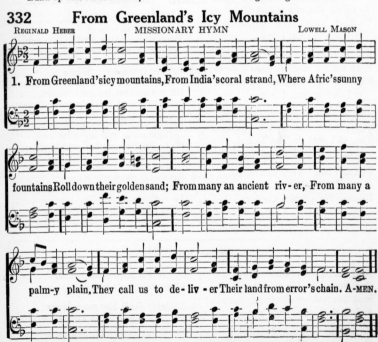

1. From Greenland's icy mountains, From India's coral strand, Where Afric's sunny

fountains Roll down their golden sand; From many an ancient riv-er, From many a

palm-y plain, They call us to de-liv-er Their land from error's chain. A-MEN.

333 Lead, Kindly Light

JOHN H. NEWMAN   LUX BENIGNA   JOHN B. DYKES

1. Lead, kind-ly Light, a-mid th' encircling gloom, Lead Thou me on:
2. I was not ev - er thus, nor prayed that Thou Shouldst lead me on;
3. So long Thy pow'r hath blessed me, sure it still Will lead me on

The night is dark and I am far from home; Lead Thou me on!
I loved to choose and see my path; but now Lead Thou me on!
O'er moor and fen, o'er crag and tor-rent till The night is gone,

Keep Thou my feet; I do not ask to see
I loved the gar - ish day, and, spite of fears,
And with the morn those an-gel fa - ces smile

The dis - tant scene; one step e - nough for me.
Pride ruled my will. Re-mem-ber not past years.
Which I have loved long since, and lost a - while. A - MEN.

Tune: Missionary Hymn

2 Shall we, whose souls are lighted
  With wisdom from on high,—
Shall we, to men benighted,
  The lamp of life deny?
Salvation! O salvation!
  The joyful sound proclaim,
Till earth's remotest nation
  Has learned Messiah's name.

3 Waft, waft, ye winds, His story,
  And you, ye waters, roll,
Till, like a sea of glory,
  It spreads from pole to pole;
Till o'er our ransomed nature
  The Lamb for sinners slain,
Redeemer, King, Creator,
  In bliss returns to reign!

Reginald Heber

Jesus Shall Reign

ISAAC WATTS   DUKE STREET. L. M.   JOHN HATTON

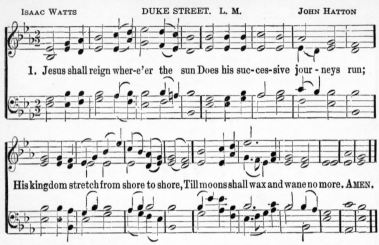

1. Jesus shall reign wher-e'er the sun Does his suc-ces-sive jour-neys run;

His kingdom stretch from shore to shore, Till moons shall wax and wane no more. AMEN.

2 To Him shall endless prayer be made,
And endless praises crown His head:
His name, like sweet perfume, shall rise
With every morning sacrifice.

3 People and realms of every tongue
Dwell on His love with sweetest song;

And infant voices shall proclaim
Their early blessings on His name.

4 Blessings abound where'er He reigns;
The prisoner leaps to loose his chains;
The weary find eternal rest,
And all the sons of want are blest.

335

Go, Labor On

HORATIUS BONAR   MISSIONARY CHANT. L. M.   HEINRICH C. ZEUNER

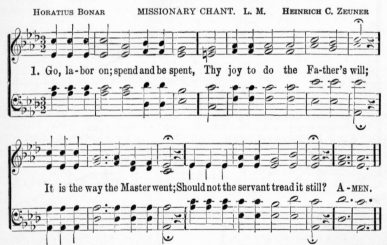

1. Go, la-bor on; spend and be spent, Thy joy to do the Fa-ther's will;

It is the way the Master went; Should not the servant tread it still? A - MEN.

2 Go, labor on; 'tis not for naught;
Thine earthly loss is heavenly gain;
Men heed thee, love thee, praise thee not;
The Master praises,—what are men?

3 Go, labor on; enough, while here,
If He shall praise thee if He deign

Thy willing heart to mark and cheer:
No toil for Him shall be in vain.

4 Toil on, and in thy toil rejoice;
For toil comes rest, for exile home;
Soon shalt thou hear the Bridegroom's voice,
The midnight peal: "Behold, I come!"

The God of Abraham Praise

LEONI

THOMAS OLIVERS

Hebrew Melody

1. The God of Abraham praise, Who reigns enthroned above; An-cient of ev-er-
2. The God of Abraham praise, At whose supreme command, From earth I rise, and

last-ing days, And God of love; Je-ho-vah, great I AM, By earth and
seek the joys At His right hand: I all on earth for-sake, Its wis-dom,

heav'n confessed; I bow and bless the sa-cred name, For-ev-er blest.
fame, and power; And Him my on-ly por-tion make, My shield and tower. A-MEN.

3 He by Himself hath sworn,
   I on His oath depend;
I shall, on eagle's wings upborne,
   To heaven ascend;
I shall behold His face,
   I shall His power adore,
And sing the wonders of His grace
   For evermore.

4 The goodly land I see,
   With peace and plenty blest;
A land of sacred liberty,
   And endless rest.
There milk and honey flow,
   And oil and wine abound;
And trees of life forever grow,
   With mercy crowned.

5 Before the great Three-One
   They all exulting stand,
And tell the wonders He hath done
   Through all their land.
The listening spheres attend,
   And swell the growing fame;
And sing, in songs which never end,
   The wondrous name.

6 The whole triumphant host
   Give thanks to God on high;
"Hail, Father, Son, and Holy Ghost,"
   They ever cry;
Hail, Abraham's God and mine!—
   I join the heavenly lays,—
All might and majesty are Thine,
   And endless praise.

337 When Morning Gilds the Skies

EDWARD CASWELL, Tr. LAUDES DOMINI JOSEPH BARNBY

1. When morning gilds the skies, My heart awaking cries, May Jesus Christ be praised:

A-like at work and prayer, To Jesus I repair; May Je - sus Christ be praised. A-MEN.

2 To Thee, O God above,
  I cry with glowing love,
    May Jesus Christ be praised:
  This song of sacred joy,
  It never seems to cloy;
    May Jesus Christ be praised.
3 Does sadness fill my mind,
  A solace here I find;
    May Jesus Christ be praised:

Or fades my earthy bliss,
  My comfort still is this:
    May Jesus Christ be praised.
4 Be this, while life is mine,
  My canticle divine;
    May Jesus Christ be praised:
  Be this the eternal song,
  Through all the ages long:
    May Jesus Christ be praised.

338 Faith of Our Fathers!

FREDERICK W. FABER ST. CATHERINE Adapted by J. G. WALTERS

1. { Faith of our fa-thers! liv-ing still In spite of dungeon, fire and sword:
  { O how our hearts beat high with joy Whene'er we hear that glorious

word; Faith of our fathers! holy faith! We will be true to thee till death! A-MEN

2 Our fathers, chained in prisons dark,
Were still in heart and conscience free,
How sweet would be their children's fate,
If they like them, could die for thee!
Faith of our fathers! holy faith!
We will be true to thee till death!

3 Faith of our fathers! we will love
  Both friend and foe in all our strife;
And preach thee, too, as love knows how,
  By kindly words and virtuous life:
Faith of our fathers! holy faith!
  We will be true to thee till death!

339 There's a Wideness in God's Mercy

FREDERICK W. FABER   WELLESLEY   LIZZIE S. TOURJEE

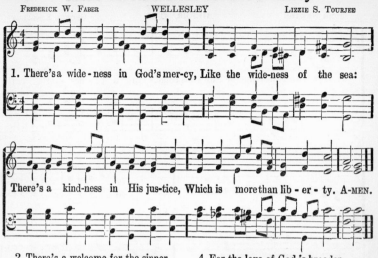

1. There's a wide-ness in God's mer-cy, Like the wide-ness of the sea:

There's a kind-ness in His jus-tice, Which is more than lib-er-ty. A-MEN.

2 There's a welcome for the sinner,
   And more graces for the good;
There is mercy with the Saviour;
   There is healing in His blood.

3 There is plentiful redemption
   In the blood that has been shed;
There is joy for all the members
   In the sorrows of the Head.

4 For the love of God is broader
   Than the measure of man's mind;
And the heart of the Eternal
   Is most wonderfully kind.

5 If our love were but more simple,
   We should take Him at His word;
And our lives would be all sunshine
   In the sweetness of our Lord.

340 I Hear the Words of Love

HORATIUS BONAR   ST. MICHAEL. S. M.   Arr. by WILLIAM H. HAVERGAL

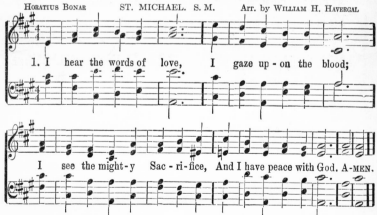

1. I hear the words of love, I gaze up-on the blood;

I see the might-y Sac-ri-fice, And I have peace with God. A-MEN.

2 'Tis everlasting peace,
   Sure as Jehovah's name;
'Tis stable as His steadfast throne,
   For evermore the same.

3 The clouds may go and come,
   And storms may sweep the sky,

This blood-sealed friendship changes not,
   The cross is ever nigh.

4 I change, He changes not,
   The Christ can never die;
His love, not mine, the resting-place,
   His truth, not mine, the tie.

How Sweet the Name of Jesus

JOHN NEWTON HEBER. C. M. GEORGE KINGSLEY

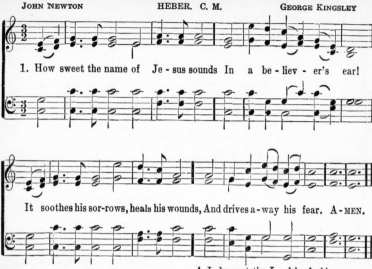

1. How sweet the name of Je-sus sounds In a be-liev-er's ear!

It soothes his sor-rows, heals his wounds, And drives a-way his fear. A-MEN.

2 It makes the wounded spirit whole,
  And calms the troubled breast;
  'Tis manna to the hungry soul,
  And to the weary, rest.

3 Jesus, my Shepherd, Guardian, Friend,
  My Prophet, Priest, and King,—
  My Lord, my Life, my Way, my End,
  Accept the praise I bring.

4 Weak is the effort of my heart,
  And cold my warmest thought;
  But, when I see Thee as Thou art,
  I'll praise Thee as I ought.

342 God Moves in a Mysterious Way

1 God moves in a mysterious way
  His wonders to perform;
  He plants His footsteps in the sea,
  And rides upon the storm.

2 Deep in unfathomable mines
  Of never-failing skill,
  He treasures up His bright designs,
  And works His sovereign will.

3 Ye fearful saints, fresh courage take:
  The clouds ye so much dread
  Are big with mercy, and will break
  In blessings on your head.

4 Judge not the Lord by feeble sense,
  But trust Him for His grace;
  Behind a frowning providence
  He hides a smiling face.

5 Blind unbelief is sure to err,
  And scan His work in vain;
  God is His own interpreter,
  And He will make it plain.

William Cowper.

343 O For a Faith That Will Not Shrink

1 O for a faith that will not shrink,
  Though pressed by every foe,
  That will not tremble on the brink
  Of any earthly woe!

2 That will not murmur or complain
  Beneath the chast'ning rod,
  But, in the hour of grief or pain,
  Will lean upon its God;

3 A faith that shines more bright and clear
  When tempests rage without;
  That when in danger knows no fear,
  In darkness feels no doubt.

4 Lord, give us such a faith as this,
  And then, whate'er may come,
  We'll taste, e'en here, the hallowed bliss
  Of an eternal home.

William H. Bathurst

344   My God, I Love Thee

GEER. C. M.

Ascribed to FRANCIS XAVIER   HENRY W. GREATOREX

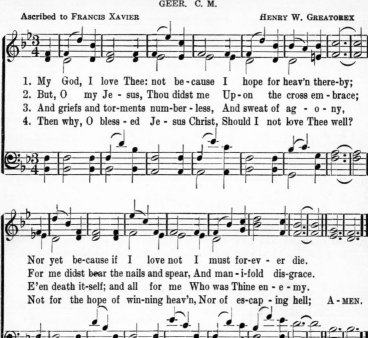

1. My   God, I love Thee: not be - cause I   hope for heav'n there-by;
2. But, O   my Je - sus, Thou didst me   Up - on the cross em - brace;
3. And griefs and tor-ments num-ber - less, And sweat of ag - o - ny,
4. Then why, O bless - ed Je - sus Christ, Should I not love Thee well?

Nor yet be-cause if I   love not I   must for-ev - er die.
For me didst bear the nails and spear, And man - i-fold dis-grace.
E'en death it-self; and all   for me Who was Thine en - e - my.
Not for the hope of win-ning heav'n, Nor of es-cap - ing hell;   A - MEN.

5 Not with the hope of gaining aught;
    Not seeking a reward;
    But as Thyself hast lovèd me,
    O ever-loving Lord!

6 E'en so I love Thee, and will love,
    And in Thy praise will sing;
    Solely because Thou art my God,
    And my eternal King.

345   O Thou, Whose Bounty

1 O Thou, whose bounty fills my cup
    With every blessing meet!
    I give Thee thanks for every drop—
    The bitter and the sweet.

2 I praise Thee for the desert road,
    And for the riverside;
    For all Thy goodness hath bestowed,
    And all Thy grace denied.

3 I thank Thee for both smile and frown,
    And for the gain and loss;
    I praise Thee for the future crown,
    And for the present cross.

4 I thank Thee for the wing of Love
    That stirred my worldly nest,
    And for the stormy clouds that drove
    The flutterer to Thy breast.

5 I bless Thee for the glad increase,
    And for the waning joy;
    And for this strange, this settled peace,
    Which nothing can destroy.

Jane Crewdson

My Jesus, I Love Thee

W. R. Featherston

A. J. Gordon

1. My Je - sus, I love Thee, I know Thou art mine; For Thee all the
2. I love Thee be - cause Thou hast first lov - ed me, And purchased my
3. I will love Thee in life, I will love Thee in death, And praise Thee as
4. In man - sions of glo - ry and end - less de - light I'll ev - er a-

fol - lies of sin I re - sign; My gra - cious Re - deem - er, my
par - don on Cal - va - ry's tree; I love Thee for wear - ing the
long as Thou lend - est me breath, And say, when the death - dew lies
dore Thee in heav - en so bright; I'll sing with the glit - ter - ing

Sav - iour art Thou; If ev - er I loved Thee, my Je - sus, 'tis now!
thorns on Thy brow; If ev - er I loved Thee, my Je - sus, 'tis now!
cold on my brow: "If ev - er I loved Thee, my Je - sus, 'tis now!"
crown on my brow: "If ev - er I loved Thee, my Je - sus, 'tis now!"

347

O Jesus, I Need Thee

1. O Jesus, I need Thee; no power but Thine
From sin can deliver a nature like mine;
O gracious Redeemer, my Saviour be Thou,
If ever, O Jesus, if ever, just now!

2. O Jesus, I need Thee; temptation's dark hour
Is closing around me, I feel its dread power;
O gracious Redeemer, my Saviour be Thou,
If ever, O Jesus, if ever, just now!

Gloria in Excelsis

Old Chant

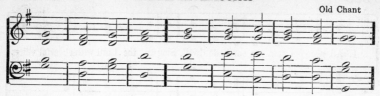

1 Glory *be* to | God on | high ‖ and on *earth* | peace, good | will · toward | men.
2 We praise thee, we bless *thee*, we | wor-ship | thee ‖ we glorify thee, we give *thanks* to | thee for | thy great | glory.

3 O Lord *God* | Heaven- · ly | King ‖ God the | Fa-ther | Al- — | mighty.
4 O Lord, the only begotten *Son* | Je-sus | Christ ‖ O Lord God, Lamb of *God* | Son— | of the | Father,

5 That takest a*way* the | sins · of the | world ‖ have *mercy* up- | on— | us.
6 Thou that takest a*way* the | sins · of the | world ‖ have *mercy* up- | on— | us.
7 Thou that takest a*way* the | sins · of the | world ‖ re- | ceive our | prayer.
8 Thou that sittest at the right *hand* of | God the | Father ‖ have *mercy* up- | on— | us.

A - MEN.

9 For thou *only* | art— | holy ‖ *thou* | on-ly | art the | Lord.
10 Thou only, O *Christ*, with the | Ho-ly | Ghost ‖ art most *high* in the | glory · of | God the | Father.

TUNE: JUBILATE DEO

3 O go your way into his gates with thanksgiving, and *into* his | courts with | praise ‖ be thankful unto *him*, and | speak good | of his | Name.
4 For the Lord is gracious, his *mercy* is | ev-er- | lasting ‖ and his truth endureth from *gener*- | ation · to | gen-er- | ation.

Glory be to the *Father* | and · to the | Son ‖ *and* | to the | Ho-ly | Ghost;
As it was in the beginning, is *now*, and | ev-er | shall be ‖ *world* without | end.— | A- — | men.

355 Old Hundred

LOUIS BOURGEOIS

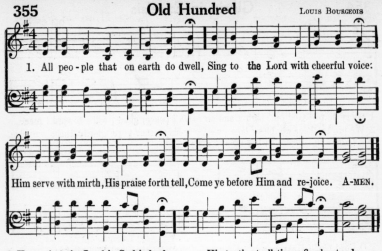

1. All peo-ple that on earth do dwell, Sing to the Lord with cheerful voice:

Him serve with mirth, His praise forth tell, Come ye before Him and re-joice. A-MEN.

2 Know that the Lord is God indeed;
  Without our aid He did us make:
  We are His flock, He did us feed,
  And for His sheep He doth us take.

3 O, enter then His gates with praise,
  Approach with joy His courts unto:
  Praise, laud, and bless His name always,
  For it is seemly so to do.

4 For why? the Lord our God is good,
  His mercy is for ever sure;

His truth at all times firmly stood,
And shall from age to age endure.

William Kethe

356 Doxology

Praise God, from whom all blessings flow
Praise Him, all creatures here below;
Praise Him above, ye heavenly host;
Praise Father, Son and Holy Ghost.

Thomas Ken

357 Glory Be to the Father

H. W. GREATOREX

Glo-ry be to the Father, and to the Son, and to the Ho-ly Ghost; As it

was in the beginning, is now and ever shall be, world without end. A-men, A-men.

358 Jesus, Lover of My Soul

1 Jesus, Lover of my soul,
　　Let me to Thy bosom fly,
　While the nearer waters roll,
　　While the tempest still is high!
　Hide me, O my Saviour, hide,
　　Till the storm of life is past;
　Safe into the haven guide,
　　O receive my soul at last!

2 Other refuge have I none;
　　Hangs my helpless soul on Thee:
　Leave, O leave me not alone,
　　Still support and comfort me.
　All my trust on Thee is stayed,
　　All my help from Thee I bring;
　Cover my defenseless head
　　With the shadow of Thy wing!

3 Thou, O Christ, art all I want;
　　More than all in Thee I find;
　Raise the fallen, cheer the faint,
　　Heal the sick, and lead the blind.
　Just and holy is Thy name,
　　I am all unrighteousness;
　False, and full of sin I am,
　　Thou art full of truth and grace.

4 Plenteous grace with Thee is found,
　　Grace to cover all my sin;
　Let the healing streams abound;
　　Make and keep me pure within.
　Thou of life the fountain art,
　　Freely let me take of Thee:
　Spring Thou up within my heart,
　　Rise to all eternity.
　　　　　　　　Charles Wesley

359 Blessed Assurance

1 Blessed assurance, Jesus is mine!
O what a foretaste of glory divine!
Heir of salvation, purchase of God,
Born of His Spirit, washed in His blood.

CHO.—‖: This is my story, this is my song,
Praising my Saviour all the day long. :‖

2 Perfect submission, perfect delight,
Visions of rapture now burst on my sight;
Angels, descending, bring from above
Echoes of mercy, whispers of love.

3 Perfect submission, all is at rest;
I in my Saviour am happy and blest,
Watching and waiting, looking above,
Filled with His goodness, lost in His love.
　　　　　　　　Fanny J. Crosby

360 Sweet Hour of Prayer

1 Sweet hour of prayer, sweet hour of
　　prayer,
That calls me from a world of care
And bids me at my Father's throne
Make all my wants and wishes known.
In seasons of distress and grief
My soul has often found relief,
And oft escaped the tempter's snare
By thy return, sweet hour of prayer.

2 Sweet hour of prayer, sweet hour of
　　prayer,
The joys I feel, the bliss I share
Of those whose anxious spirits burn
With strong desires for thy return!
With such I hasten to the place
Where God, my Saviour, shows His face,
And gladly take my station there,
And wait for thee, sweet hour of prayer.

3 Sweet hour of prayer, sweet hour of
　　prayer,
Thy wings shall my petition bear
To Him, whose truth and faithfulness
Engage the waiting soul to bless;
And since He bids me seek His face,
Believe His word, and trust His grace,
I'll cast on Him my every care,
And wait for thee, sweet hour of prayer.
　　　　　　　　W. W. Walford

361 He Leadeth Me

1 He leadeth me! O blessed thought!
O words with heavenly comfort fraught;
Whate'er I do, where'er I be,
Still 'tis God's hand that leadeth me.

CHO.—He leadeth me, He leadeth me,
　By His own hand He leadeth me;
　His faithful follower I would be,
　For by His hand He leadeth me.

2 Lord, I would clasp Thy hand in mine,
Nor ever murmur nor repine,
Content, whatever lot I see,
Since 'tis my God that leadeth me.

3 And when my task on earth is done,
When by Thy grace, the victory's won,
E'en death's cold wave I will not flee,
Since God through Jordan leadeth me.
　　　　　　　　J. H. Gilmore

362 Yield Not to Temptation

1 Yield not to temptation,
    For yielding is sin;
Each victory will help you
    Some other to win;
Fight manfully onward,
    Dark passions subdue;
Look ever to Jesus,
    He'll carry you through.

Cho.—Ask the Saviour to help you,
    Comfort, strengthen, and keep you;
    He is willing to aid you,
    He will carry you through.

2 Shun evil companions,
    Bad language disdain;
God's name hold in reverence,
    Nor take it in vain;
Be thoughtful and earnest,
    Kind-hearted and true;
Look ever to Jesus,
    He'll carry you through.

3 To him that o'ercometh
    God giveth a crown;
Through faith we shall conquer,
    Though often cast down;
He who is our Saviour
    Our strength will renew;
Look ever to Jesus,
    He'll carry you through.

H. R. Palmer

363 Oh, How I Love Jesus!

1 There is a name I love to hear,
    I love to sing its worth;
It sounds like music in mine ear—
    The sweetest name on earth.

Cho.—Oh, how I love Jesus!
    Oh, how I love Jesus!
    Oh, how I love Jesus!
    Because He first loved me!

2 It tells me of a Saviour's love,
    Who died to set me free;
It tells me of His precious blood,
    The sinner's perfect plea.

3 It tells of One, whose loving heart
    Can feel my deepest woe,
Who in each sorrow bears a part
    That none can bear below.

364 I Love to Tell the Story

1 I love to tell the story
    Of unseen things above;
Of Jesus and His glory,
    Of Jesus and His love.
I love to tell the story,
    Because I know 'tis true;
It satisfies my longings
    As nothing else can do.

Cho.—I love to tell the story;
    'Twill be my theme in glory,
    To tell the old, old story
    Of Jesus and His love.

2 I love to tell the story:
    More wonderful it seems
Than all the golden fancies
    Of all our golden dreams.
I love to tell the story;
    It did so much for me—
And that is just the reason
    I tell it now to Thee.

3 I love to tell the story;
    For those who know it best
Seem hungering and thirsting
    To hear it like the rest.
And when, in scenes of glory,
    I sing the new, new song,
'Twill be the old, old story
    That I have loved so long.

Katherine Hankey

365 Sweet By-and-By

1 There's a land that is fairer than day,
    And by faith we can see it afar,
For the Father waits over the way,
    To prepare us a dwelling-place there.

Cho.—In the sweet by-and-by,
    We shall meet on that beautiful shore;
    In the sweet by-and-by,
    We shall meet on that beautiful shore.

2 We shall sing on that beautiful shore
    The melodious songs of the blest;
And our spirits shall sorrow no more—
    Not a sigh for the blessing of rest.

3 To our bountiful Father above
    We will offer our tribute of praise,
For the glorious gift of His love,
    And the blessings that hallow our days.

S. F. Bennett

366 What a Friend

1 What a Friend we have in Jesus,
  All our sins and griefs to bear!
What a privilege to carry
  Everything to God in prayer!
O what peace we often forfeit,
  O what needless pain we bear,
All because we do not carry
  Everything to God in prayer!

2 Have we trials and temptations?
  Is there trouble anywhere?
We should never be discouraged,
  Take it to the Lord in prayer.
Can we find a friend so faithful?
  Who will all our sorrows share?
Jesus knows our every weakness,
  Take it to the Lord in prayer.

3 Are we weak and heavy-laden,
  Cumbered with a load of care?—
Precious Saviour, still our refuge,—
  Take it to the Lord in prayer.
Do thy friends despise, forsake thee?
  Take it to the Lord in prayer;
In His arms He'll take and shield thee,
  Thou wilt find a solace there.
Joseph Scriven

367 Glory to His Name

1 Down at the cross where my Saviour
    died,
Down where for cleansing from sin I cried,
There to my heart was the blood applied;
    Glory to His name!

CHO.—‖: Glory to His name; :‖
There to my heart was the blood applied;
    Glory to His name!

2 I am so wondrously saved from sin,
Jesus so sweetly abides within;
There at the cross where He took me in;
    Glory to His name!

3 O precious fountain, that saves from sin,
I am so glad I have entered in;
There Jesus saved me and keeps me clean;
    Glory to His name!

4 Come to this fountain, so rich and sweet;
Cast thy poor soul at the Saviour's feet;
Plunge in to-day, and be made complete;
    Glory to His name!
E. A. Hoffman

368 Beulah Land

1 I've reached the land of corn and wine,
  And all its riches freely mine,
Here shines undimmed one blissful day,
  For all my night has passed away.

CHORUS.—
  O Beulah Land, sweet Beulah Land,
  As on thy highest mount I stand,
  I look away across the sea,
  Where mansions are prepared for me,
  And view the shining glory shore,
  My heaven, my home forevermore!

2 My Saviour comes and walks with me,
  And sweet communion here have we;
He gently leads me by His hand,
  For this is heaven's border-land.

3 A sweet perfume upon the breeze
  Is born from ever-vernal trees;
And flowers that never fading grow
  Where streams of life forever flow.

4 The zephrys seem to float to me,
  Sweet sounds of heaven's melody,
As angels with the white-robed throng
  Join in the sweet redemption song.
Edgar Page

369 Hallelujah! 'Tis Done!

1 'Tis the promise of God, full salvation
    to give
  Unto him who on Jesus His Son will
    believe.

CHO.—Hallelujah! 'tis done! I believe on
    the Son;
  I am saved by the blood of the Crucified
    One.

2 Though the pathway be lonely, and
    dangerous too,
  Surely Jesus is able to carry me
    through.

3 Many loved ones have I in yon heavenly
    throng;
  They are safe now in glory, and this is
    their song:

4 There's a part in that chorus for you
    and for me,
  And the theme of our praises forever
    will be:
P. P. Bliss

370 Even Me

1 Lord, I hear of showers of blessing
Thou art scattering full and free;
Showers the thirsty land refreshing;
Let some drops now fall on me.
Even me, even me,
Let some drops now fall on me.

2 Pass me not, O gracious Father!
Sinful though my heart may be;
Thou might'st leave me, but the rather
Let Thy mercy rest on me.
Even me, even me,
Let Thy mercy rest on me.

3 Have I long in sin been sleeping?
Long been slighting, grieving Thee?
Has the world my heart been keeping?
O forgive and rescue me!
Even me, even me,
O forgive and rescue me!

4 Pass me not, O Holy Spirit!
Thou can'st make the blind to see;
Testify of Jesus' merit,
Speak the word of peace to me.
Even me, even me,
Speak the word of peace to me.
Elizabeth Codner

371 Take the Name of Jesus

1 Take the name of Jesus with you,
Child of sorrow and of woe;
It will joy and comfort give you,
Take it, then, where'er you go,

REF.—Precious name, O how sweet!
Hope of earth and joy of heaven;
Precious name, O how sweet;
Hope of earth and joy of heaven.

2 Take the name of Jesus ever
As a shield from every snare;
If temptations round you gather,
Breathe that holy name in prayer.

3 O the precious name of Jesus!
How it thrills our souls with joy,
When His loving arms receive us,
And His songs our tongues employ.

4 At the name of Jesus bowing,
Falling prostrate at His feet,
King of kings in heaven we'll crown Him,
When our journey is complete.
Lydia Baxter

372 Anywhere With Jesus

1 Anywhere with Jesus I can safely go,
Anywhere He leads me in this world below,
Anywhere without Him dearest joys would fade;
Anywhere with Jesus I am not afraid.

REF.—Anywhere, anywhere!
Fear I cannot know;
Anywhere with Jesus
I can safely go.

2 Anywhere with Jesus I am not alone;
Other friends may fail me, He is still my own;
Though His hand may lead me over dreary ways,
Anywhere with Jesus is a house of praise.

3 Anywhere with Jesus I can go to sleep,
When the darkening shadows round about me creep;
Knowing I shall waken never more to roam,
Anywhere with Jesus will be home, sweet home.
Jessie H. Brown

373 I Love Him

1 Gone from my heart the world with all its charm;
Gone are my sins and all that would alarm;
Gone evermore, and by His grace I know
The precious blood of Jesus cleanses white as snow.

CHO.—I love Him, I love Him,
Because He first loved me,
And purchased my salvation
On Calv'ry's tree.

2 Once I was lost upon the plains of sin;
Once was a slave to doubts and fears within;
Once was afraid to trust a loving God,
But now my guilt is washed away in Jesus' blood.

3 Once I was bound, but now I am set free;
Once I was blind, but now the light I see;
Once I was dead, but now in Christ I live,
To tell the world around the peace that He doth give.

374 Must Jesus Bear the Cross Alone?

1 Must Jesus bear the cross alone,
   And all the world go free?
   No, there's a cross for every one,
   And there's a cross for me.

2 How happy are the saints above,
   Who once went sorrowing here!
   But now they taste unmingled love,
   And joy without a tear.

3 The consecrated cross I'll bear
   Till death shall set me free;
   And then go home my crown to wear,
   For there's a crown for me.

4 Upon the crystal pavement, down
   At Jesus' pierced feet,
   Joyful, I'll cast my golden crown,
   And His dear name repeat.

Thos. Shepherd

375 O For a Closer Walk With God

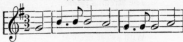

1 O for a closer walk with God,
   A calm and heavenly frame,
   A light to shine upon the road
   That leads me to the Lamb!

2 Return, O holy Dove, return,
   Sweet messenger of rest;
   I hate the sins that made Thee mourn,
   And drove Thee from my breast.

3 The dearest idol I have known,
   Whate'er that idol be,
   Help me to tear it from Thy throne,
   And worship only Thee.

4 So shall my walk be close with God,
   Calm and serene my frame;
   So purer light shall mark the road
   That leads me to the Lamb.

William Cowper

376 Rock of Ages

1 Rock of Ages, cleft for me,
   Let me hide myself in Thee;
   Let the water and the blood,
   From Thy wounded side which flowed,
   Be of sin the double cure,
   Save from wrath and make me pure.

2 Could my tears forever flow,
   Could my zeal no languor know,
   These for sin could not atone;
   Thou must save, and Thou alone:
   In my hand no price I bring;
   Simply to Thy cross I cling.

3 While I draw this fleeting breath,
   When my eyes shall close in death,
   When I rise to worlds unknown,
   And behold Thee on Thy throne,
   Rock of Ages, cleft for me,
   Let me hide myself in Thee.

A. M. Toplady

377 How Sweet, How Heavenly

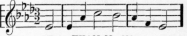

Tune, EVAN, No. 236

1 How sweet, how heavenly is the sight,
   When those who love the Lord
   In one another's peace delight,
   And so fulfil His word!

2 When each can feel his brother's sigh,
   And with him bear a part;
   When sorrow flows from eye to eye,
   And joy from heart to heart!

3 When, free from envy, scorn, and pride,
   Our wishes all above,
   Each can his brother's failings hide,
   And show a brother's love,

4 Love is the golden chain that binds
   The happy souls above;
   And he's an heir of heaven who finds
   His bosom glow with love.

J. Swain

378 Every Day and Hour

1 Saviour, more than life to me,
   I am clinging, clinging close to Thee;
   Let Thy precious blood applied,
   Keep me ever, ever near Thy side.

REF.—Every day, every hour,
   Let me feel Thy cleansing power;
   May Thy tender love to me
   Bind me closer, closer, Lord, to Thee.

2 Through this changing world below,
   Lead me gently, gently as I go;
   Trusting Thee I cannot stray,
   I can never, never lose my way.

3 I would love Thee more and more,
   Till this fleeting, fleeting life is o'er,
   Till my soul is lost in love
   In a brighter, brighter world above.

Fanny J. Crosby

379 Grow Thou in Me

Tune, RAPHAEL, No. 309

1 O Jesus Christ, grow Thou in me,
 And all things else recede;
 My heart be daily nearer Thee;
 From sin be daily freed.

2 In Thy bright beams which on me fall,
 Fade every evil thought;
 That I am nothing, Thou art all,
 I would be daily taught.

3 Fill me with gladness from above,
 Hold me by strength divine;
 Lord, let the glow of Thy great love
 Through my whole being shine.

4 Make this poor self grow less and less,
 Be Thou my life and aim;
 O make me daily through Thy grace
 More meet to bear Thy name.
      J. C. Lavater

380 'Tis So Sweet to Trust in Jesus

1 'Tis so sweet to trust in Jesus,
 Just to take Him at His word;
 Just to rest upon His promise;
 Just to know, "Thus saith the Lord."

Cho.—Jesus, Jesus, how I trust Him;
 How I've proved Him o'er and o'er.
 Jesus, Jesus, precious Jesus!
 O for grace to trust Him more.

2 O how sweet to trust in Jesus,
 Just to trust His cleansing blood;
 Just in simple faith to plunge me
 'Neath the healing, cleansing flood.

3 I'm so glad I learned to trust Thee,
 Precious Jesus, Saviour, Friend;
 And I know that Thou art with me,
 Wilt be with me to the end.
     Louisa N. R. Stead

381 Jesus, Keep Me Near the Cross

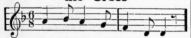

1 Jesus, keep me near the cross;
 There a precious fountain,
 Free to all, a healing stream,
 Flows from Calvary's mountain.

Cho.—In the cross, in the cross,
 Be my glory ever;
 Till my raptured soul shall find
 Rest beyond the river.

2 Near the cross, a trembling soul,
 Love and mercy found me;
 There the Bright and Morning Star
 Sheds its beam around me.

3 Near the cross!   O Lamb of God,
 Bring its scenes before me;
 Help me walk from day to day,
 With its shadow o'er me.
     Fanny J. Crosby

382 The God of Harvest Praise

Tune, ITALIAN HYMN, No. 306
or AMERICA, No. 160

1 The God of harvest praise;
 In loud thanksgiving raise
 Hand, heart and voice;
 The valleys smile and sing,
 Forests and mountains ring,
 The plains their tribute bring,
 The streams rejoice.

2 The God of harvest praise;
 Hands, hearts and voices raise,
 With sweet accord;
 From field to garner throng,
 Bearing your sheaves along;
 And in your harvest song
 Bless ye the Lord.
     J. Montgomery

383 God Be With You

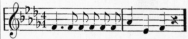

1 God be with you till we meet again;
 By His counsels guide, uphold you,
 With His sheep securely fold you,
 God be with you till we meet again.

2 God be with you till we meet again;
 'Neath His wings securely hide you,
 Daily manna still provide you,
 God be with you till we meet again.

3 God be with you till we meet again;
 When life's perils thick confound you,
 Put His arms unfailing 'round you,
 God be with you till we meet again.

4 God be with you till we meet again;
 Keep love's banner floating o'er you,
 Smite death's threat'ning wave before you,
 God be with you till we meet again.
     J. E. Rankin

Scripture Readings

From II to XXVIII a sequence of doctrine is developed that may be studied and taught with profit. Universal disregard of the divine Commandments (II) attests Man's Lost Condition (III). In mercy, Divine Atonement (IV) is provided; Exhortations (V) and Warnings (VI) are extended. Penitence (VII) and the acceptance of the Divine Invitation (VIII) lead to Pardon and Peace (IX, X). Then follow the Person and Work of the Holy Spirit (XI), Thanksgiving (XII), the blessings of Assurance (XIII), the Word of God (XIV), the office of Prayer (XVI), Union with Christ (XVII), a summary of Christian duties (XVIII-XXIV), and Kingdom teaching (XXV-XXVII). From XXVIII to the end are miscellaneous selections.

384 SELECTION I

The Apostles' Creed.

I believe in God, the Father Almighty, Maker of heaven and earth; and in Jesus Christ his only Son, our Lord; who was conceived by the Holy Ghost; born of the Virgin Mary; suffered under Pontius Pilate; was crucified, dead, and buried; the third day he arose again from the dead; he ascended into heaven, and sitteth on the right hand of God, the Father Almighty; from thence he shall come to judge the quick and the dead. I believe in the Holy Ghost; the holy catholic church—the communion of saints; the forgiveness of sins; the resurrection of the body; and the life everlasting. Amen.

385 SELECTION II

The Ten Commandments. Exodus 20:1-17; Matthew 22:37-40.

1 And God spake all these words, saying:
2 I *am* the LORD thy God, which have brought thee out of the land of Egypt, out of the house of bondage.
3 Thou shalt have no other gods before me.
4 Thou shalt not make unto thee any graven image, or any likeness *of any thing* that *is* in heaven above, or that *is* in the earth beneath, or that *is* in the water under the earth :
5 Thou shalt not bow down thyself to them, nor serve them: for I the LORD thy God *am* a jealous God, visiting the iniquity of the fathers upon the children unto the third and fourth *generation* of them that hate me :
6 And shewing mercy unto thousands of them that love me, and keep my commandments.
7 Thou shalt not take the name of the LORD thy God in vain: for the LORD will not hold him guiltless that taketh his name in vain.
8 Remember the sabbath day, to keep it holy.
9 Six days shalt thou labour, and do all thy work:
10 But the seventh day *is* the sabbath of the LORD thy God: *in it* thou shalt not do any work, thou nor thy son, nor thy daughter, thy manservant, nor thy maidservant, nor thy cattle, nor thy stranger that *is* within thy gates:
11 For *in* six days the LORD made heaven and earth, the sea, and all that in them *is*, and rested the seventh day : wherefore the LORD blessed the sabbath day, and hallowed it.

12 Honour thy father and thy mother: that thy days may be long upon the land which the LORD thy God giveth thee.
13 Thou shalt not kill.
14 Thou shalt not commit adultery.
15 Thou shalt not steal.
16 Thou shalt not bear false witness against thy neighbour.
17 Thou shalt not covet thy neighbour's house, thou shalt not covet thy neighbour's wife, nor his manservant, nor his maidservant, nor his ox, nor his ass, nor any thing that *is* thy neighbour's.

*   *   *   *   *   *   *

Hear also what our Lord Jesus Christ saith : Thou shalt love the Lord thy God with all thy heart, and with all thy soul, and with all thy mind. This is the first and great commandment. And the second is like unto it. Thou shalt love thy neighbour as thyself. On these two commandments hang all the law and the prophets.

386 SELECTION III

Man's Lost Condition. John 3:1-16.

1 There was a man of the Pharisees, named Nicodemus, a ruler of the Jews:
2 The same came to Jesus by night, and said unto him, Rabbi, we know that thou art a teacher come from God : for no man can do these miracles that thou doest, except God be with him.
3 Jesus answered and said unto him, Verily, verily, I say unto thee, except a man be born again, he cannot see the kingdom of God.
4 Nicodemus saith unto him, How can a man be born when he is old? can he enter the second time into his mother's womb, and be born?
5 Jesus answered, Verily, verily, I say unto thee, Except a man be born of water and *of* the Spirit, he cannot enter into the kingdom of God.
6 That which is born of the flesh is flesh; and that which is born of the Spirit is spirit.
7 Marvel not that I said unto thee, Ye must be born again.
8 The wind bloweth where it listeth, and thou hearest the sound thereof, but canst not tell whence it cometh, and whither it goeth : so is every one that is born of the Spirit.
9 Nicodemus answered and said unto him, How can these things be?
10 Jesus answered and said unto him, Art thou a master of Israel, and knowest not these things?
11 Verily, verily, I say unto thee, We speak that we do know, and testify that

we have seen; and ye receive not our witness.

12 If I have told you earthly things, and ye believe not, how shall ye believe, if I tell you *of* heavenly things?

13 And no man hath ascended up to heaven, but he that came down from heaven, *even* the Son of man which is in heaven.

14 And as Moses lifted up the serpent in the wilderness even so must the Son of man be lifted up:

15 That whosoever believeth in him should not perish, but have eternal life.

16 For God so loved the world, that he gave his only begotten Son, that whosoever believeth in him should not perish, but have everlasting life.

387   SELECTION IV

Christ's Atonement. Isaiah 53.

1 Who hath believed our report? and to whom is the arm of the LORD revealed?

2 For he shall grow up before him as a tender plant, and as a root out of a dry ground: he hath no form nor comeliness; and when we shall see him, *there is* no beauty that we should desire him.

3 He is despised and rejected of men; a man of sorrows, and acquainted with grief: and we hid as it were *our* faces from him; he was despised, and we esteemed him not.

4 Surely he hath borne our griefs, and carried our sorrows: yet we did esteem him stricken, smitten of God, and afflicted.

5 But he *was* wounded for our transgressions, *he was* bruised for our iniquities: the chastisement of our peace *was* upon him; and with his stripes we are healed.

6 All we like sheep have gone astray; we have turned every one to his own way; and the LORD hath laid on him the iniquity of us all.

7 He was oppressed, and he was afflicted, yet he opened not his mouth: he is brought as a lamb to the slaughter, and as a sheep before her shearers is dumb, so he openeth not his mouth.

8 He was taken from prison and from judgment: and who shall declare his generation? for he was cut off out of the land of the living: for the transgression of my people was he stricken.

9 And he made his grave with the wicked, and with the rich in his death; because he had done no violence, neither *was any* deceit in his mouth.

10 Yet it pleased the LORD to bruise him; he hath put *him* to grief: when thou shalt make his soul an offering for sin, he shall see *his* seed, he shall prolong *his* days, and the pleasure of the LORD shall prosper in his hand.

11 He shall see of the travail of his soul, *and* shall be satisfied: by his knowledge shall my righteous servant justify many; for he shall bear their iniquities.

12 Therefore will I divide him *a portion* with the great, and he shall divide the spoil with the strong; because he hath poured out his soul unto death: and he was numbered with the trans-

gressors; and he bare the sin of many, and made intercession for the transgressors.

388   SELECTION V

A Divine Exhortation. Ezek. 18:20-30.

20 The soul that sinneth, it shall die. The son shall not bear the iniquity of the father, neither shall the father bear the iniquity of the son: the righteousness of the righteous shall be upon him, and the wickedness of the wicked shall be upon him.

21 But if the wicked will turn from all his sins that he hath committed, and keep all my statutes, and do that which is lawful and right, he shall surely live, he shall not die.

22 All his transgressions that he hath committed, they shall not be mentioned unto him: in his righteousness that he hath done he shall live.

23 Have I any pleasure at all that the wicked should die? saith the Lord GOD: *and* not that he should return from his ways, and live?

24 ¶ But when the righteous turneth away from his righteousness, and committeth iniquity, *and* doeth according to all the abominations that the wicked *man* doeth, shall he live? All his righteousness that he hath done shall not be mentioned: in his trespass that he hath trespassed, and in his sin that he hath sinned, in them shall he die.

25 ¶ Yet ye say, The way of the LORD is not equal. Hear now, O house of Israel; Is not my way equal? are not your ways unequal?

26 When a righteous *man* turneth away from his righteousness, and committeth iniquity, and dieth in them; for his iniquity that he hath done shall he die.

27 Again, when the wicked *man* turneth away from his wickedness that he hath committed, and doeth that which is lawful and right, he shall save his soul alive.

28 Because he considereth, and turneth away from all his transgressions that he hath committed, he shall surely live, he shall not die.

29 Yet saith the house of Israel, The way of the LORD is not equal. O house of Israel, are not my ways equal? are not your ways unequal?

30 Therefore I will judge you, O house of Israel, every one according to his ways, saith the Lord GOD. Repent, and turn *yourselves* from all your transgressions; so iniquity shall not be your ruin.

389   SELECTION VI

A Divine Warning. Prov. 1:20-33.

20 Wisdom crieth without; she uttereth her voice in the streets:

21 She crieth in the chief place of concourse, in the openings of the gates: in the city she uttereth her words, *saying,*

22 How long, ye simple ones, will ye love simplicity? and the scorners delight in their scorning, and fools hate knowledge?

23 Turn you at my reproof; behold, I will pour out my spirit unto you, I will make known my words unto you.

24 Because I have called, and ye refused; I have stretched out my hand, and no man regarded;

25 But ye have set at nought all my counsel, and would none of my reproof:

26 I also will laugh at your calamity; I will mock when your fear cometh;

27 When your fear cometh as desolation, and your destruction cometh as a whirlwind; when distress and anguish cometh upon you.

28 Then shall they call upon me, but I will not answer; they shall seek me early, but they shall not find me:

29 For that they hated knowledge, and did not choose the fear of the LORD:

30 They would none of my counsel: they despised all my reproof.

31 Therefore shall they eat of the fruit of their own way and be filled with their own devices.

32 For the turning away of the simple shall slay them, and the prosperity of fools shall destroy them.

33 But whoso hearkeneth unto me shall dwell safely, and shall be quiet from fear of evil.

390   SELECTION VII

Penitence.   Psalm 51

1 Have mercy upon me, O God, according to thy lovingkindness, according unto the multitude of thy tender mercies blot out my transgressions.

2 Wash me thoroughly from mine iniquity, and cleanse me from my sin.

3 For I acknowledge my transgressions: and my sin *is* ever before me.

4 Against thee, thee only, have I sinned, and done *this* evil in thy sight: that thou mightest be justified when thou speakest. *and* be clear when thou judgest.

5 Behold, I was shapen in iniquity; and in sin did my mother conceive me.

6 Behold, thou desirest truth in the inward parts: and in the hidden *part* thou shalt make me to know wisdom.

7 Purge me with hyssop, and I shall be clean: wash me and I shall be whiter than snow.

8 Make me to hear joy and gladness: *that* the bones *which* thou hast broken may rejoice.

9 Hide thy face from my sins, and blot out all mine iniquities.

10 Create in me a clean heart, O God; and renew a right spirit within me.

11 Cast me not away from thy presence; and take not thy Holy Spirit from me.

12 Restore unto me the joy of thy salvation; and uphold me *with thy* free Spirit.

13 *Then* will I teach transgressors thy ways; and sinners shall be converted unto thee.

14 Deliver me from bloodguiltiness, O God, thou God of my salvation: *and* my tongue shall sing aloud of thy righteousness.

15 O LORD, open thou my lips; and my mouth shall shew forth thy praise.

16 For thou desirest not sacrifice; else would I give *it:* thou delightest not in burnt offering.

17 The sacrifices of God *are* a broken spirit: a broken and a contrite heart, O God, thou wilt not despise.

18 Do good in thy good pleasure unto Zion: build thou the walls of Jerusalem.

19 Then shall thou be pleased with the sacrifices of righteousness, with burnt offering and whole burnt offering: then shall they offer bullocks upon thine altar.

391   SELECTION VIII

The Divine Invitation.   Isaiah 55

1 Ho, every one that thirsteth, come ye to the waters, and he that hath no money; come ye, buy, and eat; yea, come, buy wine and milk without money and without price.

2 Wherefore do ye spend money for *that which is* not bread? and your labour for *that which* satisfieth not? hearken diligently unto me, and eat ye *that which is* good, and let your soul delight itself in fatness.

3 Incline your ear, and come unto me: hear, and your soul shall live; and I will make an everlasting covenant with you, *even* the sure mercies of David.

4 Behold, I have given him *for* a witness to the people, a leader and commander to the people.

5 Behold, thou shalt call a nation *that* thou knowest not, and nations *that* knew not thee shall run unto thee because of the LORD thy God, and for the Holy One of Israel; for he hath glorified thee.

6 Seek ye the LORD while he may be found, call ye upon him while he is near:

7 Let the wicked forsake his way, and the unrighteous man his thoughts: and let him return unto the LORD, and he will have mercy upon him; and to our God, for he will abundantly pardon.

8 For my thoughts *are* not your thoughts, neither *are* your ways my ways, saith the LORD.

9 For *as* the heavens are higher than the earth, so are my ways higher than your ways, and my thoughts than your thoughts.

10 For as the rain cometh down, and the snow from heaven, and returneth not thither, but watereth the earth, and maketh it bring forth and bud, that it may give seed to the sower, and bread to the eater:

11 So shall my word be that goeth forth out of my mouth: it shall not return unto me void, but it shall accomplish that which I please, and it shall prosper *in the thing* whereto I sent it.

12 For ye shall go out with joy, and be led forth with peace: the mountains and

the hills shall break forth before you into singing, and all the trees of the field shall clap *their* hands.

13 Instead of the thorn shall come up the fir tree, and instead of the brier shall come up the myrtle tree : and it shall be to the LORD for a name, for an everlasting sign *that* shall not be cut off.

392 SELECTION IX

The Way of Pardon and Peace. Psalm 32

1 Blessed *is he whose* transgression *is* forgiven, *whose* sin *is* covered.

2 Blessed *is* the man unto whom the LORD imputeth not iniquity, and in whose spirit *there is* no guile.

3 When I kept silence, my bones waxed old through my roaring all the day long.

4 For day and night thy hand was heavy upon me : my moisture is turned into the drought of summer. Selah.

5 I acknowledge my sin unto thee, and mine iniquity have I not hid. I said, I will confess my transgressions unto the LORD ; and thou forgavest the iniquity of my sin. Selah.

6 For this shall every one that is godly pray unto thee in a time when thou mayest be found : surely in the floods of great waters they shall not come nigh unto him.

7 Thou *art* my hiding place ; thou shalt preserve me from trouble ; thou shalt compass me about with songs of deliverance. Selah.

8 I will instruct thee and teach thee in the way which thou shalt go : I will guide thee with mine eye.

9 Be ye not as the horse, *or* as the mule, *which* have no understanding : whose mouth must be held in with bit and bridle, lest they come near unto thee.

10 Many sorrows *shall be* to the wicked ; but he that trusteth in the LORD, mercy shall compass him about.

11 Be glad in the LORD, and rejoice, ye righteous : and shout for joy, all *ye that are* upright in heart.

393 SELECTION X

The Means and Message of Salvation. Romans 10:4-17

4 Christ *is* the end of the law for righteousness to everyone that believeth.

5 For Moses describeth the righteousness which is of the law, That the man which doeth those things shall live by them.

6 But the righteousness which is of faith speaketh on this wise, Say not in thine heart, Who shall ascend into heaven? (that is, to bring Christ down *from above* :)

7 Or, Who shall descend into the deep? (that is, to bring up Christ again from the dead.)

8 But what saith it? The word is nigh thee, *even* in thy mouth, and in thy heart ; that is, the word of faith, which we preach ;

9 That if thou shalt confess with thy mouth the Lord Jesus, and shalt believe in thine heart that God hath raised him from the dead, thou shalt be saved.

10 For with the heart man believeth unto righteousness ; and with the mouth confession is made unto salvation.

11 For the Scripture saith, Whosoever believeth on him shall not be ashamed.

12 For there is no difference between the Jew and the Greek : for the same Lord over all is rich unto all that call upon him.

13 For whosoever shall call upon the name of the Lord shall be saved.

14 How then shall they call on him in whom they have not believed? and how shall they believe in him of whom they have not heard? and how shall they hear without a preacher?

15 And how shall they preach, except they be sent? as it is written, How beautiful are the feet of them that preach the gospel of peace, and bring glad tidings of good things !

16 But they have not all obeyed the gospel. For Esaias saith, Lord, who hath believed our report?

17 So then faith cometh by hearing and hearing by the word of God.

394 SELECTION XI

Person and Work of the Holy Spirit. John 14:15-26

15 If ye love me, keep my commandments.

16 And I will pray the Father, and he shall give you another Comforter, that he may abide with you for ever ;

17 *Even* the Spirit of truth ; whom the world cannot receive, because it seeth him not, neither knoweth him : but ye know him ; for he dwelleth with you, and shall be in you.

18 I will not leave you comfortless : I will come to you.

19 Yet a little while, and the world seeth me no more ; but ye see me : because I live, ye shall live also.

20 At that day ye shall know that I am in my Father, and ye in me and I in you.

21 He that hath my commandments and keepeth them, he it is that loveth me : and he that loveth me shall be loved by my Father, and I will love him and will manifest myself to him.

22 Judas saith unto him, not Iscariot, Lord, how is it that thou wilt manifest thyself unto us, and not unto the world?

23 Jesus answered and saith unto him, If a man love me, he will keep my words : and my Father will love him, and we will come unto him, and make our abode with him.

24 He that loveth me not keepeth not my sayings : and the word which ye hear is not mine, but the Father's which sent me.

25 These things have I spoken unto you, being yet present with you.

26 But the Comforter, which is the Holy Ghost, whom the Father will send in my name, he shall teach you all things, and bring all things to your remembrance, whatsoever I have said unto you.

395 SELECTION XII

Thanksgiving for Mercies. Psalm 116

1 I love the LORD, because he hath heard my voice *and* my supplications.

2 Because he hath inclined his ear unto me, therefore will I call upon *him* as long as I live.

3 The sorrows of death compassed me, and the pains of hell gat hold upon me : I found trouble and sorrow.

4 Then called I upon the name of the LORD ; O LORD, I beseech thee, deliver my soul.

5 Gracious *is* the LORD, and righteous ; yea, our God *is* merciful.

6 The LORD preserveth the simple : I was brought low, and he helped me.

7 Return unto thy rest, O my soul ; for the LORD hath dealt bountifully with thee.

8 For thou hast delivered my soul from death, mine eyes from tears, *and* my feet from falling.

9 I will walk before the LORD in the land of the living.

10 I believed, therefore have I spoken : I was greatly afflicted :

11 I said in my haste, All men *are* liars.

12 What shall I render unto the LORD *for* all his benefits toward me?

13 I will take the cup of salvation, and call upon the name of the LORD.

14 I will pay my vows unto the LORD now in the presence of all his people.

15 Precious in the sight of the LORD *is* the death of his saints.

16 O LORD, truly I *am* thy servant ; I *am* thy servant, *and* the son of thine handmaid : thou hast loosed my bonds.

17 I will offer to thee the sacrifice of thanksgiving, and will call upon the name of the LORD.

18 I will pay my vows unto the LORD now in the presence of all his people,

19 In the courts of the LORD's house, in the midst of thee, O Jerusalem. Praise ye the LORD.

396 SELECTION XIII

Security and Assurance. Romans 8:28-39

28 And we know that all things work together for good to them that love God, to them who are the called according to his purpose.

29 For whom he did foreknow, he also did predestinate to be conformed to the image of his Son, that he might be the firstborn among many brethren.

30 Moreover whom he did predestinate, them he also called : and whom he called, them he also justified : and whom he justified them he also glorified.

31 What shall we then say to these things? If God be for us who can be against us?

32 He that spared not his own Son but delivered him up for us all, how shall he not with him also freely give us all things?

33 Who shall lay any thing to the charge of God's elect? It is God that justifieth.

34 Who is he that condemneth? It is Christ that died, yea rather that is risen again, who is even at the right hand of God, who also maketh intercession for us.

35 Who shall separate us from the love of Christ? shall tribulation or distress, or persecution, or famine, or nakedness, or peril, or sword?

36 As it is written, For thy sake we are killed all the day long ; we are accounted as sheep for the slaughter.

37 Nay, in all these things we are more than conquerors through him that loved us.

38 For I am persuaded, that neither death, nor life, nor angels, nor principalities, nor powers, nor things present, nor things to come,

39 Nor height, nor depth, nor any other creature, shall be able to separate us from the love of God, which is in Christ Jesus our Lord.

397 SELECTION XIV

The Word of God. Psalm 19:1-14

1 The heavens declare the glory of God ; and the firmament sheweth his handiwork.

2 Day unto day uttereth speech, and night unto night sheweth knowledge.

3 *There is* no speech nor language, *where* their voice is not heard.

4 Their line is gone out through all the earth, and their words to the end of the world. In them hath he set a tabernacle for the sun.

5 Which *is* as a bridegroom coming out of his chamber, *and* rejoiceth as a strong man to run a race.

6 His going forth *is* from the end of the heaven, and his circuit unto the ends of it : and there is nothing hid from the heat thereof.

7 The law of the LORD *is* perfect, converting the soul : the testimony of the LORD *is* sure, making wise the simple.

8 The statutes of the LORD *are* right, rejoicing the heart : the commandment of the LORD *is* pure, enlightening the eyes.

9 The fear of the LORD *is* clean, enduring for ever : the judgments of the LORD *are* true *and* righteous altogether.

10 More to be desired *are they* than gold, yea than much fine gold : sweeter also than honey and the honeycomb.

11 Moreover by them is thy servant warned : *and* in keeping of them *there is* great reward.

12 Who can understand *his* errors? cleanse thou me from secret *faults*.

13 Keep back thy servant also from presumptuous *sins;* let them not have dominion over me : then shall I be upright, and I shall be innocent from the great transgression.

14 Let the words of my mouth, and the meditation of my heart, be acceptable in thy sight, O LORD, my strength, and my redeemer.

398   SELECTION XV

The Chaff and the Wheat
Jer. 23:16-29

16 Thus saith the LORD of hosts, Hearken not unto the words of the prophets that prophesy unto you ; they make you vain : they speak a vision of their own heart, *and* not out of the mouth of the LORD.

17 They say still unto them that despise me, The LORD hath said, Ye shall have peace ; and they say unto every one that walketh after the imagination of his own heart, No evil shall come upon you.

18 For who hath stood in the counsel of the LORD, and hath perceived and heard his word? who hath marked his word, and heard *it?*

19 Behold, a whirlwind of the LORD is gone forth in fury, even a grievous whirlwind : it shall fall grievously upon the head of the wicked.

20 The anger of the LORD shall not return, until he have executed, and till he have performed the thoughts of his heart : in the latter days ye shall consider it perfectly.

21 I have not sent these prophets, yet they ran : I have not spoken to them, yet they prophesied.

22 But if they had stood in my counsel, and had caused my people to hear my words, then they should have turned them from their evil way, and from the evil of their doings.

23 *Am* I a God at hand, saith the LORD, and not a God afar off ?

24 Can any hide himself in secret places that I shall not see him? saith the LORD. Do not I fill heaven and earth? saith the LORD.

25 I have heard what the prophets said, that prophesy lies in my name, saying, I have dreamed, I have dreamed.

26 How long shall *this* be in the heart of the prophets that prophesy lies? yea, *they are* prophets of the deceit of their own heart ;

27 Which think to cause my people to forget my name by their dreams, which they tell every man to his neighbour, as their fathers have forgotten my name for Baal.

28 The prophet that hath a dream, let him tell a dream : and he that hath my word, let him speak my word faithfully.

What *is* the chaff to the wheat? saith the LORD.

29 *Is* not my word like as a fire? saith the LORD ; and like a hammer *that* breaketh the rock in pieces?

399   SELECTION XVI

Christ Teaching to Pray
Luke 11:1-13

1 And it came to pass, that, as he was praying in a certain place, when he ceased, one of his disciples said unto him, Lord, teach us to pray, as John also taught his disciples.

2 And he said unto them, When ye pray, say, Our Father which are in heaven, Hallowed be thy name. Thy kingdom come. Thy will be done, as in heaven, so in earth.

3 Give us day by day our daily bread.

4 And forgive us our sins ; for we also forgive every one that is indebted to us. And lead us not into temptation ; but deliver us from evil.

5 And he said unto them, Which of you shall have a friend, and shall go unto him at midnight, and say unto him, Friend, lend me three loaves ;

6 For a friend of mine in his journey is come to me, and I have nothing to set before him?

7 And he from within shall answer and say, Trouble me not : the door is now shut, and my children are with me in bed ; I cannot rise and give thee.

8 I say unto you, Though he will not rise and give him, because he is his friend, yet because of his importunity he will rise and give him as many as he needeth.

9 And I say unto you, Ask, and it shall be given you ; seek, and ye shall find ; knock, and it shall be opened unto you.

10 For every one that asketh receiveth ; and he that seeketh findeth ; and to him that knocketh it shall be opened.

11 If a son shall ask bread of any of you that is a father, will he give him a stone? or if he ask a fish, will he for a fish give him a serpent?

12 Or if he shall ask an egg, will he offer him a scorpion ?

13 If ye then, being evil, know how to give good gifts unto your children : how much more shall your heavenly Father give the Holy Spirit to them that ask him?

400   SELECTION XVII

Union with Christ.   John 15:1-11

1 I am the true vine, and my Father is the husbandman.

2 Every branch in me that beareth not fruit he taketh away : and every *branch* that beareth fruit, he purgeth it, that it may bring forth more fruit.

3 Now ye are clean through the word which I have spoken unto you.

4 Abide in me, and I in you. As the branch cannot bear fruit of itself, except

it abide in the vine; no more can ye, except ye abide in me.

5 I am the vine, ye *are* the branches: He that abideth in me, and I in him, the same bringeth forth much fruit: for without me ye can do nothing.

6 If a man abide not in me, he is cast forth as a branch, and is withered; and men gather them, and cast *them* into the fire, and they are burned.

7 If ye abide in me, and my words abide in you, ye shall ask what you will, and it shall be done unto you.

8 Herein is my Father glorified, that ye bear much fruit; so shall ye be my disciples.

9 As the Father hath loved me, so have I loved you: continue ye in my love.

10 If ye keep my commandments, ye shall abide in my love; even as I have kept my Father's commandments, and abide in his love.

11 These things have I spoken unto you, that my joy might remain in you, and *that* your joy might be full.

401 SELECTION XVIII

Love. I Cor. 13:1-13

1 Though I speak with the tongues of men and of angels, and have not love, I am become *as* sounding brass, or a tinkling cymbal.

2 And though I have *the gift of* prophesy, and understand all mysteries, and all knowledge; and though I have all faith, so that I could remove mountains, and have not love, I am nothing.

3 And though I bestow all my goods to feed *the poor,* and though I give my body to be burned, and have not love, it profiteth me nothing.

4 Love suffereth long, *and* is kind; love envieth not; love vaunteth not itself, is not puffed up.

5 Doth not behave itself unseemly, seeketh not her own, is not easily provoked, thinketh no evil;

6 Rejoiceth not in iniquity, but rejoiceth in the truth;

7 Beareth all things, believeth all things, hopeth all things, endureth all things.

8 Love never faileth: but whether *there be* prophecies, they shall fail: whether *they be* tongues, they shall cease; whether *there be* knowledge, it shall vanish away.

9 For we know in part, and we prophesy in part.

10 But when that which is perfect is come, then that which is in part shall be done away.

11 When I was a child, I spake as a child, I understood as a child, I thought as a child: but when I became a man, I put away childish things.

12 For now we see through a glass, darkly; but then face to face: now I know in part; but then shall I know even as also I am known.

13 And now abideth faith, hope, love, these three; but the greatest of these *is* love.

402 SELECTION XIX

Christian Giving. 2 Cor. 8:9-15; 9:6-11

9 For ye know the grace of our Lord Jesus Christ, that, though he was rich, yet for your sakes he became poor, that ye through his poverty might be rich.

10 And herein I give my advice: for this is expedient for you, who have begun before, not only to do, but also to be forward a year ago.

11 Now therefore perform the doing of it; that as there was a readiness to will, so there may be a performance also out of that which ye have.

12 For if there be first a willing mind, it is accepted according to that a man hath, and not according to that he hath not.

13 For I mean not that other men be eased, and ye burdened:

14 But by an equality, that now at this time your abundance may be a supply for their want, that their abundance also may be a supply for your want: that there may be equality:

15 As it is written, He that had gathered much had nothing over; and he that had gathered little had no lack.

* * * * * * *

6 But this I say, He which soweth sparingly shall reap also sparingly; and he which soweth bountifully shall reap also bountifully.

7 Every man according as he purposeth in his heart, so let him give; not grudgingly, or of necessity: for God loveth a cheerful giver.

8 And God is able to make all grace abound toward you; that ye, always having all sufficiency in all things, may abound to every good work:

9 (As it is written, He hath dispersed abroad; he hath given to the poor: his righteousness remaineth for ever.

10 Now he that ministereth seed to the sower both minister bread for your food, and multiply your seed sown, and increase the fruits of your righteousness;

11 Being enriched in every thing to all bountifulness, which causeth through us thanksgiving to God.

403 SELECTION XX

Personal Evangelism. Acts 8:26-40

26 And the angel of the Lord spake unto Philip, saying, Arise, and go toward the south unto the way that goeth down from Jerusalem unto Gaza, which is desert.

27 And he arose and went: and, behold, a man of Ethiopia, an eunuch of great authority under Candace queen of

the Ethiopians, who had the charge of all her treasure, and had come to Jerusalem for to worship,

28 Was returning, and sitting in his chariot read Esaias the prophet.

29 Then the Spirit said unto Philip, Go near, and join thyself to this chariot.

30 And Philip ran thither to *him*, and heard him read the prophet Esaias, and said, Understandest thou what thou readest?

31 And he said, How can I, except some man should guide me? And he desired Philip that he would come up and sit with him.

32 The place of the Scripture which he read was this, He was led as a sheep to the slaughter; and like a lamb dumb before his shearer, so opened he not his mouth :

33 In his humiliation his judgment was taken away : and who shall declare his generation? for his life is taken from the earth.

34 And the eunuch answered Philip, and said, I pray thee, of whom speaketh the prophet this? of himself, or of some other man?

35 Then Philip opened his mouth, and began at the same Scripture, and preached unto him Jesus.

36 And as they went on *their* way, they came unto a certain water : and the eunuch said, See, *here is* water ; what doth hinder me to be baptized?

* * * * * *

38 And he commanded the chariot to stand still : and they went down both into the water, both Philip and the eunuch ; and he baptized him.

39 And when they were come up out of the water, the Spirit of the Lord caught away Philip, that the eunuch saw him no more : and he went on his way rejoicing.

40 But Philip was found at Azotus : and passing through he preached in all the cities, till he came to Caesarea.

404 SELECTION XXI

Service and Reward. Matt. 25:14-30

14 For *the kingdom of heaven is* as a man travelling into a far country, *who* called his own servants, and delivered unto them his goods.

15 And unto one he gave five talents, to another two, and to another one ; to every man according to his several ability ; and straightway took his journey.

16 Then he that had received the five talents went and traded with the same, and made *them* other five talents.

17 And likewise he that *had received* two, he also gained other two.

18 But he that had received one went and digged in the earth, and hid his lord's money.

19 After a long time the lord of those servants cometh, and reckoneth with them.

20 And so he that had received five talents came and brought other five talents, saying, Lord, thou deliveredst unto me five talents : behold, I have gained beside them five talents more.

21 His lord said unto him, Well done, *thou* good and faithful servant : thou hast been faithful over a few things, I will make thee ruler over many things : enter thou into the joy of thy lord.

22 He also that had received two talents came and said, Lord, thou deliveredst unto me two talents : behold, I have gained two other talents beside them.

23 His lord said unto him, Well done, good and faithful servant ; thou hast been faithful over a few things, I will make thee ruler over many things : enter thou into the joy of thy lord.

24 Then he which had received the one talent came and said, Lord, I knew thee that thou art an hard man, reaping where thou hast not sown, and gathering where thou hast not strewed :

25 And I was afraid, and went and hid my talent in the earth : lo, *there* thou hast *that is* thine.

26 His lord answered and said unto him, *Thou* wicked and slothful servant, thou knewest that I reap where I sowed not, and gathered where I have not strewed :

27 Thou oughtest therefore to have put my money to the exchangers, and *then* at my coming I should have received mine own with usury.

28 Take therefore the talent from him, and give *it* unto him which hath ten talents.

29 For unto every one that hath shall be given, and he shall have abundance : but from him that hath not shall be taken away even that which he hath.

30 And cast ye the unprofitable servant into outer darkness : there shall be weeping and gnashing of teeth.

405 SELECTION XXII

Trust for Daily Needs. Matt. 6:19-34

19 Lay not up for yourselves treasures upon earth, where moth and rust doth corrupt, and where thieves break through and steal :

20 But lay up for yourselves treasures in heaven, where neither moth nor rust doth corrupt, and where thieves do not break through nor steal :

21 For where your treasure is, there will your heart be also.

22 The light of the body is the eye : if therefore thine eye be single, thy whole body shall be full of light.

23 But if thine eye shall be evil, thy whole body shall be full of darkness. If therefore the light that is in thee be darkness, how great *is* that darkness !

24 No man can serve two masters : for either he will hate the one, and love the other ; or else he will hold to the one, and

despise the other. Ye cannot serve God and mammon.

25 Therefore I say unto you, Take no thought for your life, what ye shall eat, or what ye shall drink ; nor yet for your body, what ye shall put on. Is not the life more than meat, and the body than raiment?

26 Behold the fowls of the air : for they sow not, neither do they reap, nor gather into barns ; yet your heavenly Father feedeth them. Are ye not much better than they?

27 Which of you by taking thought can add one cubit unto his stature?

28 And why take ye thought for raiment? Consider the lilies of the field, how they grow ; they toil not, neither do they spin :

29 And yet I say unto you, That even Solomon in all his glory was not arrayed like one of these.

30 Wherefore, if God so clothe the grass of the field, which today is, and to-morrow is cast into the oven, *shall he* not much more *clothe* you, O ye of little faith?

31 Therefore take no thought, saying, What shall we eat? or, What shall we drink? or, Wherewithal shall we be clothed?

32 (For after all these things do the Gentiles seek :) for your heavenly Father knoweth that ye have need of all these things.

33 But seek ye first the kingdom of God, and his righteousness ; and all these things shall be added unto you.

34 Take therefore no thought for the morrow : for the morrow shall take thought for the things of itself. Sufficient unto the day *is* the evil thereof.

406 SELECTION XXIII

Trust in Face of Trial. Psalm 37:1-9, 23-28

1 Fret not thyself because of evil doers, neither be thou envious against the workers of iniquity.

2 For they shall soon be cut down like the grass, and wither as the green herb.

3 Trust in the LORD, and do good ; *so* shalt thou dwell in the land, and verily thou shalt be fed.

4 Delight thyself also in the LORD ; and he shall give thee the desires of thine heart.

5 Commit thy way unto the LORD ; trust also in him ; and he shall bring *it* to pass.

6 And he shall bring forth thy righteousness as the light, and thy judgment as the noonday.

7 Rest in the LORD, and wait patiently for him : fret not thyself because of him who prospereth in his way, because of the man who bringeth wicked devices to pass.

8 Cease from anger, and forsake wrath : fret not thyself in any wise to do evil.

9 For evil doers shall be cut off : but those that wait upon the LORD, they shall inherit the earth.

* * * * * * * *

23 The steps of a *good* man are ordered by the LORD : and he delighteth in his way.

24 Though he fall, he shall not be utterly cast down : for the LORD upholdeth *him with* his hand.

25 I have been young, and *now* am old ; yet have I not seen the righteous forsaken, nor his seed begging bread.

26 *He is* ever merciful, and lendeth ; and his seed *is* blessed.

27 Depart from evil, and do good ; and dwell for evermore.

28 For the LORD loveth judgment, and forsaketh not his saints ; they are preserved for ever : but the seed of the wicked shall be cut off.

407 SELECTION XXIV

The Providence of God. Psalm 139:1-14, 17, 18, 23, 24

1 O LORD, thou hast searched me, and known *me*.

2 Thou knowest my downsitting and mine uprising, thou understandest my thought afar off.

3 Thou compassest my path and my lying down, and art acquainted *with* all my ways.

4 For *there is* not a word in my tongue, *but*, lo, O LORD, thou knowest it altogether.

5 Thou hast beset me behind and before, and laid thine hand upon me.

6 *Such* knowledge *is* too wonderful for me ; it is high, I cannot *attain* unto it.

7 Whither shall I go from thy Spirit? or whither shall I flee from thy presence?

8 If I ascend up into heaven, thou *art* there : if I make my bed in hell, behold, thou *art there*.

9 *If* I take the wings of the morning, *and* dwell in the uttermost parts of the sea ;

10 Even there shall thy hand lead me, and thy right hand shall hold me.

11 If I say, Surely the darkness shall cover me ; even the night shall be light about me.

12 Yea, the darkness hideth not from thee ; but the night shineth as the day : the darkness and the light *are* both alike *to thee*.

13 For thou hast possessed my reins : thou hast covered me in my mother's womb.

14 I will praise thee ; for I am fearfully *and* wonderfully made : marvellous *are* thy works ; and *that* my soul knoweth right well.

* * * * * * *

17 How precious also are thy thoughts unto me, O God! how great is the sum of them!

18 *If* I should count them, they are more in number than the sand: when I awake, I am still with thee.

* * * * * * * *

23 Search me, O God, and know my heart: try me, and know my thoughts:

24 And see if *there be any* wicked way in me, and lead me in the way everlasting.

408 SELECTION XXV

The Second Coming of Christ.
John 14:1-3; I Thes. 4:13-18; 5:1-11

1 Let not your heart be troubled: ye believe in God, believe also in me.

2 In my Father's house are many mansions: if *it were* not *so*, I would have told you. I go to prepare a place for you.

3 And if I go and prepare a place for you, I will come again, and receive you unto myself; that where I am, *there* ye may be also.

* * * * * * *

13 But I would not have you to be ignorant, brethren, concerning them which are asleep, that ye sorrow not, even as others which have no hope.

14 For if we believe that Jesus died and rose again, even so them also which sleep in Jesus will God bring with him.

15 For this we say unto you by the word of the LORD, that we which are alive *and* remain unto the coming of the LORD shall not prevent them which are asleep.

16 For the LORD himself shall descend from heaven with a shout, with the voice of the archangel, and with the trump of God: and the dead in Christ shall rise first:

17 Then we which are alive *and* remain shall be caught up together with them in the clouds, to meet the LORD in the air: and so shall we ever be with the LORD.

18 Wherefore comfort one another with these words.

* * * * * * *

1 But of the times and the seasons, brethren, ye have no need that I write unto you.

2 For yourselves know perfectly that the day of the Lord so cometh as a thief in the night.

3 For when they shall say, Peace and safety; then sudden destruction cometh upon them, as travail upon a woman with child; and they shall not escape.

4 But ye, brethren, are not in darkness, that that day should overtake you as a thief.

5 Ye are all the children of light, and the children of the day: we are not of the night, nor of darkness.

6 Therefore let us not sleep, as *do* others; but let us watch and be sober.

7 For they that sleep sleep in the night; and they that be drunken are drunken in the night.

8 But let us, who are of the day, be sober, putting on the breastplate of faith and love; and for an helmet, the hope of salvation.

9 For God hath not appointed us to wrath, but to obtain salvation by our Lord Jesus Christ,

10 Who died for us, that, whether we wake or sleep, we should live together with him.

11 Wherefore comfort yourselves together, and edify one another, even as also ye do.

409 SELECTION XXVI

Heaven. Rev. 7:9-17

9 After this I beheld, and, lo, a great multitude, which no man could number, of all nations, and kindreds, and people, and tongues, stood before the throne, and before the Lamb, clothed with white robes, and palms in their hands;

10 And cried with a loud voice, saying, Salvation to our God which sitteth upon the throne, and unto the Lamb.

11 And all the angels stood round about the throne, and *about* the elders and the living creatures, and fell before the throne on their faces, and worshipped God.

12 Saying, Amen: Blessing, and glory, and wisdom, and thanksgiving, and honour, and power, and might, *be* unto our God for ever and ever. Amen.

13 And one of the elders answered, saying unto me, What are these which are arrayed in white robes? and whence came they?

14 And I said unto him, Sir, thou knowest. And he said to me, These are they which came out of great tribulation, and have washed their robes, and made them white in the blood of the Lamb.

15 Therefore are they before the throne of God, and serve him day and night in his temple: and he that sitteth on the throne shall dwell among them.

16 They shall hunger no more, neither thirst any more; neither shall the sun light on them, nor any heat.

17 For the Lamb which is in the midst of the throne shall feed them, and shall lead them unto living fountains of waters: and God shall wipe away all tears from their eyes.

410 SELECTION XXVII

Christ's Future Reign. Psalm 72:1-19

1 Give the king thy judgments, O God, and thy righteousness unto the king's son.

2 He shall judge thy people with righteousness, and thy poor with judgment.

3 The mountains shall bring peace to the people, and the little hills, by righteousness.

4 He shall judge the poor of the people, he shall save the children of the needy, and shall break in pieces the oppressor.

5 They shall fear thee as long as the sun and moon endure, throughout all generations.

6 He shall come down like rain upon the mown grass: as showers *that* water the earth.

7 In his days shall the righteous flourish; and abundance of peace so long as the moon endureth.

8 He shall have dominion also from sea to sea, and from the river unto the ends of the earth.

9 They that dwell in the wilderness shall bow before him; and his enemies shall lick the dust.

10 The kings of Tarshish and of the isles shall bring presents: the kings of Sheba and Seba shall offer gifts.

11 Yea, all kings shall fall down before him: all nations shall serve him.

12 For he shall deliver the needy when he crieth; the poor also, and *him* that hath no helper.

13 He shall spare the poor and needy, and shall save the souls of the needy.

14 He shall redeem their soul from deceit and violence: and precious shall their blood be in his sight.

15 And he shall live, and to him shall be given of the gold of Sheba: prayer also shall be made for him continually; *and* daily shall he be praised.

16 There shall be a handful of corn in the earth upon the top of the mountains; the fruit thereof shall shake like Lebanon: and *they* of the city shall flourish like grass of the earth.

17 His name shall endure for ever: his name shall be continued as long as the sun: and *men* shall be blessed in him; all nations shall call him blessed.

18 Blessed *be* the LORD God, the God of Israel, who only doeth wondrous things.

19 And blessed *be* his glorious name for ever: and let the whole earth be filled *with* his glory. Amen, and Amen.

411 SELECTION XXVIII

National Holidays. Deut. 8

1 All the commandments which I command thee this day shall ye observe to do, that ye may live, and multiply, and go in and possess the land which the LORD sware unto your fathers.

2 And thou shalt remember all the way which the LORD thy God led thee these forty years in the wilderness, to humble thee, *and* to prove thee, to know what *was* in thine heart, whether thou wouldest keep his commandments, or no.

3 And he humbled thee, and suffered thee to hunger, and fed thee with manna, which thou knewest not, neither did thy fathers know; that he might make thee know that man doth not live by bread only, but by every *word* that proceedeth out of the mouth of the LORD doth man live.

4 Thy raiment waxed not old upon thee, neither did thy foot swell, these forty years.

5 Thou shalt also consider in thine heart, that, as a man chasteneth his son, *so* the LORD thy God chasteneth thee.

6 Therefore thou shalt keep the commandments of the LORD thy God, to walk in his ways, and to fear him.

7 For the LORD thy God bringeth thee into a good land, a land of brooks of water, of fountains and depths that spring out of valleys and hills;

8 A land of wheat, and barley, and vines, and fig trees, and pomegranates; a land of oil olive, and honey;

9 A land wherein thou shalt eat bread without scarceness, thou shalt not lack any *thing* in it; a land whose stones *are* iron, and out of whose hills thou mayest dig brass.

10 When thou hast eaten and art full, then thou shalt bless the LORD thy God for the good land which he hath given thee.

11 Beware that thou forget not the LORD thy God, in not keeping his commandments, and his judgments, and his statutes, which I command thee this day:

12 Lest *when* thou hast eaten and art full, and hast built goodly houses, and dwelt *therein;*

13 And *when* thy herds and thy flocks multiply, and thy silver and thy gold is multiplied, and all that thou hast is multiplied.

14 Then thine heart be lifted up, and thou forget the LORD thy God, which brought thee forth out of the land of Egypt, from the house of bondage;

15 Who led thee through that great and terrible wilderness, *wherein were* fiery serpents, and scorpions, and drought, where *there was* no water; who brought thee forth water out of the rock of flint;

16 Who fed thee in the wilderness with manna, which thy fathers knew not, that he might humble thee, and that he might prove thee, to do thee good at thy latter end;

17 And thou say in thine heart, My power and the might of *mine* hand hath gotten me this wealth.

18 But thou shalt remember the LORD thy God: for *it is* he that giveth thee power to get wealth, that he may establish his covenant which he sware unto thy fathers, as *it is* this day.

19 And it shall be, if thou do at all forget the LORD thy God, and walk after other gods, and serve them, and worship them, I testify against you this day that ye shall surely perish.

20 As the nations which the LORD destroyeth before your face, so shall ye perish; because ye would not be obedient unto the voice of the LORD your God.

412 SELECTION XXIX

The Way of the Righteous Man.
Psalm 1

1 Blessed *is* the man that walketh not in the counsel of the ungodly, nor standeth in the way of sinners, nor sitteth in the seat of the scornful.

2 But his delight *is* in the law of the LORD; and in his law doth he meditate day and night.

3 And he shall be like a tree planted by the rivers of water, that bringeth forth his fruit in his season; his leaf also shall not wither; and whatsoever he doeth shall prosper.

4 The ungodly *are* not so; but *are* like the chaff which the wind driveth away.

5 Therefore the ungodly shall not stand in the judgment, nor sinners in the congregation of the righteous.

6 For the LORD knoweth the way of the righteous: but the way of the ungodly shall perish.

413 SELECTION XXX

The Shepherd Psalm. Psalm 23

1 The LORD *is* my shepherd; I shall not want.

2 He maketh me to lie down in green pastures: he leadeth me beside the still waters.

3 He restoreth my soul: he leadeth me in the paths of righteousness for his name's sake.

4 Yea, though I walk through the valley of the shadow of death, I will fear no evil; for thou *art* with me; thy rod and thy staff they comfort me.

5 Thou preparest a table before me in the presence of mine enemies: thou anointest my head with oil; my cup runneth over.

6 Surely goodness and mercy shall follow me all the days of my life: and I will dwell in the house of the LORD forever.

414 SELECTION XXXI

The King of Glory. Psalm 24

1 The earth is the LORD'S, and the fullness thereof; the world, and they that dwell therein.

2 For he hath founded it upon the seas, and established it upon the floods.

3 Who shall ascend into the hill of the LORD? or who shall stand in his holy place?

4 He that hath clean hands, and a pure heart; who hath not lifted up his soul unto vanity, nor sworn deceitfully.

5 He shall receive the blessing from the LORD, and righteousness from the God of his salvation.

6 This is the generation of them that seek him, that seek thy face, O Jacob. Selah.

7 Lift up your heads, O ye gates; and be ye lifted up ye everlasting doors; and the King of glory shall come in.

8 Who is this King of glory? The LORD strong and mighty, the LORD mighty in battle.

9 Lift up your heads, O ye gates; even lift them up, ye everlasting doors; and the King of glory shall come in.

10 Who is this King of glory? The LORD of hosts, he is the King of glory. Selah.

415 SELECTION XXXII

Faith Sustained. Psalm 27

1 The Lord *is* my light and my salvation; whom shall I fear? the Lord is the strength of my life; of whom shall I be afraid?

2 When the wicked, *even* mine enemies and my foes, came upon me to eat up my flesh, they stumbled and fell.

3 Though a host should encamp against me, my heart shall not fear; though war should rise against me, in this *will* I *be* confident.

4 One *thing* have I desired of the Lord, that will I seek after; that I may dwell in the house of the Lord all the days of my life, to behold the beauty of the Lord, and to enquire in his temple.

5 For in the time of trouble he shall hide me in his pavilion; in the secret of his tabernacle shall he hide me; he shall set me up upon a rock.

6 And now shall mine head be lifted up above mine enemies round about me; therefore will I offer in his tabernacle sacrifices of joy; I will sing, yea, I will sing praises unto the Lord.

7 Hear, O Lord, *when* I cry with my voice: have mercy also upon me, and answer me.

8 *When thou saidst,* Seek ye my face; my heart said unto thee, Thy face, Lord, will I seek.

9 Hide not thy face *far* from me; put not thy servant away in anger: thou hast been my help; leave me not, neither forsake me, O God of my salvation.

10 When my father and my mother forsake me, then the Lord will take me up.

11 Teach me thy way, O Lord, and lead me in a plain path, because of mine enemies.

12 Deliver me not over unto the will of mine enemies: for false witnesses are risen up against me, and such as breathe out cruelty.

13 *I had fainted,* unless I had believed to see the goodness of the Lord in the land of the living.

14 Wait on the Lord: be of good courage, and he shall strengthen thine heart: wait, I say, on the Lord.

416 SELECTION XXXIII

The Lord Is Good. Psalm 34:8-18

8 O taste and see that the Lord is good: blessed is the man that trusteth in him.

9 O fear the Lord, ye his saints: for

there is no want to them that fear him.

10 The young lions do lack, and suffer hunger: but they that seek the Lord shall not want any good thing.

11 Come, ye children, hearken unto me: I will teach you the fear of the Lord.

12 What man is he that desireth life, and loveth many days that he may see good?

13 Keep thy tongue from evil, and thy lips from speaking guile.

14 Depart from evil, and do good; seek peace, and pursue it.

15 The eyes of the Lord are upon the righteous, and his ears are open unto their cry.

16 The face of the Lord is against them that do evil, to cut off the remembrance of them from the earth.

17 The righteous cry, and the Lord heareth, and delivereth them out of all their troubles.

18 The Lord is nigh unto them that are of a broken heart; and saveth such as be of a contrite spirit.

417 SELECTION XXXIV
Our Refuge. Psalm 91

1 He that dwelleth in the secret place of the most High shall abide under the shadow of the Almighty.

2 I will say of the Lord, He is my refuge and my fortress: my God; in him will I trust.

3 Surely he shall deliver thee from the snare of the fowler, and from the noisome pestilence.

4 He shall cover thee with his feathers, and under his wings shalt thou trust: his truth shall be thy shield and buckler.

5 Thou shalt not be afraid for the terror by night; nor for the arrow that flieth by day;

6 Nor for the pestilence that walketh in darkness; nor for the destruction that wasteth at noonday.

7 A thousand shall fall at thy side, and ten thousand at thy right hand; but it shall not come nigh thee.

8 Only with thine eyes shalt thou behold and see the reward of the wicked.

9 Because thou hast made the Lord, which is my refuge, even the Most High, thy habitation;

10 There shall no evil befall thee, neither shall any plague come nigh thy dwelling.

11 For he shall give his angels charge over thee, to keep thee in all thy ways.

12 They shall bear thee up in their hands, lest thou dash thy foot against a stone.

13 Thou shalt tread upon the lion and adder: the young lion and the dragon shalt thou trample under feet.

14 Because he hath set his love upon me, therefore will I deliver him: I will set him on high, because he hath known my name.

15 He shall call upon me, and I will answer him: I will be with him in trouble; I will deliver him, and honor him.

With long life will I satisfy him, and show him my salvation.

418 SELECTION XXXV
Thanksgiving. Psalm 95:1-6

1 O come, let us sing unto the Lord: let us make a joyful noise to the Rock of our salvation.

2 Let us come before his presence with thanksgiving, and make a joyful noise unto him with psalms.

3 For the Lord is a great God, and a great King above all gods.

4 In his hand are the deep places of the earth: the strength of the hills is his also.

5 The sea is his, and he made it: and his hands formed the dry land.

6 O come, let us worship and bow down: let us kneel before the Lord, our Maker.

*　*　*　*　*　*　*

Psalm 96:1-4

1 O sing unto the Lord a new song: sing unto the Lord, all the earth.

2 Sing unto the Lord, bless his name; shew forth his salvation from day to day.

3 Declare his glory among the heathen, his wonders among all people.

4 For the Lord is great, and greatly to be praised: he is to be feared above all gods.

419 SELECTION XXXVI
Gratitude. Psalm 103

1 Bless the Lord, O my soul: and all that is within me, bless his holy name.

2 Bless the Lord, O my soul, and forget not all his benefits:

3 Who forgiveth all thine iniquities; who healeth all thy diseases;

4 Who redeemeth thy life from destruction; who crowneth thee with loving kindness and tender mercies;

5 Who satisfieth thy mouth with good things; so that thy youth is renewed like the eagle's.

6 The Lord executeth righteousness and judgment for all that are oppressed.

7 He made known his ways unto Moses, his acts unto the children of Israel.

8 The Lord is merciful and gracious, slow to anger, and plenteous in mercy.

9 He will not always chide: neither will he keep his anger for ever.

10 He hath not dealt with us after our sins; nor rewarded us according to our iniquities.

11 For as the heaven is high above the earth, so great is his mercy toward them that fear him.

12 As far as the east is from the west, so far hath he removed our transgressions from us.

420 SELECTION XXXVII

Keeping. Psalm 121

1 I will lift up mine eyes unto the hills, from whence cometh my help.

2 My help *cometh* from the LORD, which made heaven and earth.

3 He will not suffer thy foot to be moved: he that keepeth thee will not slumber.

4 Behold, he that keepeth Israel shall neither slumber nor sleep.

5 The LORD *is* thy keeper: the LORD *is* thy shade upon thy right hand.

6 The sun shall not smite thee by day, nor the moon by night.

7 The Lord shall preserve thee from all evil: he shall preserve thy soul.

8 The Lord shall preserve thy going out and thy coming in from this time forth, and even for evermore.

421 SELECTION XXXVIII

Kingdom Blessings. Isaiah 35:1-10

1 The wilderness and the solitary place shall be glad for them; and the desert shall rejoice, and blossom as the rose.

2 It shall blossom abundantly, and rejoice even with joy and singing: the glory of Lebanon shall be given unto it, the excellency of Carmel and Sharon, they shall see the glory of the LORD, *and* the excellency of our God.

3 Strengthen ye the weak hands, and confirm the feeble knees.

4 Say to them *that are* of a fearful heart, Be strong, fear not: behold, your God will come with vengeance, *even* God *with* a recompence; he will come and save you.

5 Then the eyes of the blind shall be opened, and the ears of the deaf shall be unstopped.

6 Then shall the lame *man* leap as an hart, and the tongue of the dumb sing: for in the wilderness shall waters break out, and streams in the desert.

7 And the parched ground shall become a pool, and the thirsty land springs of water: in the habitation of dragons, where each lay, *shall be* grass with reeds and rushes.

8 And an highway shall be there, and a way, and it shall be called The way of holiness; the unclean shall not pass over it; but it *shall be* for those: the wayfaring men, though fools, shall not err *therein.*

9 No lion shall be there, nor *any* ravenous beasts shall go up thereon, it shall not be found there; but the redeemed shall walk *there:*

10 And the ransomed of the LORD shall return, and come to Zion with songs and everlasting joy upon their heads: they shall obtain joy and gladness, and sorrow and sighing shall flee away.

422 SELECTION XXXIX

The Beatitudes. Matt. 5:1-12

1 And seeing the multitudes, he went up into a mountain: and when he was set, his disciples came unto him.

2 And he opened his mouth, and taught them, saying,

3 Blessed *are* the poor in spirit: for theirs is the kingdom of heaven.

4 Blessed *are* they that mourn: for they shall be comforted.

5 Blessed *are* the meek: for they shall inherit the earth.

6 Blessed *are* they which do hunger and thirst after righteousness: for they shall be filled.

7 Blessed *are* the merciful: for they shall obtain mercy.

8 Blessed *are* the pure in heart: for they shall see God.

9 Blessed *are* the peacemakers: for they shall be called the children of God.

10 Blessed *are* they which are persecuted for righteousness' sake: for theirs is the kingdom of heaven.

11 Blessed are ye, when *men* shall revile you, and persecute *you*, and shall say all manner of evil against you falsely, for my sake.

12 Rejoice, and be exceeding glad: for great *is* your reward in heaven: for so persecuted they the prophets which were before you.

423 SELECTION XL

Christian Example. Matt. 5:13-20

13 Ye are the salt of the earth: but if the salt have lost his savour, wherewith shall it be salted? it is thenceforth good for nothing, but to be cast out and to be trodden under foot of men.

14 Ye are the light of the world. A city that is set on a hill cannot be hid.

15 Neither do men light a candle and put it under a bushel, but on a candlestick; and it giveth light unto all that are in the house.

16 Let your light so shine before men, that they may see your good works, and glorify your Father which is in heaven.

17 Think not that I am come to destroy the law, or the prophets: I am not come to destroy, but to fulfill.

18 For verily I say unto you, Till heaven and earth pass, one jot or one tittle shall in no wise pass from the law, till all be fulfilled.

19 Whosoever therefore shall break one of these least commandments, and shall teach men so, he shall be called the least in the kingdom of heaven: but whosoever shall do and teach *them*, the same shall be called great in the kingdom of heaven.

20 For I say unto you, That except your righteousness shall exceed *the righteousness* of the scribes and Pharisees, ye shall in no case enter into the kingdom of heaven.

Topical Index

(Titles Capitalized)

Topical Index (Continued)

Topical Index (Continued)

Hymn Tunes

Index of Titles and First Lines

(Titles Capitalized)

Index of Titles and First Lines (Continued)

Index of Titles and First Lines (Continued)

Index of Titles and First Lines (Continued)